An Illustrated Encyclopaedia

WONDERS *of* ANIMAL LIFE

also available by the same editor

An Illustrated World Gazetteer

Peoples of all Nations

Their Life Today and Story of Their Past

In 14 Volumes

Volume One
Abyssinia **to** Azerbaijan
Volume Two
Belgium **to** British Empire in America
Volume Three
British Empire in Asia **to** Canada
Volume Four
Ceylon **to** Dahomey
Volume Five
Danzig **to** England
Volume Six
Esthonia **to** France
Volume Seven
Georgia **to** Iceland

Volume Eight
India **to** Italy
Volume Nine
Japan **to** Mexico
Volume Ten
Monaco **to** Oman
Volume Eleven
Palestine **to** Rumania
Volume Twelve
Russia **to** Sin-kiang
Volume Thirteen
South Africa **to** The Ukraine
Volume Fourteen
The United States **to** Wales
with General Index

About the Editor

Sir John Alexander Hammerton (1871-1949) was an English statesman and author, best-known for his editorship of popular encyclopaedias published in the first half of the 20th century, such as the 10-volume New Book of Knowledge.

From 1914 to 1919, Hammerton was joint editor with HW Wilson of the periodical "The Great War: The Standard History of the All-Europe Conflict", published by the Amalgamated Press. It was lavishly illustrated with photographs and with realistic drawings which were sometimes hardly distinguishable from photographs.

He was also a contemporary and friend of Arthur Mee, about whom he wrote a biography.

An Illustrated Encyclopaedia

WONDERS
of
ANIMAL LIFE

by Famous Writers on Natural History

Volume One

Edited by

J.A. Hammerton

Over Three Thousand Illustrations from Photographs and Thirty-three Colour Plates

LOGOS PRESS, NEW DELHI

ISBN -13: 978-81-7268-175-3 (Set)
ISBN -10: 81-7268-175-5 (Set)

ISBN -13: 978-81-7268-176-0 (Vol. I)
ISBN -13: 978-81-7268-177-7 (Vol. II)
ISBN -13: 978-81-7268-178-4 (Vol. III)
ISBN -13: 978-81-7268-179-1 (Vol. IV)
ISBN -13: 978-81-7268-180-7 (Vol. V)
ISBN -13: 978-81-7268-181-4 (Vol. VI)
ISBN -13: 978-81-7268-182-1 (Vol. VII)
ISBN -13: 978-81-7268-183-8 (Vol. VIII)

ISBN -10: 81-7268-176-3 (Vol. I)
ISBN -10: 81-7268-177-1 (Vol. II)
ISBN -10: 81-7268-178-X (Vol. III)
ISBN -10: 81-7268-179-8 (Vol. IV)
ISBN -10: 81-7268-180-1 (Vol. V)
ISBN -10: 81-7268-181-X (Vol. VI)
ISBN -10: 81-7268-182-8 (Vol. VII)
ISBN -10: 81-7268-183-6 (Vol. VIII)

Edition : 2008

Printed & Published by

LOGOS PRESS

Building No. 4788-90, Street No. 23, Ansari Road, Darya Ganj, New Delhi-110 002 (India)
Phone : 23272187

Foreword

Here is not a 'natural history' in the accepted meaning of that description. There exist many and excellent natural histories and more than fifteen years ago the present editor was associated with the publication of one which, in its authoritative letter-press and profuse illustration, had wide acceptance. But it is undeniable that the general reader finds large and exhaustive treatises on animal life, encumbered with Latin names, somewhat hard reading, however fine their illustrations, if they are arranged on the approved scientific divisions—order, family, genus, species—into which naturalists split up animated nature. A proper natural history, however, must follow this method of treatment if it is to form the basis of a scientific knowledge of the subject.

Does the ordinary reader desire such knowledge? Does he require it?

The answer to both questions is a negative: emphatic in the first and modified in the second case. No matter how slightly youth is drawn to the conventional study of zoology, not even the forbidding scientific approach to natural history can rob it of its inherent fascination.

A boundless curiosity about the infinite diversity of creatures that share the life of the globe with him is a deep and abiding and a most natural trait in man. The stories of a Adam naming the beasts, and of the animals, two by two, going into the ark are ancient evidence of man's interest in his fellow-creatures of the so-called lower orders. A study of the life-histories of many animals and birds, fishes and reptiles, or of the astounding social systems of certain insects, is calculated to limit man's pride in himself as the incarnation of the highest intelligence or the finest physical product of the animal world. Especially is it likely to extend his sympathy to all lowly things that are living out their little days with him upon this planet. It lies at the root of humanitarianism. Interest in animal life is never an idle curiosity, and it may prove more absorbing than any other interest that could be named.

Not, then, to add a new natural history to a list already adequate, but to meet this universal and most healthy interest in the astonishing realities and the mysterious ways of the animal kingdom is the purpose of WONDERS OF ANIMAL LIFE. Its title adequately suggests its scope: to enquire into and to illustrate all that is of uncommon interest in the life of the animal kingdom.

While the reader will find in our pages a constantly changing panorama of animal life, with no more apparent order than the naturalist finds in the Brazilian jungle, he can hardly fail to be interested and he is certain to be instructed, for though the only method that is observed throughout our chapters is a rough alternation of interest, now in mammals, next in reptiles, then in birds, fishes, insects, each chapter of this work is written either by one of the leading specialists on his subject or—where expert knowledge is less needed than vividness of descriptive style—by a popular author.

A glance at the list of contributors, their scientific and literary credentials, and the subjects allotted to them in our scheme, will indicate to the reader that though WONDERS OF ANIMAL LIFE is designedly popular in its appeal, it is not the less authoritative in being more entertaining than the conventional sort of natural history.

Never before has there been brought together so representative and so varied a collection of photographic documents covering the whole range of animated nature. In the last decade, and particularly within the latter part of it, naturalists have acquired an immense amount of new knowledge, and marked progress has been made in recording the wild life of the world by means of direct photography.

The exploits of the camera experts employed by the organizers of some of the great 'nature and adventure' films—'Simba' is a fine example—that have fascinated millions throughout the world in these years have produced so rich a body of material for illustrating such a work as this that editorially we are in a more favoured position than any of our predecessors in the same field and we hope the reader will agree with us in thinking that we have taken advantage of that fortunate circumstance for his entertainment and instruction.

J.A. HAMMERTON

Publisher's Note

We are happy to present the illustrated encyclopaedia—Wonders of Animal Life—to the learned readers. As its title suggests, it attempts to enquire into the astonishing realities and the mysterious ways of life of the animal kingdom—mammals, reptiles, birds, fishes and insects.

Presented in eight volumes, each chapter of this work is written either by one of the leading specialists on the subject or—where expert knowledge is less needed than vividness of descriptive style—by a popular author. The text is enriched with a representative and varied collection of photographic documents covering the whole range of animated nature. Our other notable illustrated encyclopaedias include *The Living Animals of the World* (4 volumes), *The Wonders of the World* (4 volumes), *Peoples of All Nations* (14 volumes), and *The Earth and Its Inhabitants* (8 volumes).

TABLE OF CONTENTS

Volume One

List of Colour Plates

Volume Two

List of Colour Plates

Volume Three

List of Colour Plates

Volume Four

List of Colour Plates

Volume Five

List of Colour Plates

Volume Six

List of Colour Plates

Volume Seven

List of Colour Plates

Volume Eight

List of Colour Plates

Chapter I

Man's Nearest Kin in the Animal World

By Professor Sir Arthur Keith, F.R.S.

President of the British Association 1927-28; Author of "The Antiquity of Man."

So vast has the number of known animals become and so diverse are they in structure and nature that the editor of a modern work such as this has now to employ an army of specialists.

It was not so 200 years ago; in 1735 a young Swedish naturalist named Carl Linné, or Linneus, enumerated all the living things then known, both plants and animals, gave them names, and arranged them in Orders or main groups. To the highest or first Order of animals he gave the name Primates, animals with teeth which were arranged according to a stated formula and with only one pair of breasts, set upon the chest, not on the flanks. As Man answered to these criteria Linneus gave him the highest place amongst the Primates.

The second place in this Order he gave to a group or genus which he named Simia. It was in this group, which is now to engage our attention, that he placed apes and monkeys. The third and fourth groups or kinds of animals which Linneus included among the Primates, the lemurs and the bats, do not concern us here.

In the middle part of the eighteenth century, when Linneus was issuing edition after edition of his System of Nature, the twelfth and last edition of which appeared in 1766, large parts of the earth were still unknown. Only the fringe of the great African continent had been charted, a continent three times the size of Europe, and the modern headquarters of the Simian world. The jungles of the distant East, of Borneo, Sumatra, and Farther India, representing a combined area equal to a third of Europe, the home of so many interesting Simian forms, were unexplored. The immense forests of South America had not yet revealed their secrets. All that was then known in Europe of the apes and monkeys of these distant lands were such specimens as sailors secured in the course of their voyages and such tales as travellers gathered from coastal natives and recounted on their return home.

F. W. Bond

CLOTHES MAKE THE APE MORE MAN-LIKE

When man-like apes are dressed in human garb, like this chimpanzee, even those who doubt the theory of evolution will not deny the suggestion of human kinship in their appearance.

Linneus was an earnest seeker after truth, but found it hard to separate fact from fiction in the publications of his time. When so much of the earth was still unknown every fabulous thing was still possible. Among the races of mankind Linneus accepted, in all seriousness, the existence of *Homo caudatus*, tailed men, of *Troglodyta bontii*, hairy men, and of two other mythical human races.

But, having now searched the earth, we can say with complete confidence that the monstrous forms of humanity in which our forefathers believed have no existence in reality and that all living races of mankind, much as they differ in appearance and in habit, are yet members of a single species, for we know that children may be born to parents who represent the most diverse of living racial stocks. Yet the world of humanity was not always thus; we know, from the geological records, that in past times the earth was inhabited by races so diverse in structure and nature that we must ascribe them to separate species and even to separate genera.

Before diving into the Simian world as we know it to-day we must consider for a moment what Linneus knew of apes and monkeys. He made three divisions; the first included those which had no outward trace of a tail; the second, those which had short tails; the third, those which had long tails; a scheme which had at least the merit of simplicity. When we remember that the Manx cat is tailless, and yet is none the less a cat, and that tailless breeds of dogs and of fowls are known, it may be thought that Linneus was much at fault in selecting such a structure as the tail as a basis for classification. As a matter of fact modern inquiry has proved that when Linneus grouped together the tailless apes he showed real insight, for the absence of a tail is an outward sign of a profound change which has affected all parts of the inward body. The tailless apes of Linneus are the man-like, or anthropoid, apes of our scientific classification of to-day.

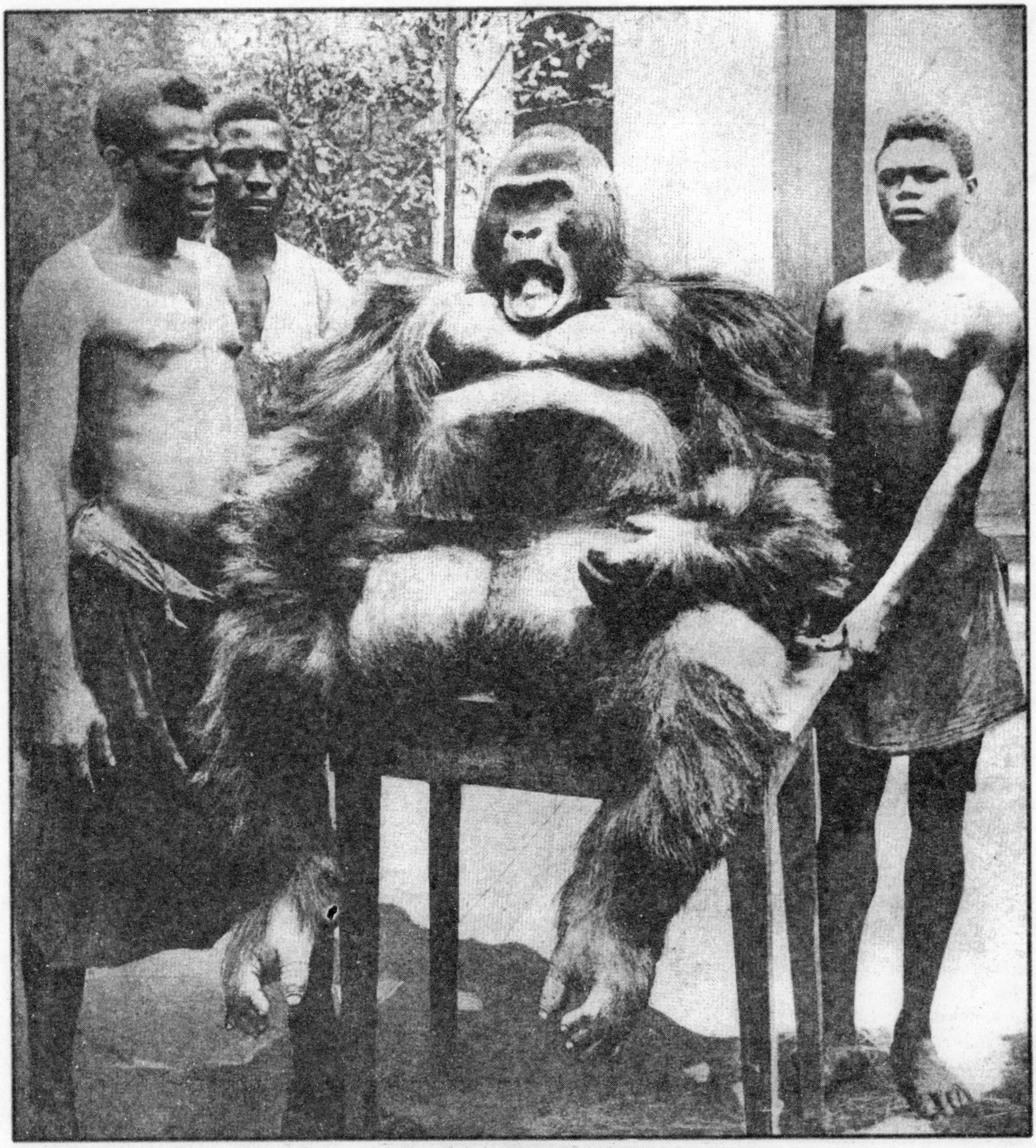

THE BIGGEST GORILLA EVER SEEN BY MAN

The enormous size of the adult gorilla can be easily appreciated in this photograph of a specimen shot in the Cameroon forest. It is said to be the largest gorilla ever seen by man and was seven feet high, while its weight was about a fifth of a ton. Of all the great anthropoids the gorilla has its lower limbs best developed, and in its leg is often found a certain muscle which is also present in the leg of man, but not in that of any other animal. The gorilla's footprint is three times the size of that of a full-grown man.

The jungles of the Old World and of the New have now been explored, superficially at least, and we are convinced that of the many kinds of anthropoid, or tailless, apes which lived in past geological times, only four now survive. Two of these live in Africa, the gorilla and chimpanzee; a third, the orang-utan, inhabits Borneo and Sumatra; the fourth, the gibbon, lives in the forests of Farther India, and of the islands of Hainan, Borneo, Celebes, Java, and Sumatra.

Time has justified Linneus in placing man at the head of the Order Primates, and in brigading certain apes together just because they were destitute of an outward tail. To an inexperienced onlooker it may seem equally hazardous when we of to-day employ a character so variable as size of body as a means of separating the tailless, or anthropoid, apes into two categories, the small anthropoids and the great.

THE GORILLA AS HE FACES AN ENEMY IN THE STEAMING AFRICAN FOREST

The gorilla will stand up in this way to face a foe although his usual attitude when moving about is on all fours. In muscular development he vastly surpasses the most powerful human prize-fighter. So bulky does he become in adult life that he finds himself unable to climb the trees as the females and younger members of his family can. At night he sleeps by the foot of the tree in whose boughs his family is safely bestowed. No full-grown male has been photographed alive, and this picture is from a stuffed specimen.

Everyone knows how the dog, horse, and ox may vary in size of body, and yet, great or small, they are still dogs, horses, and oxen. A dwarf or pigmy is none the less human because he is small. Yet the fact remains without question that size of body, among the Primates, is linked to hundreds of changes in structural organization.

Geological records reveal the earliest Primates as small animals, no bigger than rats or squirrels; we do not encounter larger forms until we have followed primate evolution at least half-way along its geological history. The gibbon, we now know, represents an ancient type, and is a small anthropoid varying from fourteen pounds to twenty-eight pounds, that is, from one to two stones. On the other hand, the chimpanzee, gorilla, and orang are great anthropoids. In size of body they are human or ultra-human, varying in weight from eight or twelve

Autotype

THE SILVERY GIBBON OF JAVA

Curiously enough, the gibbons, although the lowest and smallest of the man-like apes, are the only ones that habitually walk in an upright position. Their arms are so long that they touch the ground when walking upright. They are very affectionate creatures.

stones among chimpanzees to twelve or thirty stones among gorillas. And their weight is due not to the accumulation of fat, but of solid bone, muscle, and viscera. In size of body, as well as in many details of structure, man agrees with the great anthropoids; anthropologists often find it convenient to have a name for this big-bodied group, and speak of its members as the Great Primates.

I have introduced the reader to the most recent conception of the animals whose lives I am to sketch. But how we have blundered as we reached forwarc to come by it! To illustrate our initial mistake: let us suppose for a moment that the mastery o the world had fallen not to strong-legged man bu to the arboreal chimpanzee, and that in the cours of marauding expeditions along our coasts chimpanzee sailors had captured stray waifs here anc there and carried them away home to their Africar headquarters.

There the unhappy children are encaged in a treetop and the chimpanzee public crowds round tc gaze at them with curious eyes. We can see th learned professor of the jungle step forward anc explain to his interested audience what poor, weak helpless, and ignorant beings these human captive: are. Compared with themselves, how ill adaptec such anomalous beings are for all the purposes o arboreal life. Just look at their feet! Could anyon conceive structures more awkwardly fashioned fo the purposes of climbing, or hands and arms mor useless for a life in the jungle? It puzzles thi learned chimpanzee to know why Nature should eve have made such weaklings, for he supposes that th captives before him are adults.

Now it is after this manner that men made thei acquaintance with the great anthropoids. In the time of Linneus naturalists had only an occasiona opportunity of seeing an anthropoid waif captured on the coast of Africa or of Borneo, and strange to say they confused the one with the other, for the Malay name orang-utan, or man of the woods, was given indiscriminately to both orang and chimpanzee. It wa not until about the middle of the 19th century when trained naturalists such as Russel Wallace, o adventurous explorers like Du Chaillu, began tc penetrate the tropical jungles of the East and o Africa and observe anthropoid life in its nativ setting, that we began to realize the number anc extent of our original misconceptions.

Our knowledge of the gorilla began in 1847. In that year Dr. Savage, an American medical missionary in the French Gaboon, made its existence known tc the world. Our pioneer explorers had to make th acquaintance of anthropoid apes gun in hand; in no other way could they come by the knowledge we all desired. The harsher methods of the early pioneers are now being replaced by more gentl and more profitable modes of inquiry. When ou modern explorers bring their harvests home we shal understand the simian world better than our forefathers did.

I do not, of course, undervalue the knowledge which has been gained by those who have studied the apes in captivity. It was thus that Darwin became acquainted with their modes of expression and behaviour. Sally, an accomplished and intelligent chimpanzee which lived eight years in the Zoological Gardens, London, some forty years ago, had her mental gifts measured and registered by Dr. G. J. Romanes. In more recent years trained psychologists have built laboratories for the study of anthropoid apes and monkeys, such studies being carried out over periods of months and even years. Just before the Great War the Germans established such a laboratory in the Island of Teneriffe. Dr. Köhler, Professor of Philosophy in the University of Berlin, has summed up what he learned while in charge of that laboratory in a book called "The Mentality of Apes."

THE most painstaking and illuminating researches so far made are those of the American psychologist, Dr. Robert M. Yerkes, who has published his studies on the mentality of gorillas and chimpanzees, orangs and monkeys in many recent monographs and books. In intelligence he places the chimpanzee first, the orang second, the gorilla third, but has some doubt as to the real place of the gorilla, as that animal is naturally undemonstrative and seems to possess an ability which it declines to exhibit.

We learn from the experience of Dr. Yerkes that the first requisite for an experimenter is to place himself on the best terms possible with the subject of his inquiry. He must wait patiently hours or days for requisite opportunities. He found that individual apes vary as much in their intelligence as do men and women; their moods change from hour to hour and from day to day. Their minds react according to their state of health. To set their minds working there must be an incentive, and the mental stimulus on which every experimenter depends is that of food. To ascertain the mental resources of apes, psychologists have devised an infinite variety of food-finding problems, bananas suspended so high that they can be reached only by placing boxes upon one another, or placed so far outside the cage bars that they can be reached only by the aid of a stick. Some anthropoids have solved these problems unaided, but the majority require tuition or example, and to be trained they have to be taken in hand during childhood; adults stubbornly refuse to learn. In all of these points anthropoid apes may be described as human.

I made the acquaintance of apes as a young medical man in the jungles of the East some forty years ago. I dissected examples to discover whether or not they suffered from malaria, which plagued us poor humans. In the course of long journeys through the primeval forest I observed how the families or small bands of gibbons which abounded in those parts differed from ordinary apes. Ordinary or dog-like monkeys run along branches on all fours. When they plunge heavily from tree to tree they use their hinder limbs as the impelling power. The gibbon, on the other hand, ran along branches with its body upright, supporting itself upright on its lower limbs and using its arms lightly on branches overhead. Then, when it leapt from tree to tree (and I have seen it clear an open space of forty feet), it derived its impetus, like a gymnast, from the

F. W. Bond

YOUNG GORILLA THAT LIVED IN LONDON FOR SOME YEARS

It used to be thought that gorillas could not be kept in captivity, but this one, known to his friends as John Daniel, lived in a London house and used to travel about the town. At night he slept in an ordinary bed, and his meals were taken at table with knife, fork, and spoon just as though he were human. After being parted from his mistress, he died of a broken heart.

swing of the arms. Its arms are particularly long; the biceps and neighbouring muscles of the arm are strong and highly specialised, and its long, narrow hands serve as flexible hooks.

Ordinary monkeys—there were families of macaques as well as of semnopithecques in the district—were pronograde, or horizontal, in their posture of body and mode of climbing, whereas the gibbon was orthograde, or upright, in his carriage. I soon found that this mode of holding the body was reflected in every detail of the gibbon's anatomy—in the muscles of the back, in the arrangement of heart, lungs, and viscera, and in every joint and bone of its body. And in all, or nearly all of these orthograde adaptations, he resembled man. And yet in size, in the soft fur of his body, in the callosities on which he sits and sleeps, even in the volume of his brain, he differed little from the ordinary dog-like, or cynomorphous, monkey. Somehow the assumption or evolution of the orthograde posture had brought about the complete disappearance of the tail and a radical transformation of the muscles which, in pronograde apes, move the basal part of the tail.

It was then that I began to realize that posture has played an exceedingly important part in the evolution of the primates—that it was a fundamental character. At first I supposed that the gibbon was merely an ordinary type of monkey which had taken to climbing in an orthograde, hand-over-hand way, but I soon became disillusioned on this score, and found that if we were to solve the enigma of the history of the gibbon and of other orthograde forms, such as the orang, chimpanzee, and gorilla, it was necessary to search for the infancy of the primate order in the geological deposits of the Eocene period, that is the oldest period of the Age of Mammals, deposits laid down two and a half million years ago, or more.

In that long-past era a most interesting evolutionary experiment was launched; the early primate world was rent in twain. In the New World, as we now name it, were isolated the early ancestors of the modern monkeys of America; the Old World retained the ancestral types which in the course of time have given us our present dog-like, or pronograde, monkeys, the small orthograde anthropoid, now represented by the gibbon, and the great orthograde anthropoids exemplified to-day by the orang, chimpanzee, and gorilla.

In the course of their evolution American apes have become adapted to various forms of progression. The spider monkey, with its long limbs and strong, flexible, prehensile tail, may be compared in point of specialisation to the gibbon, but is really a five-handed type and mainly pronograde in habit. On the other hand the little marmoset has retained, more than any other living monkey, the size and posture of body which distinguished the primates before a separation took place into New and Old World forms.

Even in the long geological period which succeeded the Eocene—the Oligocene—we find the Old World primates still small in size and retaining many marks of affinity to their separated cousins in the New World. It is at this time, too, we find early stages in the divergence of the Old World stock into orthograde and pronograde forms. Each type proceeded to diverge more and more, and to split up into a diversity of forms. In the Miocene jungles of Europe, that is those of the middle period of the Mammal Age, a phase following on the Oligocene, we find fossil remains of small orthograde anthropoids, or gibbons, and of large orthograde anthropoids—the extinct *Dryopithecques*, or tree apes, animals which varied in size but for the greater part resembled the chimpanzee.

In the Miocene and in the still later Pliocene forests of India great anthropoids, of many species, were abundant. The Miocene period has been described as the hey-day of the great anthropoids. All the facts known to us lead to the belief that the great anthropoid was evolved from the small, and that the modern gibbon represents a very ancient and persistent type which carries the imagination back to that distant and early stage in the evolution of the order of beings which in due time, in the shape of man, was to conquer the world.

I have touched on the gibbons of the distant East and have made a digression in order to explain to the reader why anatomists are so interested in this marvellous little gymnast. Every large district of the area in which the gibbon is found has its own particular species or breed, there being about ten distinguishable forms. The most distinct type of all is the Siamang, which now lives in the upland forest areas of Sumatra and in those of the southern half of the Malay peninsula. The siamang is of interest not only because of peculiarities in its structure, but because of its size of body. It may reach thirty pounds in weight, double that of an ordinary gibbon. It is the occurrence of such a type which justifies us in believing that great anthropoids may have been evolved, at a distant period, from the small.

We now turn to make a brief survey of the three great anthropoid types which have survived intc

MAN AND HIS NEAREST RELATIVES

The resemblances and differences between man and his nearest relatives, the anthropoid apes, are best seen by comparing their skeletons as in this group at the Public Museum, Liverpool, which shows from left to right the gibbon, orang, chimpanzee, gorilla, and man.

our time. The continent of Africa, the home of the chimpanzee and gorilla, is being rapidly opened up. We now know that a great belt of primeval forest, the larger part of which is an almost impenetrable jungle, stretches right across equatorial Africa, beginning at Sierra Leone in the West and ending on the East at the great central chain of lakes. The total length of this forest belt is some three thousand miles ; it varies in width from three hundred to eight hundred miles.

This belt is the home of the chimpanzee ; but the animal occurs also just beyond the belt. The total area of its distribution is about three million square miles, an area almost as large as Europe, but there are many tracts of this vast district which have no chimpanzee population.

" Natural History." N.Y.

FOUR CHIMPANZEE FRIENDS READY FOR A RIDE

The anthropoids are remarkably like children in that they delight in anything on wheels, and are always ready for a ride. These four chimpanzees of varied ages were closely attached to one another, and if one screamed, the big ape on the right invariably rushed to help his friend. While the photograph was being taken, however, the animals remained still.

THE chimpanzee is a social animal and lives in family bands, numbering from twelve to forty individuals of all ages and both sexes. From the accounts given by travellers one infers that in the districts which are occupied they do not average more than one animal to each ten square miles. If we presume that only half of the three million square miles are actually occupied, we arrive at a crude census of the chimpanzee population, namely 150,000, an estimate which I am certain errs in exaggerating the actual number. Man encroaches upon their territory more and more every year, and when the great forest belt disappears the chimpanzee will go with it.

Although Dr. Yerkes gives the chimpanzee first place in order of intelligence, it comes third in actual size of brain as well as in size of body. The female chimpanzee has a smaller brain than the male, but the proportional sex difference in favour of the male is rather less than holds for human races and much less than is the case in the orang and gorilla, where the male greatly overshadows the female in size and strength of body as well as in size of brain. In weight of body the chimpanzee varies from eight to twelve stones, thus resembling man, but it differs from man in having a longer trunk but much shorter lower limbs, its total height seldom exceeding four feet eight inches.

At birth the chimpanzee is only about one-third the weight of a human baby. Its mother suckles it for a year at least, until a young brother or sister comes along. The baby begins to cut its teeth at two months, whereas a human baby usually gets its first teeth at six months, and has not cut all its milk teeth until towards the end of the second year. The chimpanzee arrives at the same stage of dentition when about one year old. The chimpanzee child begins to fend for itself at the age of two, and its permanent teeth begin to appear about the end of the fourth year, nearly two years earlier than in human children. All the permanent teeth, which are the same in kind and in number as in man, are cut and in use about the end of the fifteenth year, four or five years sooner than in man. Chimpanzees are quite adult in their fourteenth or fifteenth year, and from certain inquiries I have made I have formed the opinion that they are, in general wear of body, as old in their fortieth year as a man is in his seventieth.

Chimpanzees are the most active, enterprising, and happy of all the great anthropoids. They are playful in youth and retain through life the attributes of youth more than is the case with the orang and gorilla, but not so much as is the case with man. They interest us, too, because of certain primitive features. They are orthograde in posture, spending most of their time on the trees, using arms and legs equally. But they are also at home in the wild undergrowth which covers the floor of the jungle. Their limbs are much less specialised than those of the other great primates.

THERE is no doubt that the gorilla represents a very distinctive type of ape, and yet many find it hard to distinguish the young gorilla from the young chimpanzee. No doubt the gorilla and chimpanzee are evolutionary cousins; they have arisen at some distant period from a common ancestor. The gorilla, sooty-faced from infancy, can always be recognised by its nose. Not only is the gorilla's nose long, but its wings form rounded, fleshy folds which run down on to and merge with the upper lip. The ears of the chimpanzee are large and outstanding, while those of the gorilla are small and pressed tightly against the sides of the head. When gorillas open their mouths and show their teeth there can be no longer any doubt; the molar teeth of the gorilla are so massive and so strongly cusped. In mental nature gorillas and chimpanzees are totally different; the chimpanzee is playful and social, while the gorilla, even in childhood, is taciturn, self-contained, and irresponsive.

The gorilla also occupies the great equatorial forest belt of Africa, but its distribution is much more restricted than that of the chimpanzee. Gorillas prefer hilly country covered with jungle, and are fond of descending on disused clearings which men have made and forsaken. They also carry out marauding expeditions on native plantations, being particularly fond of shoots of the plantain and of sugar canes. They are gross feeders; bamboo shoots and succulent roots form their staple diet; quantity rather than quality is their motto. Their droppings are massive and resemble those of a horse.

On the west coast they extend northward into the Cameroons, while on the south they reach the mouth of the Congo, but never beyond it. They

H. Shepstone

F. W. Bond

HOW CHIMPANZEE AND ORANG-UTAN APPEAR IN AN ERECT POSTURE

Although it is not common or easy for any of the larger man-like apes to maintain an upright position they do stand erect when occasion demands, and these two photographs show how very upright their attitude can be. The chimpanzee (left) seems perfectly comfortable as he stands with folded arms: but the orang (right), though quite as straight, seems less at ease. Note that while the chimpanzee supports himself on the soles of his feet, with his toes tucked underneath, the orang stands on the sides of his feet, a most uncomfortable position.

F. W. Bond

AGED MALE ORANG WITH CHEEK POUCHES

The male orang-utan in his later adult years develops cushions or pouches on the sides of the face. The female never possesses such facial ornaments and therefore remains more human in appearance. The white marks are wisps of straw from the ape's bed.

stretch to the east as far as the great lakes. It was only at the beginning of the present century that they were discovered in the volcanic mountains to the west of Lake Kivu, and they even reach the neighbouring frontier of Uganda. In Eastern Central Africa gorillas live in the damp, cold, bleak bamboo jungle which clothes the ravines and sides of these high mountains. They are found living at a height of eight or even ten thousand feet. Although we have many records of the occurrence of gorillas in the western and eastern extremities of the forest belt, they have been seen only very rarely in the intermediate areas.

GORILLAS live in small bands, which seldom contain more than ten individuals, each band being led by a massive old male with usually a young male or two to serve as understudies. Each band apparently represents a family, and includes two or three adult females with young at various stages of growth. How sparse the gorilla population is, even where the animals abound most, may be seen from the records of Du Chaillu. That traveller, in the course of four years, covered eight thousand miles on foot, and yet succeeded in shooting or capturing only seventeen individuals. If we estimate the total gorilla population at fifty thousand, I feel certain that we have exaggerated the numbers. If all were gathered together they could be accommodated in one of our smaller county towns. Nor are their numbers increasing; the opposite is the case. The gorilla is a dying race.

The gorilla changes exceedingly as he grows up—far more than the chimpanzee and man do. He is born small, being less than half the weight of a new-born human infant, but the adult male usually weighs as much as two ordinary men. An old male gorilla which Mr. T. A. Barns shot on the volcanic highlands of the Eastern Congo near Lake Kivu, weighed 450 pounds, over 32 stones. It took ten natives to lift and carry his carcase, and they staggered under their burden. The gorilla child cuts its teeth and becomes mature at very much the same time-periods as the chimpanzee, but growth, especially of the male, is much more rapid. Although the prevailing colour of hair is some shade of dark-brown or even black, a touch of red is common, especially in the hair of the scalp. In old age the hair turns grey.

The gorilla is the Hercules of primates. His strength of jaw and limb is enormous; in muscular development the adult male surpasses the strongest of our Jack Johnsons; an ordinary average specimen has the strength of five men. The evolutionary trend of the gorilla has been toward the acquisition of sheer brute strength and mass of body. The male animal has become a veritable giant—not in height, for its total stature reaches only about six feet, but in bulk of body and power of limb.

F. W. Bond

"APING" THE MAN

There are few human actions that a chimpanzee cannot be taught to imitate but in the use of a hair-brush he needs no teaching at all. He has only to see a man brush his hair and if the brush s passed to him he will quickly reproduce the action on himself.

In the chimpanzee the evolutionary trend has been in the opposite direction; the chimpanzee represents the light cruiser, whereas the gorilla is modelled on heavy battleship lines. The trend towards sheer strength has brought about a change in the habits of the gorilla of a very interesting kind. Every structure of the gorilla's body proclaims that it was originally designed for life in the trees, but with the evolution of bulk the old male has become too heavy for climbing, and has been forced to spend his adult life on the ground among the undergrowth of the jungle, supported on his bowed legs and using his long, stout arms as crutches. The females and the young still retain their arboreal habits. Most of their time, however, is passed on the jungle floor.

Of the great anthropoids, gorillas have the lower limbs best developed; it is remarkable that in their legs a certain special muscle is occasionally developed, a muscle which otherwise is found only in the leg of man. It is also remarkable that many gorillas also possess a special muscle for the thumb, one which is constantly found in man, but in no other animal. The hand of the gorilla is massive and extremely clumsy, while the sole of his foot makes an imprint which covers three times the area of that made by the foot of adult man.

I have made no mention of the nest-building habits of the chimpanzee; such nests are rough, temporary platforms fashioned out of bent and broken branches—not unlike nests made by our wood-pigeons, but of even cruder workmanship and measuring three or four feet in diameter. The great anthropoids share man's habit of sleeping in a reclining position; hence every night they have to provide themselves with sleeping platforms or beds.

At night the old male gorilla makes a shake-down of branches at the foot of a tree, while the young animals and females of his band spend the night on platforms roughly fashioned on neighbouring trees. Dr. Dyce Sharp informed the writer that all members of a family post themselves at night within sight of the old gentleman's bed. Orangs also build similar platforms or beds.

The orang builds very rapidly. Some years ago an adult orang escaped from his cage in the Zoological Gardens, London, and in less than half an hour constructed a platform on a tree adjoining the anthropoid house.

We must not suppose we have discovered all the secrets of the gorilla world. It was only at the beginning of the present century that Captain von

F. W. Bond

BOSOM FRIENDS IN CAPTIVITY: TWO YOUNG ORANGS AT LONDON'S ZOO

Orang-utans are easily tamed and trained, and owing to their very human appearance they are great favourites in all zoos, where children and grown-ups alike love to watch their quaint antics. They are fond of companionship, and two young orangs like these will form as close a friendship as any human beings could do. The one on the right is showing marks of real affection as he embraces his companion, while the other solemnly waves his arm as though he is wishful of attracting the attention of the photographer or of some other visitor.

THE ORANG'S BED IN THE TREE-TOPS
The orang-utan builds a platform of branches in the tree-tops and uses it as a bed, where it can sleep in peace, safe from enemies that might attack it if it were caught on the ground. This platform is well constructed, and is put together with amazing rapidity.

Beringe discovered the Highland or Kivu gorilla in the volcanic mountainous ranges near Lake Kivu. The Kivu gorilla can be distinguished at a glance from the gorilla of the West by his hairiness, his occipital crest, and his stocky build of body. But in muscle and bone and brain the eastern gorilla differs in no distinctive way from the gorilla of West Africa. There are thus at least two distinct races of gorillas—the lowland, or western, gorilla and the highland, or eastern, gorilla.

In spite of his great strength, his powerful jaws, and dagger-like canine teeth the male gorilla is not an offensive animal, but can be terrible in defence. He will fight ferociously, but only when attacked or when his home is invaded and his followers threatened. He never runs away when the safety of his band is endangered, but courageously faces his foe.

We must, in concluding, touch upon the great anthropoid of the East, the orang-utan. In recent years whole families have been captured in Sumatra and brought to Europe for a medical purpose of most doubtful utility. No one who has viewed a family of father, mother, and baby orangs in captivity behind the iron bars of a cage will ever forget the sight, so pathetic is it. Such a scene cannot fail to move the most thoughtless. It is much to be desired that such a nefarious trade and practice should be made impossible. For by nature the orang is the most timid and inoffensive of animals. The male orang is a massive anthropoid weighing 170 to 200 pounds, covered with long red hair, and in late adult years developing curious cushions on the sides of the face, in front of the ears. The female orang never possesses these facial ornaments and is a much smaller animal than the male, weighing twenty to thirty pounds less. The newly born baby is only about one-third the weight of a human baby; it reaches maturity about the fourteenth year and is old at forty.

The orang is purely arboreal, descending to the ground only under compulsion. He is a slow climber, lethargic in his movements, using his long arms and hook-like hands as the main means of progression from branch to branch and from tree to tree.

This predominant use of the arms has led to a remarkable atrophy of the lower extremities, which serve purely as grasping organs. It is also noteworthy that the thumb and great toe are much reduced in size and are apparently on the way to become mere vestiges—if the orang race survives long enough for such a process to be completed.

The area occupied by the orang is much less than that held by chimpanzees in Africa. Orangs are found within a wide tropical belt which covers the western parts of Borneo and in the north-western half of Sumatra. The total area inhabited by them cannot exceed 200,000 square miles; even if we allow one animal to every five square miles—a too liberal allowance—the total orang population would amount to only forty thousand. It is very possibly little more than half this number.

The anthropoid world, which I have hurriedly surveyed with the eyes of a registrar-general rather than of a naturalist, differs altogether from that of man. Anthropoids are the slaves of circumstances, being dependent, from day to day, upon what they

C. E. Akeley

HOW THE GORILLA MOVES ABOUT
Habitually the gorilla does not adopt an upright attitude, but moves about on all fours with a curious swinging motion, using its arms as crutches and bringing its huge body forward with a kind of jump. When facing an enemy, however, it will rise as shown in page 5.

Autotype

THE FIERCE MIEN OF THE MALE GORILLA WHEN DEFENDING HIS FAMILY FROM ATTACK

Though ordinarily the gorilla is not aggressive, he can become terribly ferocious in defence of his females and their young, and when he opens his mouth he displays huge, dagger-like canine teeth that are truly formidable. The evolutionary trend of the gorilla has been toward the acquisition of brute strength and he could easily master five men. The museum specimen from which this head was photographed was one of the finest ever shot, and the picture gives a good idea of the animal when roused to wrath.

can gather from Nature's table—and a jungle table is a precarious one. All of them remain far below the level of organization at which the brain becomes capable of conscious effort; they are untutored children of Nature, ignorant of tools, and incapable of the simplest mechanical invention.

Man, even the lowest we know of, has risen far above the anthropoid level and become a conscious inventor. Man has succeeded in making ten square miles of land support a population of five thousand individuals—an area which, in its virgin condition, would provide sustenance for only one ape. The result has been that humanity now numbers about 1,800 million souls, all being varieties of one species; whereas the great anthropoids, which represent three different genera, cannot muster a total of 300,000 amongst them, a number equal only to the population of a single modern city.

We see, too, how precarious is their hold on life in our world. The primitive tropical forests are disappearing before the growing needs of civilized man, and when these tropic jungle belts have gone no home will be left any longer for animals which have, or should have, man's most sympathetic consideration. For there was a time when mankind was just as sparsely represented as these animals now are and was just as dependent on what fell from Nature's table. From the anthropoid world of to-day man can obtain a glimpse of his own remote past. For there was a time when mankind was also divided into very diverse forms, each native to a confined area of the earth's surface.

Chapter II

The Wonder of the White Ant

By Hamilton Fyfe

If an explorer were to tell us he had found a race of men who could control, not merely the sex but the character and the bodily structure of their children; if he were to relate how they produced, according to the needs of the community, labourers or soldiers, parents or nurses, we should at first almost certainly disbelieve him.

Were he to convince us of the truth of his story, we should call this one of the marvels of the universe. We should want to learn as much as we could about it. The methods employed would be of enormous interest to us. We should feel that the scope of Will and Intellect had been vastly enlarged, that one of Nature's most jealously guarded secrets now lay open before us.

That is the feeling created in every mind capable of reflection and imagination by a study of the Termites. They are not indeed human beings, but does that make them any less wonderful? Surely it is more wonderful that tiny, weak creatures, the easy prey of countless enemies, without any of the advantages which man prides himself on possessing, should know so much that is hidden from us; that they should have been able for unnumbered ages to do as a matter of course and daily habit what we with all our skill and ingenuity cannot either accomplish or understand.

That ants and bees are in their way as astonishing as man is known to all who have read even simple accounts of their activities. The hive is a model state which in its working and results surpasses any system of civil government elaborated by human beings. It is not fantastic to say that bees and ants have civilizations of their own, for a civilization implies a discipline which allots to every citizen his or her duty and keeps always the general good in view. Such discipline is far stronger in the hive and possibly in the ant-heap than it has ever in any age been among men. Among the termites we see it even more efficient.

Prof. R. W. Doane

TURRETS BUILT BY AMERICAN TERMITES

Some white ants instead of building towering structures of Gothic appearance erect slender turrets like these. The one on the left was built near a house in California, and that on the right is interesting as standing quite out of its centre of gravity.

These insects are commonly known as white ants —commonly, but erroneously, for they are neither ants nor white. Their colour is as a rule more or less that of the earth in which they live. They are a distinct genus, unlike ants in most important particulars and carrying on perpetual war with them. There is a wide range of variation among termites; nearly fifteen hundred different kinds are known. They are found only in hot climates, which has saved the north of Europe from them. They are reckoned to have been in existence on the earth for between two and three million years—yet it was only a century and a half ago that they began to be studied seriously.

This was all the more curious seeing that their homes and their habits are so much in evidence in the countries where they live. In Africa one sees often tall columns which appear to be of earth. For the most part these are from six to ten feet high; they may run up to twenty. In Australia the termitaries reach a height greater than that. Sometimes the mounds and columns have a large circumference. They are always plainly visible; indeed they are often the most prominent objects in the landscape. The termite is very seldom seen himself, but he makes no attempt to conceal his buildings. These are unnecessarily, even dangerously, conspicuous.

Nor is it possible in a tropical country to remain unacquainted with the destructive habits of the termites. Everything that is not of metal they can eat, and do eat if they take a fancy to it. Nor do they eat in an open, straightforward, honest way. They never start on the outside of anything. They gnaw their way in somehow, and continue gnawing until nothing but the outside is left. Thus, you may see what looks like a perfectly good tree, but at a touch it crumbles. You may sit on what appears to be a sound chair and have it collapse under you. You may push open a door and see it fall off its hinges because the termites have hollowed out the door-posts, which dissolve into dust.

"In the hot and tropical parts of the surface of the earth," testifies W. W. Froggatt, the Australian naturalist, "there is no family of insects whose members wage such an unceasing war against the work of man." Jamestown in St. Helena was once attacked by them; a large part of it had to be rebuilt. The most surprising stories are told about their ingenuity and cunning. They can even bite through metal if they have time to rust it with a juice which they exude. In an account of Oriental travel an author named Forbes told of all his pictures and picture-frames being eaten away as they hung on his walls. Only the glass was left, and that had been cemented to the walls!

There is so much that seems incredible in the lives of termites that it would be rash to exclude any possibility. M. Maeterlinck is indeed inclined to credit them with an intelligence superhuman in some directions. In his book "The Life of the White Ant" there is much poetry and not a little philosophy added to a passionate interest in his subject and a comprehensive acquaintance with it. Some think that he falls into the error which poets are prone to make of speaking about creatures without self-consciousness as if they could experience "misery," "joy" or "resignation," in the same degree as we do. Yet M. Maeterlinck throughout most of his book keeps close to facts, drawing them from naturalists of authority; and the story he tells is one that leaves the mind of the reader, as it left his mind, groping eagerly for answers to the many questions it suggests.

In size the termite is not much larger than a wasp or small beetle; in shape it is like an ungainly ant. Once all termites must have had wings. Now it is only what we may call (for convenience rather than with any approach to exactitude) the royal line that emerges into the world able to fly, and for all but a very few of the "princes and princesses" this means immediate destruction.

This royal line is kept up for the purpose of insuring that the termite race shall not die out. Its members are the only residents in the termitary capable of reproduction. In each termitary there is a queen's cell. There lies the mother of the community, engaged in her business of laying eggs. That is her sole function, her sole occupation. She is enormously larger than any of her "subjects." She is hideously bloated and swollen. Her consort, small and timid, remains near to his immense spouse, but keeps as much as possible out of sight.

The domed cell, which we might almost call a sanctuary, is filled with worshippers who show their devotion by caressing, licking, even biting their huge, sausage-like divinity. There are guards who do their best to prevent her from being bitten, and who "move on" throngs which gather in too large numbers at any particular point. There are also soldiers of more formidable aspect who stand sentinel all round the cell.

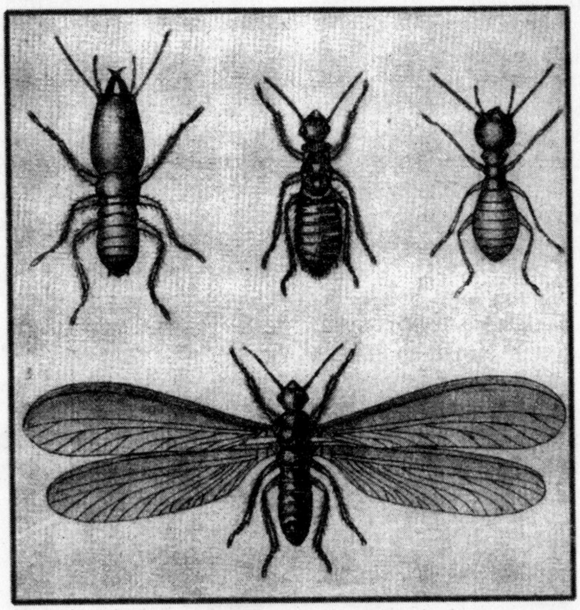

H. Bastin

MEMBERS OF THE TERMITE FAMILY

The various castes in a white ant family vary greatly in appearance as can be seen here. At the top reading from the left are a worker, a reserve female not yet distended with eggs, and a soldier, while below is a typical winged male.

The queen is fed by her attendants; she cannot feed herself. As the eggs drop, they are received by other servitors, washed and carried away to be stored in heaps in chambers above. Should the queen cease for any reason to lay eggs, which she does at the rate of sixty a minute, 86,000 a day, thirty millions a year, she is doomed. Her normal term of existence is from four to five years. During that period, if she remains healthy, she continues to produce eggs at the same rate without ceasing, day or night. If the flow is interrupted, the community recognizes that her value to it has gone. Her attendants stop feeding her. She perishes of starvation. Then her corpse is devoured and a fresh egg-producing machine is installed in her place.

Here we come to the marvel of the termitary which has probably the most vivid interest for most human beings. It is not necessary to keep a stock of reserve royal mothers, though sometimes this is done, and sometimes a queen whose fertility diminishes is allowed to live and to share her position and duty with associate egg-layers. If there is no individual of the royal line to take the place of a queen who has lost her powers, the termites can turn into a queen any of the millions of larvae which are stored in their "nursery," or can force any egg to yield the sort of creature they require.

Exactly how this miracle is accomplished is not yet known. Diet, massage, surgery, regulation of air and temperature, may all be employed. How the eggs are treated is a mystery even more profound.

ONE OF THE BAFFLING MYSTERIES OF THE WHITE ANT SOLVED

Existing in countries subject to droughts, it has long been a mystery how the termites obtain the moisture they need. This was solved by accident. At a place where a 65 ft. shaft had been sunk in vain to obtain water, it was found by Mr. Eugene N. Marais, that the termites succeeded where man had failed: they went deeper down. Our diagram shows on the left a section of the well-shaft, and zig-zagging down the same earth is the termites' tunnel with fungus seed beds ' y ' planted at effective positions. In the lower centre the explorer is examining a portion of the termites' tunnel and seed beds, the latter on an enlarged scale. Above is a sectional view of the termitary.

One further point to notice. Since the associate-queen produced in this way has no need to fly or to see, as have the princes and princesses who take part in the annual flight, she is provided neither with wings nor with eyes. If that be not accepted as proof of an intellectual process, maybe far in the past, it is very hard to know how to account for it.

This annual flight, or swarming, suggests, on the other hand, the maintenance of a tradition which might long ago have beneficially been discarded if intelligence were supreme in the termitary. What happens is this. As the summer draws to its end, the walls, which at all other times are so carefully kept solid in order to exclude both light and other enemies, are pierced by a number of openings. From these fly out masses of perfectly formed termites, with eyes and wings and reproductive organs. They have been nourished at the expense of the community. They are unable to feed themselves. When they are hungry, they tap a nurse or a worker with their antennae and receive a morsel of food already digested which the others exude from their stomachs if it is for the young; from their intestines for the fully-grown.

Why does the community allow so vast a proportion of its members to live without working? Why does it persist in producing so vast a quantity of consumers who contribute nothing to the common stock? Certainly the termites must secure the continuance of their race. They need a certain number of mothers and fathers. But nothing, it seems, can explain the immense cloud of possible parents which issues from the termitary once a year save mechanical adherence to an ancient habit for which the reason has long passed away.

For as soon as they have issued, almost all these possible parents are destroyed. An array of enemies, warned in some way of the feast that will be spread before them, awaits the unsuspecting swarmers as they come forth in a dense cloud and attempt to fly towards the upper air. The effort is quickly over. Their wings fail them, they fall to the ground, they become the helpless prey of the ants and other insects, the birds, the snakes and toads, the cats and dogs, the men even (baked or toasted, royal termites are eaten by the natives of several countries), who have been on the look-out for them. In a short time none are left on the ground. Only a small number have managed to escape; by them new colonies will be formed. They will be the kings and queens of new termitaries. Wasteful Nature thus appears to us to sacrifice countless lives in order that a few pairs may be able to come together and carry on the reproduction of the species.

A. Montgomery

F. Martin Duncan

THE PRISONER QUEEN AND HER ARMY OF ATTENDANTS

The sole function of the white ant queen is to carry on her race. She lays eggs at the rate of 86,000 every 24 hours. The average life of this astounding egg-producer is five years, during which time she lays about 150 million eggs. The lower photograph (approximately life-size) shows a queen with a soldier termite for comparison, and above she is seen surrounded by her attendants, who feed her and carry away the eggs.

The moment the flight has taken place and all the winged termites have quitted their home, the openings in the walls are closed up again. This is done with astonishing speed; the method of it is not less strange. Much of the building material of the termites is, to begin with, swallowed by them. They extract what nourishment is in soil or wood or grass; the waste matter they discharge. Sometimes this is eaten again and again

W. Saville Kent

CATHEDRAL-LIKE EDIFICES OF THE WHITE ANTS IN AUSTRALIA

The industry of the white ant, or termite, is indeed amazing. In a short time it throws up a building with spire rising on spire, like some Gothic cathedral. In the upper picture is a landscape in North Queensland dotted all over with termite hills 13 or 14 feet high, made by a species that always builds with the long axis in an exact line with the North and South poles of the Magnetic meridian. The bottom left picture shows an end-on view of one of these buildings of the Meridian termite and on the right is the hill of another species found in West Australia.

until all the food value has departed from it. Sometimes it is used as building material along with sand and wood.

A French naturalist, M. Bugnion, has described vividly how they use it. He cut into a termitary in Ceylon nineteen years ago. He made a hole in the wall nearly an inch long.

Immediately ten or a dozen soldiers appeared at the hole, then advanced a little and formed a circle with the horns on the front of their heads pointed outwards as though they were prepared to meet the invader. A quarter of an hour later the work of repairing the damage that had been done was busily in progress. A file of soldiers lined the gap, their heads outside, their bodies within. Waving their antennae, they were biting the edges of the opening and making it wet with their saliva. Already I could see all round it a trace of moisture which made it deeper in colour than the rest of the wall.

Soon a worker termite appeared. It examined the gap with its antennae, then it turned round and from its rectum expelled a tiny drop of thick brownish fluid. Another worker then brought a grain of sand, which was placed upon the drop.

This went on over and over again in the most methodical fashion. For half an hour I watched workers come up one by one, inspect the gap, turn round and deposit their tiny drops, and other workers bearing grains of sand or little scraps of wood place them in position. All the time the soldiers, moving their antennae briskly, seemed to be there for the purpose of guarding the workers and directing their labours.

The repairing of the inch-wide breach, done entirely from inside, took an hour and a half.

This same M. Bugnion saw and photographed a host of 300,000 termites marching to and from a tree that happened to have on its bark a lichen of which they are very fond. They went at the rate of three feet a minute and marched between two rows of soldiers who protected them from hostile and marauding ant skirmishers and occasionally fought rearguard actions to cover the retreat of their comrades loaded with lichen.

These soldiers were armed, not with the powerful curved scissor-blade mandibles which distinguish most of the termites, but with syringes, from which they discharge a sticky fluid. The syringes are part of their anatomy, growing in place of a head. As they are without heads, they are without eyes, but they seem to have some sense which tells them where enemies are, for they manage to direct their squirting quite accurately.

Another French naturalist, M. Bathelier, of Saigon in Indo-China, put some of these squirt-carriers into a basin with some large red ants. The ants were soon put out of action. The fluid made their legs and wings stick to their bodies.

M. Bugnion, too, had a good opportunity to observe the syringes in use. He had put a number of the termites who have these soldiers into a box with a glass top to it. The top did not fit well, and when he came in one morning and saw the table on which the box stood covered with ants of a very fierce kind, he feared his termites must have been annihilated. But he then saw the syringe soldiers standing on the table round the box, and also by the groove into which the glass top did not fit. They had been on guard all night. Not a single ant had got past them.

The more usual kind of soldier-termite fights with its scissor-mandibles and is protected by a covering of horn. If ants or other foes succeed in piercing a termitary wall, they rush to the spot as soon as the alarm has been given and thrust their weapons outwards, thus stopping up the breach with their heads. While the battle goes on they make rhythmic noises which can be heard from a distance of several feet. If ants fight their way into the termitary, the soldiers engage them while the workers close up all the passages. Thus the home is saved, but its defenders are sacrificed, for they are left outside.

The workers, like the soldiers, are sexless and blind. Unlike the soldiers, they have no defensive apparatus. Another point of difference is that the workers can feed themselves, since they are provided with digestive organs. With these they do the digesting for the whole community. It is no easy task, for termites live on cellulose, and cellulose is very hard to assimilate. The workers are able to assimilate it by reason of the organisms known as protozoa, which swarm in their intestines. The protozoa are able to digest cellulose (which is the substance of trees, plants, grasses, roots) ; the termites are able to digest them.

Some sorts of termites go to work another way to overcome the difficulty of assimilating cellulose. They cultivate large quantities of an infinitesmal mushroom which feeds on cellulose, and they live on these mushrooms, which give them their nutriment in a pre-digested form. Only in termitaries will the mushrooms grow. Efforts made by men to produce them have failed. The termites collect the spores, sow them on prepared beds, and keep them weeded and watered. When a move is made, the founders of a new colony always carry with them mushroom spores so that they may supply themselves with food.

The workers are, as we have seen already, divided into two categories. Some are large and have sharp, strong mandibles, something like those of the soldiers, but not so powerful. These do all the hard work. They build and repair ; they go forth on foraging expeditions ; they cut up wood and other substances which are needed for food. The smaller kind of workers remain in the home. They are the housekeepers, the nurses. They feed all those who cannot feed themselves. They look after the eggs and the larvae. They store up the food which the foragers bring in to the termitary.

Here we come to another of the specially wonderful sides of the termites' activity. Not only is it necessary to keep the whole place pretty warm. It is essential that the temperature of the "nursery," where the larvae remain until they hatch out completely, should be higher than that of the rest of the termitary. This is managed by regulation of the heat generated from the fermenting of vegetable matter stacked at various points. The termites, in fact, invented central heating a million years or so before even the Romans thought of it. They make the warm air circulate in little corridors running through the termitary in every direction. As for ventilation

Leon Bayer, M.D.

A SKYSCRAPER BUILT BY THE LITTLE WHITE ANTS OF AFRICA

The tallest skyscrapers built by man are like bungalows compared with the homes erected by the white ants, if we take into consideration the relative sizes of the two builders. Here is a great column nearly twenty feet high, built of the hardest material—man can produce nothing to equal it—by the termites of East Africa. It was photographed by Dr. Leon Bayer, who says it is hollow and probably helps to regulate the moisture in the termite galleries that lead many feet below the surface. Openings at the base often shelter small mammals which is equally important, that is secured by means not less adroit. The walls have numberless tiny apertures in them to admit air.

But there is something else which the termites must have in addition to warmth and a fresh atmosphere; this is moisture. When Maeterlinck wrote his book it was not known how they were able to obtain this. In the hottest of African or Australian summers, with all parched for miles around them, they live in an atmosphere pleasantly humid. How they do it has been until lately a complete mystery. Dr. Livingstone, the great traveller and missionary, was so puzzled by this that he thought they might have succeeded in making synthetic water. He suggested the possibility of their combining the oxygen of the air with the hydrogen of vegetable food so as to produce what is known to chemistry as H_2O. It was a fascinating theory and captured the imagination of M. Maeterlinck. But now we know that such a far-fetched explanation is not required. The mystery has been solved.

IN the Transvaal a naturalist of Dutch stock, Mr. Eugene Marais, has investigated the problem on a farm (Pietfontein, No. 1368) and discovered the termites' method. For three years the land had suffered from unbroken drought. The soil was baked, springs were dried up, trees were withering from the dryness of their roots, not a blade of green grass could be seen. A well shaft was sunk to a depth of 65 feet, no trace of water being found. But in the course of their efforts to strike on a spring or a subterranean stream the well-sinkers had opened up several termitaries and had been amazed to see that there was no lack of the usual moisture in them. The termites were quite happy; the mushroom beds were in their normal condition of dampness; the "nursery" was in its accustomed atmosphere of warm humidity.

"How," they asked each other, "could the termites maintain this state of things while all around them the earth and everything in or upon it was parched and bone-dry?" Then, by accident, they hit upon the explanation.

Making another attempt to strike water, they uncovered a shaft constructed by termites which was evidently connected with a colony up above. The shaft was full of termites, some going up, others descending. The well-sinkers suspected at once that these were fetching water for the termitary, and when they had excavated to the base of the shaft they confirmed their guess. Observation was now kept on the termites, who continued to go up and down, although they were exposed to the light of day. A most valuable addition to our knowledge of their methods was made by Mr. Marais, who watched them, and by marking certain of them with dye discovered that the same individuals came again and again, daytime and night alike.

Their well had been sunk to a greater depth than that of the men and they had got down to the water level. It took the water-carriers as long as half an hour to travel from the termitary to the bottom of the shaft and back again. They had no intervals of rest. They disregarded the danger which threatened them when the shaft had been uncovered. Ceaseless the movement of descending workers on the left side, ceaseless the climbing of those who bore their load on the right. Besides carrying water, they took up mushroom spores for replenishing the beds; these came from nursery gardens planted at intervals on the way down.

The termites were clearly excited by their struggle to save themselves from perishing by lack of moisture and at the same time to wall themselves up afresh and keep out the light which, in spite of their blindness (or possibly because of that), seems to be an agony to them. The watcher had evidence of their perturbation not only in their hasty movements, but in the noises he could hear—the same rhythmic noises that they make when they battle with armies of invading ants.

The fresh knowledge thus acquired about the termites' ingenious ways is not only most interesting in itself, it gives encouragement to hope that further discoveries may be made and more of their secrets laid bare. The only one that we can hardly expect to learn is the great secret of all: Why do they do it? Or, as M. Maeterlinck asks, "What governs here? What is it that issues orders, foresees the future, elaborates plans and preserves equilibrium, administers, and condemns to death?"

Are we to go on attributing to instinct the brilliant ability which the termites show in the ordering of their State, the devotion they display to the interest of the community instead of their own interest, their heroic courage, their sublime self-sacrifice, their ingenuity in meeting difficulties and dangers? Or must we allow them the gift of intellect, not dissimilar in essence from that bestowed on us, and in some directions superior to it?

THE Belgian poet takes refuge in a misty speculation. He suggests that the termitary itself is the source of all the activities connected with it. He imagines vaguely some Occult Power, directing the energies of the termites with the sole aim of keeping the termitary secure and ensuring the continuance of the race.

Like Nature, as she appeared to Tennyson, this Power would be "careless of the single life." It would sacrifice the parts to the whole. In other words, the termitary would be the individual, its inhabitants merely infinitesimal cellules composing it.

This is rather a theory to play with than a serious conjecture. If we are to come nearer to solving the many problems which the termites offer to us, we are more likely to be helped by the patient study of naturalists than by the notions, stimulating though they be, of an imaginative writer. We can scarcely, however, look forward to the solution of them all, for if we knew what goes on in the minds of termites, we should, to quote Tennyson again, "know what God and man is." We should then have nothing more to learn.

A. J. Shipley

W. Saville Kent

TERMITE BUILDINGS THAT IN SIZE AND SKILL RIVAL THE WORK OF MAN

If man, in proportion to his size, could build as skilfully and industriously as the white ant, he could set up a building as big as Mount Everest. Some species of termites in South Africa erect homes forty feet high and in the upper picture we see part of one of these vast structures being demolished on a farm. It takes a whole army of men to undo the work of the tiny termite. Below is a termite mound at Port Darwin, in Australia, of the columnar type. Its size—it is 18 feet high—can be judged by the waggon standing at its side.

Chapter III

The Marvel of Animal Coloration

By W. P. Pycraft

Author of "Camouflage in Nature"

WHETHER we consider the beasts of the field or the fowls of the air in regard to their coloration we are soon faced with strange contrasts. It is as though we were looking at some old illuminated manuscript enriched with scrolls and arabesques and gorgeous blendings of gold, lapis-lazuli, and vermilion set on the fringe of a crowded text formed of letters presenting a dreary uniformity; which may, or may not, after due study, prove edifying.

Why are the peacock and the bird of paradise so gaily apparelled while the sparrow and the wren wear plain russet the year round? We may go farther and ask, Why are they coloured at all, and whence come their hues?

Our search for an interpretation soon brings out the fact that coloration, in itself, is not an essential; since myriads of animals have translucent bodies, to wit, myriads of the microscopic protozoa, jelly-fish, and those strange, incipient vertebrates the salpae, as well as larval fishes, and newts. These living ghosts, however, it will be noted are all aquatic.

When we come to survey that larger assemblage of animals whose bodies are more or less conspicuously coloured we are tempted to conclude that somehow this coloration, from its very universality, must have some deep meaning: that it must, in short, be essential to their well-being.

But such a conclusion would be only partly justified. For it becomes apparent, after a little search, that coloration is an inherent quality wherever it is met with, quite apart from any relation it may have acquired with the outer world.

This much is forcibly demonstrated in the case of the cone-shell. As will be seen in the photograph on page 29, showing two such shells, the surfaces are marked by a very definite pattern. Yet, so long as the creature lives that pattern remains invisible; for it is hidden under a thick layer of epidermis. Only after death, when all the perishable tissues have vanished, is that pattern revealed.

The living conus has a coloration absolutely different from that which covers the concealed shell. Has this also no meaning?

Enough has now been said to show that we may not formulate theories without carefully weighing the facts on which such theories are based. We have to suspend judgment till we have studied the coloration in relation to its environment, in relation to its character, and in relation to the habits and sex of the individual presenting this or that combination of colours which we call the "coloration." But of this more presently.

What follows will be the more easily grasped if something is said now as to the source of this coloration. Briefly, then, it is due in all cases, directly, or indirectly, to pigments which are of two main types—melanin pigments and lipochrome pigments. The melanin pigments are derived from the blood. They are waste-products, deposited in the skin, hair, feathers, or scales, as the case may be, instead of being carried out of the system altogether with other waste products. Dark brown and black are among the most conspicuous of the various melanin pigments.

Yellow and red are lipochrome, or fat, pigments, and hence are derived from the reserves of the body. Other pigments known as derived pigments, because they are drawn directly from the corresponding constituents of the food, as in the case of the green colours of caterpillars, are found only in a few cases.

But however derived, it does not always follow that these pigments serve any useful purpose. They may, indeed, be accidental properties of the substance they pervade. The red colour of blood, for example, or the green colour of the bones of some fish, like the gar-pike or the American amia, cannot be regarded as purposeful colours.

BUT be this as it may, one may safely say that the coloration of most creatures is purposeful. Any animal which tended to develop a coloration rendering the body conspicuous would expose itself thus marked to its enemies, while those of duller hues would escape. The recognition of this fact was first made by Darwin. It was left to Professor Poulton to work out its full significance.

To-day we recognize several distinct types of coloration. Of these the most important are protective and warning coloration, mimicry, and the coloration associated with what are known as the secondary sexual characters.

Examples of protective coloration might be cited by the hundred. But none more convincing can be found than are furnished by the sitting pheasant, or partridge, or wild duck. So long as they remain perfectly motionless they are invisible.

We see here that the precise pattern of the individual feathers is of no consequence; for each of these species has its own peculiar patterning, but the general effect in all cases is the same—a mantle of invisibility.

In some birds the coloration is associated with a special posture of the body when fear induces a desire to escape detection. In the bittern the whole body is held vertically, the beak pointing skywards. At the same time, care is taken always to present the under surface to the source of danger, as if conscious of the qualities of its coloration. For the front of the neck and breast now present a series of dark vertical lines on a paler background, harmonising perfectly with the shafts of light seen between the

W.S. Berridge

MOST BRILLIANTLY COLOURED OF ALL THE MAMMALS

The mandrill offers an unsolved problem in animal coloration. Its amazing colour scheme, scarlet nose and cobalt blue cheeks, which are furrowed as though a miniature plough had been over them, puzzles the scientists, who cannot say how such brilliant hues were first developed or of what use they are to the male, who alone wears them. No other mammal is so brightly coloured.

tall reed-stems. The Norfolk plover (*Oedicnemus*), again, matches the sandy wastes on which it lives. When alarmed the bird throws itself flat upon the ground, with the neck stretched straight out and pressed as close to the earth as possible. So long as it remains perfectly still only by the merest accident will it be discovered. The night-jar, similarly, lies along, instead of across, the bough of the tree wherein the hours of daylight are spent. And in this position it so closely resembles the bark that detection is well-nigh impossible.

But it is not only the creatures which desire to escape being eaten that wear a mantle of invisibility. The wolf must wear sheep's clothing if his fashion is to steal upon his prey unawares. And so the tiger haunting grass jungles wears a hide which is vertically striped; the leopard, lying up in a tree, is spotted; the spots harmonising with the play of light through the leaves, and breaking up the solid appearance of the body, thus causing it to blend with its surroundings.

That these harmonies between coloration and environment are no mere coincidences is further emphasised by the fact that deer which live in tropical forests, like the axis deer, have a spotted hide the year round; while such as live in woodland glades, leafless for half the year, have a spotted hide only in summer, the winter covering being unicoloured.

Sometimes, as in the case of butterflies and moths, two quite different liveries are worn at one and the same time; one being exposed during flight, the other when at rest. In other words, the upper and under sides of the wings are differently coloured. The butterflies, when at rest, keep the upper surface of the wings closely pressed together above the back, and this surface is generally much more conspicuously coloured than the under, though the swallow-tail and some others are exceptions to this rule.

The famous kallima butterfly of India, the Malay Archipelago, and Africa affords a peculiarly striking example of an insect which is able to change his coat, so to speak, in the twinkling of an eye; how the racecourse welsher must envy him! During flight the wings present a broad expanse of dark blue, relieved by a wide band of golden yellow. But the flight is erratic, and if pursuit becomes at all pressing it will cease instantly, the gaudy body vanishing as it were into thin air. What has happened? Keep a watchful eye on the leaves of the bush over which the flight ceased. Sooner or later one of the leaves will show the faintest suspicion of a double edge, and the next moment the gap may widen, revealing the blue and gold of the lost fugitive. If the under side of the wings of a captive specimen be examined the mystery will be explained. For the coloration reproduces that of a dead leaf with the most astounding fidelity. There is the mid-rib, the venation, and even spots and clear spaces as though due to the attacks of fungus. The mid-rib runs down into a short stalk, formed by projecting spurs from the hind wings; these, when brought close together, form the stalk, and apparently spring from the stem like a leaf.

F. Martin Duncan

BUTTERFLY THAT PRETENDS TO BE A LEAF

This butterfly, the Kallima, is of purplish-blue and yellow, and in flight is very conspicuous. If pursued by a bird it disappears, the explanation being that it has alighted and closed its wings which, on the underside, resemble a dead leaf.

With the moths the wings, when closed, are held horizontally over the back, the fore-wings completely concealing the hind-wings. When the wings are expanded it is found that it is the upper, and not the under, surfaces which have to be considered in regard to their coloration. Where this is of a protective character the necessary camouflage is borne by the front-wings, and when these are expanded they disclose a blaze of colour, as, for example, in the red and yellow underwing moths. The poplar hawk-moth, and some others, when at rest, thrust the hind-wings slightly forward, so that they stand out a little beyond the outer edge of the fore-wing, thus giving a leaf-like appearance to the body; the coloration, of course, adding the finishing touch to the deception.

Occasionally not merely the coloration but the whole body is shaped to perfect this likeness to the external surroundings. Many of the looper caterpillars, for example, as of our swallow-tailed moth, peppered moth, and brindled beauty, take on so close a likeness to the bare twigs among which they hide as to make detection extremely difficult. These have long, cylindrical bodies, and have reduced the number of their legs to help the deception. Grasping the twig on which it is resting by a pair of clasping-legs at the extreme end of the body, the creature

TWO REMARKABLE EXAMPLES OF PROTECTIVE COLOURING IN ANIMALS

The colouring of defenceless animals is often of such a nature as effectively to conceal them from their enemies and the giraffe (below) and zebra (above) are two notable examples. The vertical stripes of the zebra, which make it so conspicuous in a zoo, harmonise with the long grass of the haunts in which it is found. Similarly the tall motionless figure of the giraffe, with its body colour broken up into blotches, blends so completely with the trees and shrubs amid which it rests, that it is lost sight of, even though it may have been located while moving.

The photographs are from Mr. and Mrs Martin Johnson's famous film "Simba."

contrives to stand out stiffly at a wide angle from the supporting twig, as if it were a part of the plant. And it will maintain this position without the slightest suspicion of a tremor throughout the long hours of daylight, unseen and unsuspected. Some of these caterpillars, like those of the purple-thorn, develop excrescences on the body simulating the leaf-scars on the surrounding twigs.

A SPIDER found in Java, and another nearly-related species found in Ceylon, spin silken webs on a leaf to simulate the liquid part of a bird's excrement. Taking its place in the centre of this the spider forms the darker area of the patch, and here it awaits butterflies and other insects coming to sip at the welcome moisture. As soon as they alight they are seized!

A few of the mantises have, by a seemingly diabolical cunning, so changed their bodily shape and coloration as to cause them to be mistaken for gaily-hued flowers. We say seemingly advisedly, for it is not to be supposed that this is a conscious likeness, or has been assumed by taking thought. A striking instance of this disguise is furnished by the Indian mantis (*Hymenopus bicornis*). The general coloration of the body is pink, and the petals of the flower are simulated by the flattening out of the legs. Hanging head downwards it awaits its unsuspecting victim, which presently comes near enough to be seized by the long fore-legs, fashioned to form deadly traps by reason of the fact that they are enabled to fold back the terminal segment of the leg upon the segment next above it, like the blade of a clasp-knife; the edge of the blade being armed with formidable teeth. Nothing can escape their deadly grip. Butterflies and other insects come to this lure for a draught of nectar. Their end is swift!

Some use lures of a more active type. The matamata water-tortoise, whose shell has been modified to form a series of bosses simulating stones lying at the bottom of the stream, lies in wait for small fish. As these approach, a long, worm-like tongue is thrust out, and given a wriggling motion. The fish respond to the tempting-looking bait, and are instantly engulfed by the inrush of water caused by the sudden opening of the mouth.

The angler-fish is an expert in the use of lures. The skin surrounding the huge mouth is, as it were, frayed out. Currents of water induced by breathing set the ragged fringe in gentle motion, attracting the attention of small fishes; or they are brought within range by the waving movement of a flap of skin borne at the end of a long rod formed by one of the rays of the dorsal fin, which has become split up into a number of isolated rods widely separated from one another, the foremost being situated immediately over the rim of the mouth. Attracted by

Oliver G. Pike

SITTING PARTRIDGE HIDES IN THE HERBAGE SURROUNDING HER NEST

The hen partridge, when sitting on her eggs, is difficult to find, as her brown and black plumage blends remarkably well with the tangle of grass and bramble round about, and the human eye is deceived. The camera, however, is able to pick out the detail. Were it not for this protective colouring birds with nests on the ground would be at the mercy of many enemies.

M. H. Crawford

THE SWALLOWTAIL IS ALWAYS CONSPICUOUS

Most British butterflies that are brightly coloured on the upper side, have dull undersides, so that when they alight and close their wings they may remain unnoticed by enemies. The swallowtail is a curious exception, being brightly coloured on both sides.

the foremost lure the fish come unsuspectingly to the very jaws of death, for the fisherman lies half concealed in the mud. When the victims are sufficiently close the mouth is suddenly opened, and with the consequent inrush of water the poor dupes are swept in.

It would almost seem as though these creatures were conscious of the benefits they derive from the likeness they present to their surroundings. Take the case of the spider-crab, for example. Here the body is made to match its surroundings, not by its natural coloration, but by fixing pieces of seaweed to bristle-like hooks which cover the shell and legs. Take a captive spider-crab, strip him of his covering, and pitch weed and crab into a large bowl of sea-water. Presently the captive will begin to place every scrap of weed back again. If, instead of the weed, small stones are thrown into the dish till the bottom is covered, the crab will fasten on the stones instead, till once more it matches its background.

The remarkable univalve molluscs, known as carrier-shells (*Xenophorides*), fasten to their shells pieces of coral, the shells or fragments of shells of other molluscs, and even those containing living occupants; while some of the hermit-crabs, in like manner, use live sea-anemones. When it becomes necessary to move into a larger shell the anemone is gently unseated, and placed on the new home to serve as a living mascot.

SOMETHING must now be said of creatures which can change their coloration with the most astonishing rapidity, not merely by the incidence of light falling upon prismatic surfaces, as in the case of the metallic feathers of the peacock, which at one moment may show green, the next blue, the next copper, for here the coloration is fixed, the changes are due to the effect of lighting.

The colour changes to which attention is now drawn are to be seen in their highest perfection in, say, the octopuses and squids, and some of the tropical fishes. And this because the pigments lie immediately under the outer surface of the skin.

They consist of little droplets of pigment, enclosed within a series of small, closed membranes or pouches, richly supplied with nerves and subservient strands of muscular fibres. The various pigment-sacs are attuned to respond to differing intensities of light received through the eye, as is shown by the fact that blind fishes make no colour change. By this mechanism trout, for example, are able to adjust their coloration to harmonise with the colour of the bottom of the stream in which they live. But this change is effected slowly. Very different is the case with the Nassau grouper of the Bermudas, shown in the photographs in page 29. In the upper figure it is seen as a dull lead-coloured fish, while below it is seen banded and marbled with pure white; and this change takes place within a few seconds.

Some of these tropical fishes display the most astonishing range of coloration, and captive specimens lose none of their ability for such transformation. Different individuals in the same tank will produce the most dazzling effects. Thus, a uniformly yellow fish will suddenly assume an orange tint on the back, and this will gradually deepen into brownish red, while the sides and under parts will become paler. At the same moment a greenish fish will suddenly flash out red. Another will change from yellow to deep bronze, striped with blue; and the stripes may change from longitudinal to vertical with the most disconcerting rapidity.

In these cases it is clear that the sudden changes

E. J. Manly

A FISH THAT CHANGES COLOUR

The Nassau grouper, a fish of Bermuda waters, is normally of a dull leaden colour, as in the upper picture, but under the stimulus of light it changes colour and, within a few seconds is conspicuously banded and marbled with white, as in the lower photograph.

are due rather to emotional than to light stimuli. But whatever the stimulus the effect is the same—at one moment all the pouches containing blue or yellow pigment are, as it were, squeezed flat, so as to spread their contents into a thin layer; while the bronze or the red pigment-pouches will contract to assume a spherical form like so many little pudding-bags, whereby the pigment is concentrated into a small, inconspicuous droplet, having no effect at all on the coloration.

LET us pass now to the theme of warning coloration, the very antithesis of protective or concealing coloration. Always and everywhere it is associated with nauseous qualities. The evidence shall speak for itself. Perhaps the most convincing and most striking instance of this type is that furnished by the skunk of North America. This creature is most conspicuously marked with longitudinal bands of black and white. When alarmed, instead of seeking safety in concealment it ostentatiously parades before its potential enemy. Should this be a wolf or dog it waits until the oncomer is within a few feet, then suddenly turns its tail to the attacker and squirts, from glands near the base, a most virulent and evil-smelling liquid. Blindness may follow should it touch the eyes; and foaming at the mouth results from the smallest particle of this corrosive spray which may touch the tongue. Never again will that black and white demon be molested! Should the dog's owner, standing several yards off, receive the smallest particle of this spray on his clothes, they will be unwearable for weeks. So nauseating is the smell that in some people it induces fainting.

There are several species of skunk, differing one from another in size, as well as in markings, but in all of them, these markings consist in strongly contrasted areas of black and white. A precisely similar warning livery is worn by the African zorillas, and the Cape pole-cat; and these, in like manner, discharge from glands at the base of the tail an acrid liquid having a most repulsive odour.

Emphasis must be laid on the fact that all these creatures, though technically carnivores, feed upon insects, worms, roots, and fruit, as well as on mice, frogs, lizards, and so on. Hence they are not dependent on concealment for the capture of lively prey. In this it is important to note that they differ conspicuously from their near relations the stoats, weasels, and martens, which are wholly carnivorous, and protectively coloured.

BLACK and yellow and black and red are common types of warning coloration. The hornet and wasp are familiar examples of the black-and-yellow types; and there is no need to stress the power of these insects to inflict punishment on the unwary. The black-yellow salamander, though powerless to injure man, is effectively protected against aggression by animals which seize their victims in their jaws. For the salamander when taken into the mouth exudes from glands on each side of the back of the head an acrid juice. One such lesson suffices.

The small toad known as the fire-bellied toad presents a very singular form of warning coloration, since when at rest it is protectively coloured. But when alarmed it throws itself upon its back, revealing great blotches of black and red. Some of the South American tree-frogs of the genus Dendrobates, display warning colours in great variety. Some are black and white, some black and red, some black and yellow, while one is vermilion coloured with dark patches on the back and legs. All, however, are highly poisonous. This fact is well known to the natives, who apply this poison to the tips of their arrows when shooting monkeys. Thus introduced

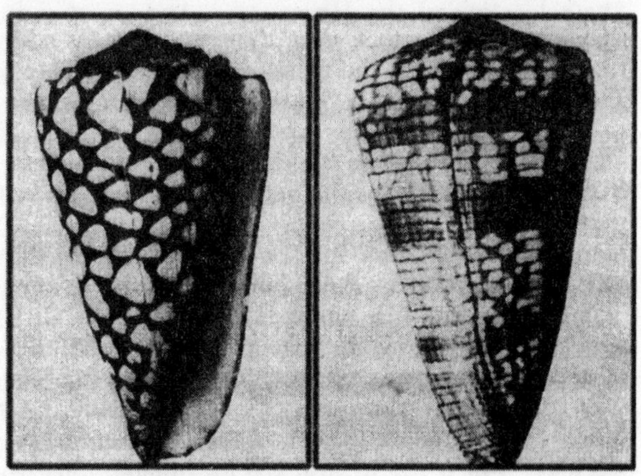

E. J. Manly

SHELL MARKINGS SEEN ONLY AFTER DEATH

The conspicuous markings of the cone-shells, two examples of which are given here, are familiar to all, but when the mollusc that inhabits this type of shell is alive the pattern is quite invisible, being covered by skin, which perishes at death and lays bare the pattern into the victims' blood-system the heart and central nervous system are swiftly deranged, and they fall helpless to the ground. It is also worth noting that the only lizard possessing poison fangs, the gila monster or heloderm lizard, is coloured black and red.

Experiment has shown that the gaily coloured caterpillars, like the black-and-yellow larvae of the cinnabar moth, are never eaten by birds save in the direst need. Throw a number of protectively coloured and warningly coloured caterpillars to the fowls in the farmyard, and watch the result. All will be instantly snapped up, save the black-and-yellow-coloured. If any of these do happen to be seized they are quickly dropped.

The remarkable facts which have been embodied to form the theory of mimicry are intimately associated with warning coloration. The phenomena are best exemplified among the butterflies, which, indeed, led to the discovery of the strange facts about to be described.

The traveller-naturalist Bates, collecting natural history specimens on the Amazons more than half a century ago, was struck by the singular uniformity in the coloration of the butterflies at each of his several halting-places. However varied their patterns, when the collection was seen as a whole, the colours were always the same—black and yellow—colours, be it noted, associated with nauseous qualities. It was not until he began to study his spoils at leisure, after his return to England, that he solved his puzzle.

THE most numerous forms were always some species of Heliconias, a broad-winged, slow-flying insect; like the skunk, indeed, advertising the fact that all who attacked would do so at their peril. All the remaining butterflies were of different genera, belonging to the Pieridae, to which our cabbage-white belongs. There could be no mistake, because the venation of the wings, and other deep-seated characters, which distinguish the Heliconias and the Pieridae, are quite distinct. The Pieridae had, in short, completely disguised themselves by assuming the coloration of the Heliconias. And, in so doing, they masked the fact that they were really edible species by assuming the guise of the nauseous species. This type of mimicry is known as Batesian mimicry, to distinguish it from an even more remarkable form of this subterfuge known as Mullerian mimicry, from the discovery by the naturalist Muller, that the various species of the genus Heliconias were closely mimicked by as many species of the equally inedible genus Melanitis. He then showed that this common likeness conferred an immense advantage on all the species concerned ; since it would spread the incidence of attack from inexperienced birds, and other foes, over the whole community, and it would at the same time immensely reduce the number of such attacks. For if the several species differed, one from another, in coloration each would have to bear the brunt of experiment.

Our own bee-hawk and clear-wing moths furnish us with good instances of Batesian mimicry, for they bear a most uncanny likeness to bees, hornets, and wasps. And to effect this, too, they have to rid the wings of their scales, to make them transparent. The innocuous hover-flies, so common in our gardens during the summer, bear a striking likeness to bees.

It is not to be supposed that these creatures consciously assume the coloration of the inedible species. The likeness, to put it briefly, has come about through the agency of natural selection, whereby any variation towards the coloration of the inedible gave the variants a better chance of escape from their enemies than the more conservative individuals. Doubtless it has taken an immense time to bring about these results, but Nature is never in a hurry.

Throughout the animal kingdom we find marked differences in coloration between the sexes. Nowhere is this more apparent than among the birds, and nowhere can the facts associated therewith be so easily studied. The inferences to be drawn therefrom will be found to apply with almost equal force in regard to other groups.

THIS survey must of necessity begin with species in which male and female are coloured alike, and of relatively sombre hues as, for example, in the wren. Where any advance in the direction of a resplendent dress is found it will be noted that it starts with the male, as in the case of the common sparrow.

When all the evidence comes to be surveyed the conclusion seems to be irresistible that the evolution of a resplendent dress was at first an evanescent, seasonal phenomenon, due to the activities of the reproductive glands at the time of the spring moult ; as, for example, in the case of that remarkabe member of the plover tribe, the ruff. At the autumn moult he sheds his splendours and assumes again a plumage like that of his mate.

That foundation once laid there grew up a tendency to retain the resplendent or nuptial plumage for longer and longer periods, till at last it becomes the permanent livery of the male. The mallard is a good illustration of this phase. For he wears his ancestral dress, resembling that of the female, for no more than a few weeks. The cares of a family have hardly begun—and he leaves these to her—than he goes into eclipse, assuming a livery often confused with that of the female, and at this time he is flightless, owing to the fact that all the quills or flight feathers are moulted at once, instead of in pairs as is the rule among birds. Being flightless, the protection afforded by his concealing coloration is all-important.

By the late summer the new quills have hardened, and he then proceeds to moult again, resuming the characteristic resplendent dress we know so well. In some of the game birds, like the blackcock, no more than a vestige of this ancestral " female " dress remains, for its last traces are seen in the head and neck, which, for a short space, stand out in sharp contrast with the rest of his plumage, since they are coloured like that of the hen. In *Gallus*, the neck hackles are for a short space discarded. In the pheasant the resplendent dress is never lost.

The gorgeous birds of paradise for a short space are hen-coloured, and this is true also of many brilliantly coloured weaver finches and tanagers, which wear two distinct liveries known as the winter and summer plumages. These changes are often striking, as in the scarlet tanager which has a summer or nuptial dress of scarlet and black but in the winter a dress of green and black.

The next phase in the evolution of a permanently resplendent dress is seen where the female acquires the like splendours of her mate, leaving the ancestral, sombre dress to the young, as in the case of our starling. Finally, we have the case of the kingfisher where male, female, and young are all resplendent. But much is yet to be known. Why, for example, is the house-sparrow resplendent, after his fashion, leaving the drab hues to the female and young, while with the tree-sparrow, not only the male, but female and young are all resplendent?

In this brief chapter it has been impossible to do more than trace the broad outlines regarding the coloration of animals and its significance, but enough has been said to show what a fascinating theme it is.

r Martin Duncan

INSECTS SHAPED AND COLOURED LIKE LEAVES

The leaf-walking insect, two examples of which are given in this photograph, is a native of India. It cannot fly for it has no true wings, but the wing-cases are shaped like a leaf and the colour varies according to the foliage it frequents.

The Living Rainbow of Animal Colour

THE large three-fold colour plate **facing the preceding page** is not intended as a scientific contribution to the subject of Animal Coloration which **Mr. Pycraft deals with in** Chapter **III**. It has been designed chiefly to illustrate in a novel, yet accurate, manner the fact that all the colours of the rainbow are also displayed in animal life.

The animals have been skilfully grouped by the artist along the respective **colour bands** of the rainbow to which their predominant hues most nearly correspond. The result is at once pleasing and instructive, and the editor doubts if so large a variety of birds, beasts, fishes, reptiles and insects has ever been represented so effectively in the same space.

There are in all 197 figures (naturally, relative sizes could not be shown), and below a complete key-list is provided, numbered in the order of the colours from left to right. The scientific names are given only in those cases where no 'popular' names are available. Typical black and white and grey animals are shown in the right bottom corner of the plate.

RED: 1, Coccinella septempunctata; 2, Cardinalis Cantharis; 3, Xanthospilopteryx superba; 4, Zygaena filipendulae; 5, Cantharis Nuttalli; 6, Ampelis carnifex; 7, Rhamphocelus ignescens; 8, Rhomalea; 9, Cardinalis Virginianus; 10, King Bird of Paradise; 11, Cardinal Lory; 12, Cock of the Rock; 13, Red and Blue Macaw; 14, Crimson-breasted Barbet; 15, Golden Pheasant; 16, Banded Snake; 17, Pterois miles; 18, Streaked Gurnard; 19, Golden Red Perch; 20, Actinia chiococca; 21, Sun Star; 22, Giant Crab of Japan; 23 and 25, Actinia mesembryanthemum; 24, Red Coral.

ORANGE: 1, Orange-tip Butterfly; 2, Hypotrabala Neavei; 3, Curculio brunnens; 4, Callioratis Millari; 5, Large Copper Butterfly; 6, Phromnia rubra; 7, Horia maculata; 8, Miniodes discolor; 9, Arctia caja; 10, Danais archippus; 11, Giant Swift Moth of Australia; 12, Arctia caja L.; 13, Blue-breasted Lory; 14, Short-billed Minivert; 15, Toto Toucan; 16, Sappho sparganura; 17, Orange Fruit Pigeon; 18, Selatophorus rufus; 19, Rhamphastos maximus; 20, Xanthornus aurantius; 21, Weaver Bird; 22, Gila Monster; 23, Solverenus; 24, Amphiprion Cicinctis; 25, Bunodes coronata; 26, Balanophyllia regia; 27, Comet Goldfish; 28, Spinous Cockle; 29, Stomphia Churchiae; 30, Sagartia troglodyte; 31, Orange-disk Anemone; 32, Pecten opercularis; 33, Mauritius Star Fish.

YELLOW: 1, Brimstone Butterfly; 2, Niasia difformis; 3, Opisthograptis luteolata; 4, Cassida micans; 5, Clouded Yellow Butterfly; 6, Geana sulphurea; 7, Madagascar Giant Moth; 8, Blue and Yellow Macaw; 9, Muscicapa chrysomela; 10, Black-tipped Sulphur Butterfly; 11, Zygaena filipendulae; 12, Golden Oriole; 13, Paradisea apoda; 14, Golden Conure; 15, Heniochus macrolepidotus; 16. Beaked Chaetodon; 17, Gemmous Dragonet; 18, Camel; 19, Cystagnathus Senegalensis; 20, Salamander; 21, Jaguar; 22, Leopard; 23, Giraffe; 24, Antilope scripta; 25, African Fennec; 26, Tiger; 27, Lion.

GREEN: 1, Polyommatus Endymion; 2, Curculio Latreillii; 3, Great Green Grasshopper; 4, Ityraea electa; 5, Cantharis vesicatoria; 6, Melachius marginellus; 7, Buprestis bicolor; 8, Cassida bicornis; 9, Enchloron megaera; 10, Ornithoptera Priamus; 11, Puss Moth Caterpillar; 12, Swallow-tail Butterfly Caterpillar; 13, Emperor Moth Caterpillar; 14, Oleander Hawk Moth Caterpillar; 15, Leaf Insect; 16, Pseudochalcothea auripes; 17, Mantis; 18, Chameleon; 19, Livingstone's Turaco; 20, Rana esculenta; 21, Ceratophrys ornata; 22, Green Lizard; 23, Australian Frilled Lizard; 24, Alexandrine Parakeet; 25, Budgerigar; 26, Glossy Starling; 27, Trogon pavoninus; 28, Psittacus aestivus; 29, Pionus menstruus; 30, Green Woodpecker; 31, Peacock; 32, Actinia mesembryanthemum; 33, Sagartia troglodytes; 34, Sagartia chrysosplenium; 35, Globe Fish; 36, Kelloggella cardinalis; 37, Rainbow Leaf-worm.

BLUE: 1, Apoderus ruficollis; 2, Curculio sexdecimpunctatus; 3, Rhynchites pubescens; 4, Calopteryx splendens; 5, Neurobasis; 6, Morpho cypris; 7, Adonis Blue Butterfly; 8, Desmocerus cyaneus; 9, Calopteryx virgo; 10, Orthetrum cancellatum; 11, Oedionychis cincta; 12, Coris aygula; 13, Polyommatus venus; 14, Polyommatus marsyas; 15, Erycina melibaeus; 16, Physalia pelagica; 17, Abudefduf Lencopomus; 18, Garfish; 19, Blue Wren; 20, Cacreba cyanea; 21, Blue Creeper; 22, Pica colliei; 23, Small Racquet-tailed Kingfisher; 24, Lanius bicolor; 25, Ampelis cotinga; 26, The Blue Bird; 27, Common Kingfisher; 28, Hyacinthine Macaw; 29, Blue Tit; 30, Edolius coerulescens; 31, Indian Black-naped Flycatcher; 32, Blue Bird of Paradise.

INDIGO: 1, Victoria Crowned Pigeon; 2, Tectocoris Banksii; 3, Blue Crossbeak; 4, Lyrurus tetrix; 5, Mikado Pheasant; 6, Pelrossirus atrodosalis gunther; 7, Geotrupes stercorarius; 8, Scincus caelestinus; 9, Oceanops Latorittata; 10, Brachyluphus fasciatus; 11, Cychlae fasciata; 12, Gomphosus coeruleus; 13, Blue Shark; 14, Sailfish.

VIOLET: 1, Ianthina globosa; 2, Australian Star Fish; 3, Sea Slug; 4, Purple and Gold Bird of Paradise; 5, Violet Plantain Eater; 6, Purple Hairstreak Butterfly; 7, Goliathus magnus; 8, Rhinoscapna Bennetti; 9, Mouhotia Batesi.

WHITE: Polar Bear, Arctic Fox, Stoat, Ptarmigan.

GREY: Grey Falcon, Grey Parrot, Striped Hyena, Indian Buffalo, Boatbill, Grey Lag Goose, Peccary.

BLACK AND WHITE: Malay Tapir, Ostrich, Zebra, Porcupine, Guereza Monkey.

BLACK: American Black Bear, Raven, Black Panther, White-handed Gibbon.

THE GIANT DRAGON OF KOMODO, MOST STRIKING OF ALL THE LARGER REPTILES

It is only within recent years that the great lizards living on the East Indian island of Komodo have been proved realities. For generations the natives of adjacent islands told tales of great and fearful dragons that lived at Komodo, their terrified imaginations magnifying the sizes of the monsters till they were supposed to be between twenty and thirty feet long. Many people, however, were sceptical about their existence till 1912, when an expedition went out and actually found these huge lizards. Monsters were seen as long as fifteen feet. Some of the dragons were caught alive, including the one shown here with its tongue projecting, and brought to the London Zoo, where their habits are now being carefully studied.

Chapter IV

Dragons That Are Alive To-Day

By Joan B. Procter, F.Z.S., F.L.S

Curator of Reptiles to the Zoological Society of London

The thanks of the Editor are due to Miss Procter for enabling him to publish the unique series of illustrations of the Komodo lizards under her care at the London Zoo, these photographs having been specially taken by Mr. F. W. Bond for WONDERS OF ANIMAL LIFE. For the illustrations which appear in pages 38 and 39 and the lower photograph in page 35, he is indebted to the courtesy of the American Museum of Natural History, New York.

To the minds of many people, the word dragon suggests a purely mythical beast ranking with the phoenix and the unicorn. They think of winged serpents, and if they happen to be reporters writing articles on the real dragons at the Zoo, they cannot resist at least one reference to St. George! In other words dragons are relegated to the past; to art, mythology, and the world of imagination. And yet almost all fictitious dragons are based on living reptiles, usually lizards, but sometimes giant pythons and crocodiles. Some are actual reptiles which I shall describe, and others composite beasts made up on the "Makara" principle, like the nursery game, "Head, body, and tail."

In the East there are several lizards with crests, wattles, and other decorations, and those of the genus *Draco* have brilliantly coloured wings with which they can volplane from tree to tree. Their wings are supported by prolonged ribs, and superficially resemble those of butterflies. These lizards also have gular sacs, and if they were not small in size would be very impressive.

Another species which resembles the Chinese dragon, is *Phisignathus cochinchinensis*, which is found in Siam, Annam, and Cochin China, and which is also very beautifully coloured and crested.

It happens, however, that the dragon of the Dutch East Indies, so much dreaded by the natives, is a genuine creature, a colossal monitor-lizard living on Komodo Island, which lies between Sumbawa and Flores, in the Lesser Sunda Islands.

But although only lizards, and not even prehistoric, they are quite equal to the dragon of fable. They are certainly the most powerful living lizards, with wonderful muscles and large heads, limbs, tails, claws, broad snouts, red mouths, long, forked, snake-like yellow tongues, strong recurved teeth, brilliant eyes; and perhaps a quality that is more important than the rest: a curious dignity, given to them by the regal way in which they hold their heads and carry themselves as they move about.

The skin is coarsely scaled and very delicately shaded in several colours. They are always described as brown, but this is only the general effect, caused by the fact that each scale has a brown spot almost reaching to its edge. But the skin itself is almost carrot-orange on the shoulders and back, and lime-green on the neck and chest, and black predominates on the head and limbs. The general effect is mainly chestnut, with brighter shades on the front part of the body, and darker limbs. The upper eyelids and long, thin tongue are pale yellow.

Naturally, as the lizards grow older, the juvenile colours give way to dull browns and blacks, but the description in this chapter is based on two healthy seven-feet specimens which cannot be said to be very young, and the pair have grown noticeably brighter as they have become healthy and contented, although one would not have expected their coats to improve to such an extent in captivity.

There is no doubt that this monitor is the most striking of all the larger reptiles. The natives call it *Boeaja darat*, or land crocodile, and herpetologists, or reptile students, have compared it with *Tyrranosaurus* and many other prehistoric monsters. It was discovered to science as a reality only recently, and was first described in 1912 as *Varanus komodoensis* by the zoologist Ouwens, who sent collectors to Komodo to search for the lizards, because certain pearl-fishers had corroborated the dragon stories of the natives of the adjacent islands. Five specimens were killed for him, the largest of which measured about nine and a half feet. At this time the species was thought to attain a length of at least 23 feet, but now that we know more about it, it seems probable that 15 feet is about the maximum.

Then in 1926 the American Douglas Burden Expedition went to Komodo and explored the island and rounded up many dragons, the largest of which was just over nine feet. The principal object of the expedition was to get material for a dragon 'group' for the New York Natural History Museum, and for this they brought back twelve dead specimens together with masses of useful photographs of the lizards in their natural habitat. They also brought two live specimens for the Bronx Zoo, which, however, soon pined to death. Burden says of these, "It was painful to see the broken-spirited beasts that barely had strength to drag themselves from one end of their cage to the other."

We now come to the much happier dragons in the New Reptile House at the London Zoo. They arrived on Whit Sunday, 1927. We christened them Sumba and Sumbawa, and they are now almost as well known and as much photographed as Douglas Fairbanks and Mary Pickford.

They were obtained for us by Dr. Malcolm Smith, the herpetologist, to whom they were sent by the Governor of the Dutch East Indies, and as soon as we knew that they had been shipped we began to arrange a perfect home for them in the new house.

Their enclosure contains a cave, electrically heated rocks, a swimming pool, growing palm-trees, overhead heat-beam radiators and ultra-violet artificial sunlight lamps, focussed in parallel, vita-glass lights, and other arrangements, which, working together, produce a miniature Komodo, with correct climate and surroundings.

Owing to the enormous strength of the lizards, the ceiling apparatus had to be protected by steel bars, and the lower portions of the partitions are disguised sheet metal. We also provided four doors, one in each corner of the enclosure, for the safety of keepers, because, according to the American accounts, the dragons might be expected to be ferocity personified.

When the dragons arrived, they were ill and miserable; so we gave them warm baths, drinks, and medical attention. It is not possible to give their correct lengths, as both of them have lost quite six inches of tail, but they are about seven feet each, and weigh approximately between four and a half and five stones. They differ from *Varanus salvator* in almost every particular, but chiefly in relative bulk, for in head and body they are more than twice as large as a seven-foot *V. salvator* in our collection. In the latter somewhat slender species, quite two-thirds of the total length is tail, as against barely one-half in the very powerfully-built *V. komodoensis*. It is almost certainly this fact which has given rise to the stories of their gigantic size, for estimating upon the lines of better-known species, one would get entirely wrong figures.

Further, Dr. Dunn, who was with Burden, says that when the lizards are tracked and watched in their wild state, they give quite an overpowering impression of size, so much so that as each lizard was shot its actual measurement was invariably a surprise and disappointment. Moreover, they carry themselves with such dignity, and are so muscular, that even half-grown specimens must appear alarming to people who do not understand reptiles. Mrs. Burden was evidently terrified by them, for she writes: "The creature was now less than five yards away, and its subtle reptilian smell was in my nostrils. Too late to leap from hiding. If I did, he would surely spring upon me, rending me and devouring my remains as he had devoured the dead deer."

Yet Sumbawa can be trusted with small children!

In fact, almost everything that has been written about these dragons proves to be inaccurate. After the opportunity of studying the lives and domestic

A "CLOSE-UP" OF THE GIANT LIZARD, SHOWING THE MUSCULAR DEVELOPMENT OF ITS FOREQUARTERS

Seen in this fore-shortened position, the Komodo monitor looks as formidable as any dragon of the story-books, yet its keeper can lead it about as tamely as Saint Martha led the monster Tarasque in the legend of Tarascon. This photograph very clearly illustrates the immensely strong neck and breast muscles and powerful forelegs. The skin of these huge lizards, which is covered with scales, is in their earlier years delicately shaded in several colours. They have been kept so ingeniously in their London captivity that they are now perfectly healthy.

DRAGON'S JAWS THAT CAN BITE THROUGH SOLID METAL

These photographs afford some idea of the massive heads and muscular jaws possessed by the great lizards of Komodo. They can even bite through metal, and yet during the whole time that the dragons have been at the London Zoo they have never attempted to snap at a human being. The long yellow bifurcated tongue, like that of the snakes, is used as a sensory organ.

routines of our now perfectly healthy, spirited, and normal Sumba and Sumbawa for over 15 months, it seems amazing that so much nonsense should have found its way into scientific literature! One of the worst items is that the species is described as stone-deaf, when in actual fact they have the same sense of hearing as the other members of the genus. Of course, it is very difficult to test the hearing of wild animals, but the fact that they frequently take no obvious notice of sounds is no proof whatever that they are deaf. On Komodo Island what have they to fear, and consequently to listen for? The only large mammals are buffalo and harmless deer; all other creatures on the island, such as pig, and smaller mammals, water-fowl, smaller monitors, and so on, are preyed upon by the dragons, who hunt by sight and smell. Experiments show, however, that our Sumba and Sumbawa will turn their heads sharply when called now that they have learned to associate the call with food, but, of course, only if they are hungry, and if they feel in a responsive mood. I have on these occasions taken great care that they should not catch sight of me, or pick up vibrations of footsteps. If you take a Siamese cat, as another example of a protected animal of independent character, you will find that it will not so much as turn its head when you speak to it, unless it happens to feel in the mood; why should it? And if you call to it to come in when it is stalking birds, it will not pay the slightest attention to you, and yet who would dare to say that cats are deaf? The behaviour of these lizards cannot be construed on the same lines as that of domestic dogs, or timorous antelopes.

Then there is the question of the way the eyes are described, and also portrayed in the stuffed specimens, as beady. The living lizards have large, very bright, and gentle eyes, like the eyes of Alsatian wolf-dogs. And the upper lid is not at all flattened or beetly, but rounded, and of a pale lemon yellow, like the long lithe tongue.

POWERFUL AND FEARSOME REPTILES THAT ARE AS GENTLE AS LAMBS

Although many stories have been told of the ferocity of the giant lizards of Komodo, their dragon-like form, huge size, and voracity seeming to lend confirmation to such reports, yet a close acquaintance with two of the reptiles at the London Zoo has quite discounted this estimate of their character. They like to be stroked and patted. The Curator of Reptiles at the Zoo takes one of the dragons with her when she goes on a round of inspection. As seen in the lower photograph the dragons carry themselves with great dignity, a fact that seems to impress all who see them.

The question of the ferocity of these lizards is, perhaps, the most misunderstood of all. All the lizards of the genus *Varanus* are savage, predatory, and highly strung, and they use their teeth, claws and slashing tails with great effect, as I have personal cause to know. At the Zoo we consider any large monitor more dangerous to deal with than a crocodile twice its size. But, allowing for this, *V. komodoënsis* is the gentlest, most intelligent, and most tractable of them all. This is comparing them with specimens only half their weight of species such as *niloticus, albigularis, bengalensis, salvator, nebulosus, varius,* and so on. It is quite true that they are very nervous, and also that they could no doubt kill one if they wished, or give a terrible bite when taking food from the hand greedily, but there is no vice in them.

THE DRAGON SWALLOWS A CHICKEN WHOLE

The giant lizards of Komodo in their native haunts seize pigs and small deer for food, but in London they are fed chiefly on fowls and eggs. The lizard swallows a fowl whole in two gulps, its great mouth opening wide enough to take the bird, as seen in the lower picture. Its jaws are very powerful and once, when being given an egg in an iron table-spoon, it bit off the bowl.

Sumba is the more nervous of the two, and if he is meddled with or bothered, as for instance if one picks ticks off him, or if he is frightened, he will turn at bay and open a large red mouth. He also slashes with his tail, but on the other hand he takes food from our hands, and will sometimes permit his head to be stroked and his back scratched. Sumbawa, the heavier, larger dragon, has never attempted to bite at all, even though she has had to submit to surgical dressings, cauterization of septic tick-bites, and daily dental treatment. The more treatment she receives the more tractable and gentle she becomes.

TELEPHOTOGRAPHIC IMPRESSION OF TWO OF THE LIZARDS OF KOMODO FORAGING FOR FOOD IN THEIR NATIVE HAUNTS

This picture, reproduced from the touched-up print of an instantaneous photograph taken on the Island of Komodo by the Burden Expedition, is not offered as a faithful reproduction of the dragons in detail; but it has definite value as illustrating their movements in pursuit of food. Having been "snapped" at a distance in unfavourable light, the details of the original photograph are necessarily indistinct, though the general impression of the scene and the motion of the reptiles are graphically conveyed.

When they first arrived they both required a great many painful dressings, for they had canker of the jaw, injured tails, septic paws, torn claws, and abscesses. Now, however, they are very well, greedy, and generally fit. There is nothing of the craven captive about either of them, and there is also no question of their being sluggish, for they have a tropical climate, and about eight hours of artificial sunlight each day. Sumbawa comes for daily walks with me on my rounds of inspection, investigating everything that might be of interest.

She has no objection to my holding the end of her tail and using it as a rudder, and she is good at walking up and down stairs. Only a few weeks after her arrival she gave a children's tea-party, and she does not mind small children bullying her. Except when she is actually bolting food, she is absolutely safe. When she is in a tiresome mood one can wrestle with her, and she will struggle like a naughty child and persist in what she is doing, but she never bites or attacks. Of what other reptile of that or any other weight can this be said? For one must always remember that it is certainly true that these monitors do tear down pig and deer and swallow large fowls in two gulps. Certainly I dare not touch our large *V. salvator* without two men to help. But *V. komodoensis* has the natural temperament of a nice large dog, and I am not quoting from our own London Zoo dragons alone, for I have just heard that one has arrived in Berlin, and that this specimen is also really gentle with human beings.

Like most intelligent creatures they have varying fancies about food. Sometimes it is large fowls and at others vast quantities of eggs, each one carefully picked up whole. Both Sumba and Sumbawa will take an egg off a spoon

"THE HABITATION OF DRAGONS WHERE THEY DWELL"

The great monitor lizards of Komodo make homes for themselves among the rocks of their East Indian island by digging out the earth with their powerful claws. Selecting a place sheltered by trees they scratch away the soil till the roots are exposed, and into the den thus formed they crawl when darkness falls and remain under cover all night. Then, when morning breaks, they come out and prowl among the rocks for food, seizing any unlucky mammal or bird that comes their way. Their dens can accommodate two or three men.

very neatly, but to give some idea of the strength of their jaws it must be added that once Sumbawa bit the spoon off the handle along with the egg, and it was a very stout metal tablespoon! Sumba, having grasped the fact that his mate gets more food than he does by coming out among the public, has now become a "gate-crasher," which is a little tiresome, because his manners are not so reliable. So now that we are in a position to understand the psychology of these terrible dragons we are more surprised with them than ever. But personally I prefer to enjoy their friendship in London, and not to visit them on Komodo for the purpose of trapping and shooting them. On the whole, two healthy living specimens teach far more about the species than many dead ones stuffed. And as even dragons are mortal, the British Museum will ultimately receive their bodies for morphological research.

GIANT DRAGON FROM A FAR EASTERN ISLAND IN ITS TROPICAL LONDON HOME:
The "dragons" of Komodo are the Goliaths of the land reptiles and may grow to a length of fifteen feet, though the more common size is twelve feet. They are really carnivorous lizards that could no doubt easily kill a man, but the stories told of their ferocity are almost certainly exaggerations. Two specimens are living today in the London Zoo and Miss Joan Procter, the scientist who has charge of them and who has written about them in the accompanying chapter, states from experience that they are perfectly gentle, tractable, and never aggressive. In addition, they are

F. W. Bond

THE LIZARD OF KOMODO RESTING ON HEATED ROCKS AND BASKING IN ARTIFICIAL SUNSHINE

described as remarkably intelligent and they certainly appear to be perfectly happy in their London home, which has been so constructed as to reproduce in every important detail the conditions of their native island of Komodo in the Dutch East Indies. Like the dragons of romance, those of London live in a cave, and this has a commodious swimming pool, electrically heated rocks, growing palm-trees, overhead heat-beam radiators, ultra-violet artificial sunlight lamps, and vita-glass lights. With Shakespeare we might almost say: "Did ever dragons keep so fair a cave."

Chapter V

The Amazing Story of the Common Eel

By E. G. Boulenger

Director of the Zoological Society's Aquarium

Of the many solid achievements which the present age may count to its credit, the solving of the eel mystery may be considered as one of the most important, involving as it does not merely the unravelling of the life history of an individual animal, but marking an epoch in deep sea exploration and economic oceanography.

The eel's sudden appearance in vast numbers and its equally sudden disappearance, its presence in isolated waters far from the sea or rivers, these facts among others baffled the best scientific brains for centuries. Not that the tale is even now altogether told. The newly-laid eel's egg, if it is laid at all, has not yet been discovered, nor has a wholly-ripe female eel, that is, one containing mature eggs.

So late as the latter part of the seventeenth century, when man had fairly set out to map the world and catalogue its treasures, this fish, abounding in home waters, was the subject of conjectures and learnedly-propounded theories that to-day merely provoke our mirth.

Izaak Walton, writing in 1653, says: "Eels growing old breed other eels out of the corruption of their own age, which exceeds not ten years. As, also, worms are made of glutinous dew-drops which are condensed by the sun's heat, so eels are bred of a particular dew falling about May or June on the banks of ponds and rivers." Eels were likewise supposed to be generated from horse-hair, straw, and so on, after prolonged saturation in fresh water.

It must be borne in mind that the trawl and all other complex apparatus at the command of modern investigators were as yet not even contemplated. It was known, however, that eels were often, as they still are, dug out of the mud and even brought to light by the plough far from any water. The various-coloured varieties were known, and also the fact that the adult fish might often be caught hurrying seawards. Further, the elver fishing of the Severn and many other rivers was a much-looked-for event. Millions of tiny little elvers about the thickness of a straw were caught at the surface in the spring, being netted or even baled out with pails and blankets, and such fry were converted into cakes. Eel fairs, though now on the decline, still exist in certain districts, but to-day the bulk of the home supply comes from the Netherlands.

Early marine biologists of all countries have recorded captures of the glassy, transparent creature termed a leptocephalus, or small-head. The first taken in British waters was caught near Holyhead in 1763. Some of the specimens captured later were kept alive long enough for them to undergo some startling changes before metamorphosing into a juvenile eel. Their eyes became much smaller, their teeth fell out, the whole creature became opaque, and cylindrical instead of compressed and leaf-like. Such experiments cast a flood of light upon the entire eel question, and the next problem presenting itself was whence came the leptocephali.

This was a harder proposition, since it could only be solved upon the high seas. Two Italian investigators in 1893 found large numbers in the Straits of Messina, but no trace of them outside the Mediterranean. At this point progress came to a halt until 1904, when the Danish Fisheries Board began investigations, and Dr. Johannes Schmidt succeeded in capturing off the Faroe Islands a leptocephalus seven and a half centimetres long, or roughly three inches, a form known by the laboratory researches to be the larva of the common European eel.

From this point onwards investigations proceeded apace. The seas were scoured for leptocephali from Iceland to Morocco. Such a task was obviously impossible for a single ship, and numerous commercial trawlers and cargo vessels were enlisted to help with the work. These towed small fish trawls at varying depths, from the surface to near the sea-floor, for several hours a day, carefully preserving the catch, with date, position, temperature, and other necessary data. As a result it was established that the eel larvae decreased in size from east to west, but at the

COMMON EEL IN ITS SILVER LIVERY

The common eel changes colour several times during its life. When it first appears in our rivers it is olive green. As it grows this changes to olive brown, and when its breeding time arrives it assumes a silver livery, such as it is wearing here.

same time increased in numbers, and the pursuit of the leptocephali led the investigators further westward.

It was in the neighbourhood of Bermuda that they were found to mingle with those of the nearly-related American eel, but the two species were never found together east or west of a prescribed area. The American eel larvae, for instance, were only taken between the West Indies and the mainland. Careful records of the young eels caught further established the fact that the American eels grew much more rapidly than the European.

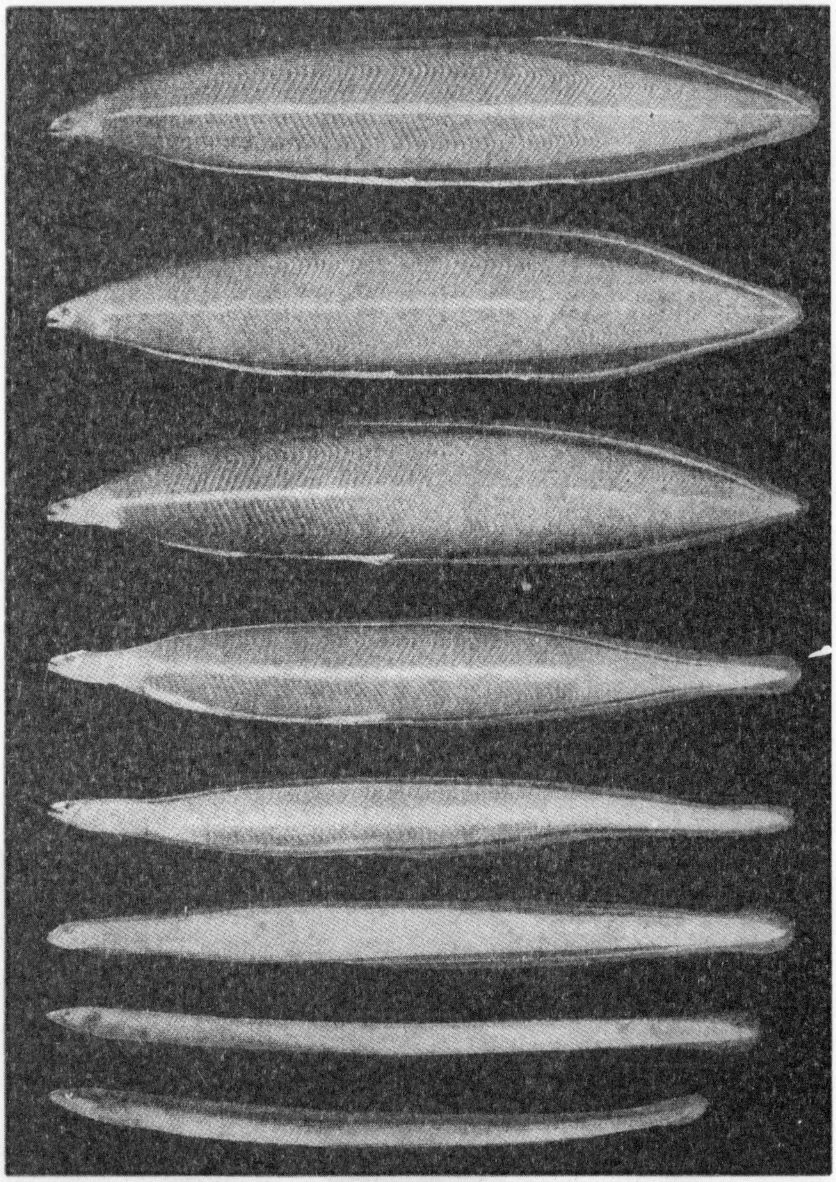

EIGHT STAGES IN THE EARLY LIFE OF AN EEL

In this picture, for which we are indebted to Dr. Johannes Schmidt of Copenhagen, we are shown various stages in an eel's early life. Born deep down in mid-Atlantic it is first of all a tiny leaf-like creature as thin as paper. Gradually it becomes more cylindrical, till at last it is like the bottom specimen here, and then begins to make its way across the sea to the rivers.

FROM early spring to late summer the eels of the two hemispheres congregate in countless hosts in deep water in the western Atlantic, where one can only assume that the parents die. In their stead arise millions upon millions of leptocephali of two species differing from each other only in obscure details.

The American eels at once head westward and in a year reach the coast and proceed to the interior via the rivers. The European eels make east, at first travelling not far from the sea-floor, but rising by easy stages as they head for their goal, a three years' journey beset with innumerable perils. Only a small minority of those hatched survive the ordeal. In the course of their progress young eels eat everything within their compass, chiefly the minute floating plants and animals termed collectively plankton—young jellyfish, sea squirts, molluscs, crustaceans, and fish. This minority of surviving eels, forming at times a huge expanse of glassy appearance, drifts ever eastwards. Gulls attack the swarms from above, while flying-fish, mackerel, and other surface swimmers likewise take their toll. Yet, even after three years of steady persecution the hosts of infant eels colour the estuarine waters as they forge their way inland.

By this time a subtle change which began when the larval eel left the breeding grounds is almost completed. The body is snake-like in form, and of a dull, olive green. The appetite steadily increases, and larger and still larger animals come within its scope. No river is safe from the incursions of the growing eel. With the advent of its first winter it haunts the lower waters, eventually coming to rest on the river-bed. Winter finds it deep in the mud, but the spring brings it once more into activity.

With the advent of summer it is literally a giant refreshed, and nothing it can engulf is safe from its voracious jaws. It may forge its way up tributaries and canals, and even gain an entry to water-mains. So, slowly watching for the wherewithal to stay its insatiable appetite, it snatches mayfly from the surface and digs the crayfish from its burrow. Nothing living is deemed inedible by this ever-hungry eater, even its own brothers and sisters.

The entire form now makes for easy and swift progression. The long body is barrel-shaped and wonderfully supple. The slightly prehensile tail becomes compressed into a flattish paddle and may anchor the eel in swift currents leaving its head free to snap at and engulf such creatures as are within its reach. Forward movement is accomplished by sinuous movements of the body and fins, which are employed to a certain extent in walking, for as an eel grows, the more complete is its conquest, not only of the water, but the land. The dart-shaped head is perfectly formed for exploring the burrows of water rats and can force its way through mud or dense reed thickets. And where the head can go the body can follow. Moreover the gill chambers are capable of retaining a large quantity of moisture which the eel can draw upon for its life's blood in periods of drought.

Thus, well equipped for the battle of life, the eel steadily forages onwards. So long as feeding is good it stays more or less in one place. The food supply exhausted, the onward march begins again. The stay in fresh waters may extend for ten years and possibly more. In a sudden drought it will lie in the mud or on some shelving bank till the rain swells the stream. Under cover of night it may progress overland through the dew-drenched grass, possibly eating as it goes, and only such behaviour explains the presence of eels in the Swiss lakes three thousand feet above sea level.

The female of the species is more deadly than the male, for the father eel seldom exceeds three feet in length, whilst the mother may reach nearly double that size and a weight of 25 pounds. The female develops a protruding jaw, an index to her pugnacity and voracity. The sexes live apart so far as mating is concerned until they meet again, as we shall see later, at their common birthplace in the far western Atlantic. Doubtless many a female eel engulfs a male and occasionally vice versa in European waters. It depends of course upon the size of the fish as to which engulfs which.

A large eel has been known to migrate from stream to pond and there drag down to destruction moorhen chicks and ducklings as soon as they were hatched. Even the constricting powers of a large eel are not to be despised. Authentic cases are recorded of monster specimens that have been speared by herons and so involved their slimy coils with the avian necks that fish and bird died together. In all probability the birds died first, as the eel's vitality is amazing.

The fish is probably quite a stranger to pain as we understand the term, for a large eel caught not long ago in Lancashire was found to have three hooks embedded in its interior and they had evidently been there for many months buried deep in the intestinal fat. Yet the fish rose eagerly to a worm which proved its undoing. Even after being skinned and cut in pieces reflex action may cause the dismembered fragments to seem unpleasantly alive.

A FISH of such active habits in all situations would be seriously hampered by a covering of stiff unyielding scales. The eel's scales are minute and embedded in the skin, and a plentiful supply of very active slime glands accounts for the proverbial slipperiness. Being unusually sensitive to atmospheric pressure the fish is in many parts regarded as weatherwise. A thunderstorm, for instance, invariably arouses the creature, however great its previous lethargy. This may be explained by the fact that a thunderstorm always means the washing of much bankside food, worms, insects, and so on, into the stream, besides a dramatic disturbance of the stream bed. Ancient chronicles told how the old-time fishermen took advantage of this weakness on the eel's part and in the Fen districts actually beat drums on sultry nights to make the eels 'run.' The vibration near shallow waters lured the fish from their snug hiding places.

Eels are most active and adventurous after dark. In an aquarium they may be found in the morning several tanks away from where they went to bed. A specimen kept in the Regent's Park under-water zoo left its tank night after night to seek that inhabited by some sea anemones a considerable distance away. Every morning it was replaced in its own aquarium, but as soon as it was dark it wandered forth to seek the home of its choice. Eventually the zoo officials gave in and the obstinate

J. J. Ward

UNFISHLIKE SKIN OF THE EEL

A fish of such lithe activity as the eel would be greatly handicapped by a covering of stiff scales like those of ordinary fish. It has, therefore, only very minute scales embedded in its skin, a portion of which is shown in this micro-photograph.

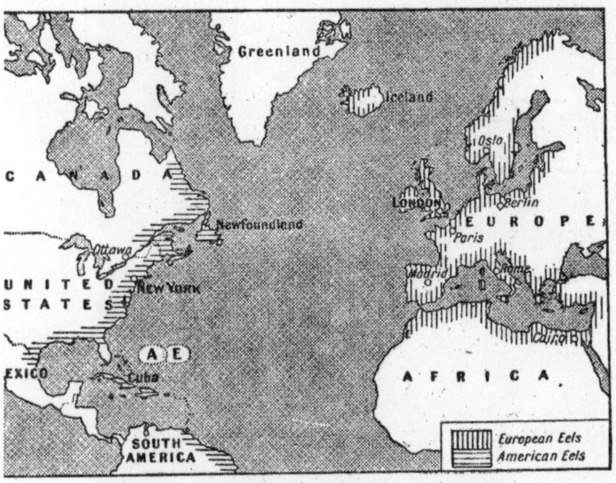

THE EELS' MID-ATLANTIC NURSERY

ll the eels found in the rivers of Europe and America have been ›rn far off in the dark depths of the Atlantic. Their breeding area marked here with two small overlapping ovals, and the eels ıen travel east and west to the areas marked on the coasts, hence they pass up the estuaries in vast numbers and into the smaller rivers.

reature was left undisturbed to enjoy the company f the anemones, which it found such an attraction.

Sex becomes assertive when the eel is anything :om seven to ten years old. :xact figures are impossible, his being among the minor eel uestions still unsolved. Once, owever, that the eel hears the all, it turns about and makes ›r the sea. The eel, having eaded eastward, runs an even arder gauntlet than that which t hazarded when travelling rom the Bermudas to, let us ay, the Grand Junction Canal. Iow it is fat and full grown nd fair game to every man vho is skilled to catch it. All nanner of nets are placed in anks across its path, and in)enmark alone the eel catch is vorth annually over £100,000.

These eels, like all mature els, have exchanged their olive rown clothing for a bright ilver livery and are known as ilver eels. In the Baltic at least hey hug the coast for many niles and it has been found ›ossible to mark specimens nd note the rate of progress.)ne eel travelled at the average ate of just under ten miles ›er day for thirty days in uccession. Other cases show uch rates of travel as 230 miles n 29 days and 750 miles in 93 lays. An eel marked and iberated in Finland in August vas captured the following November off Jutland. In the Mediterranean region the eel is trapped in exaggerated lobster pots, huge cages three feet in length laid at intervals of twenty yards, each cage strung on a common rope.

It is sufficient tribute to the eel's fecundity that despite all the obstacles from the spawning to the fattening grounds and back again there is no marked shortage in the eel supply. In spite of the creature's increase in bulk the adult must find the homeward journey a very difficult one, as sharks, skates, and other sea beasts that may have easily overlooked the eel in its baby clothes now realise its existence and are bent on its extermination.

The common eel, like the rat and the sparrow, is one of those animals that has made its way in the world by virtue of its marvellous powers of adaptability, the true keynote of success in Nature. The common eel ranges from the Bermudas to the Swiss Alps, while all other species of eels and congers other than the common European and American species are, as at present known, confined to the sea.

There are many unfulfilled gaps in the life story of other members of the eel family and the scientific trawl and tow net continually bring to light fresh species of those curious transparent leptocephali.

A GOLIATH OF THE EEL FAMILY: THE GREEN MORAY

The common eel of European waters is not very big, but it has relations in the tropical seas that grow into giants ten or eleven feet long. The two eels shown in this photograph are goliaths of this kind. They are known as green morays and are found in the Atlantic and Pacific. They have been known to attack men. Fishermen catch them for food purposes.

F. W. Champion

AN AUTO-PORTRAIT OF THE KING OF THE INDIAN JUNGLE TAKEN AT NIGHT BY FLASHLIGHT AS HE TROD UPON A WIRE

This magnificent photograph of a tiger taken in the foot-hill jungle of the Himalayas, shows the animal at a distance of only thirteen feet from the camera. It is the finest picture of a tiger in its native lair ever taken, and great preparations and enormous patience were needed to get it. The photographer, Mr. F. W. Champion, having first of all discovered the track which the tiger regularly used, arranged the camera and flashlight apparatus to face this path, and then set a trip-wire in such a way that if the tiger passed he would probably catch his foot in it, so setting off the light and releasing the camera-shutter. For two nights nothing happened, but on the third night the tiger came and took this splendid portrait of himself.

Chapter VI

When Night Falls on the Jungle

A Chapter of Personal Adventure

By The Rt. Hon. Lord Lugard, G.C.M.G.

Formerly Governor-General of Nigeria; Author of "Our East African Empire"

MAN is undisputed lord of forest and plain in the hours of daylight. Elephant and buffalo, lion and tiger that fear no other living creature, will move away when his scent is borne towards them on the breeze, though they may challenge him if he comes unexpectedly upon them. The "rogue" and the "man-eater" alone have for one reason or another cast off the natural and instinctive dread of man. But when night falls man's supremacy is in abeyance, and he feels it. If he must perforce sleep in the open, he protects himself by a blazing camp-fire. If he ventures into the jungle he takes refuge in a tree. It is "night, wherein all the beasts of the forest do creep forth. The young lions roar after their prey . . . The sun ariseth . . . Man goeth forth unto his work and to his labour until the evening."

No one, I think, who has traversed the jungle by night, but has experienced that curious feeling of powerlessness—the consciousness that every hostile beast has quicker hearing, and scent, and better sight in the dark than he has. His heavy foot is incapable of their noiseless tread, his weapons are discounted against their sudden onset in the darkness.

THE sportsman who has planned to spend a night watching some jungle pool has, however, generally settled himself comfortably before sunset that he may not miss the earlier visitors. The dead silence which falls on the jungle when the sounds which by day reach the ear without creating any distinct impression—the twitter of birds, the occasional scream of the fish eagle, the hum of insects—wholly cease, and all is still save the dancing fire-flies, and the noiseless passage of a night-jar, or a bat, or some night moth, is a silence like no other.

It was over forty years ago that as a youngster I was fired with ambition to achieve the distinction of killing a tiger—the Mansur man-eater in the Central Provinces of India, which had been responsible for the deaths of a great number of natives, and had baffled the efforts of a number of sportsmen. There was a big reward on his head and a big reputation to be won! Did ever a British subaltern exist who in such circumstances would not risk his skin to the uttermost? Had not the noted Padre shikari, brother to my old friend Sir James Willcocks, who had bagged the equally noted Higginghat man-eater, devised a plan and been covered with ridicule—and straw—in its failure?

It was in this wise: The Mansur man-eater was known to lie beside the road along which the laden country carts brought their produce by night to the neighbouring city. The tinkling bells of the oxen warned him of the approach of a ghari, and he had sprung on the sleeping driver and carried him off. So the Padre filled a ghari with straw and sat in it, putting a dummy man on the driver's seat. The tiger got the dummy all right, but his impact upset the empty cart, and the Padre was buried beneath his own straw!

So I thought I would take no chances, if that is the right way of putting it, and I spent day after day following with my trackers the actual spoor of the tiger, and sitting at night in a machan over the water where he was due to drink. A machan, I must explain, consists of a few sticks lashed crossways to the boughs of a tree to form a seat, and there is sure to be one, made by natives to shoot pea-fowl, over any permanent pool in the jungle.

It is a thrilling experience to watch breathlessly, as the sun goes down, and the moon begins to throw a fitful and weird light between the forest trees, when at any moment you may hope to see the great head of the tiger emerge noiselessly from the jungle.

On two occasions I had rather comical little adventures. The first was when a sudden storm with thunder and lightning and a deluge of rain came on. The peasants who make these machans are careful to put them high in the tree, well out of the way of danger, and consequently I was rocked about and my rifle slipped from my hands and fell. It banged against the tree trunk lower down but fortunately did not go off, and with some misgivings I made up my mind to go after it.

IT was pitch dark, and as I was drenched to the skin I thought it best to shed my clothes first. I retrieved the rifle and regained my seat, but as the man-eater might for all I knew be looking on I did not spend more time about it than I could help. Had he come I think he could hardly have helped laughing—before he proceeded to business—at the ridiculous picture of a naked white man groping about for his rifle. I always had a small basket with a cold fowl and a piece of bread, and it was a relief when daylight broke to put on my partially dried clothes and light a pipe after breakfast.

My second absurd adventure was on a later occasion, when after the same man-eater in a different part of the jungle. I had been on his fresh tracks all day. We had come to the conclusion that he had not drunk any water, and my native shikaris were convinced that he would unquestionably drink at a particular pool, the only one in the vicinity.

When we got there we found a lean and scraggy bullock which someone had tied up as a bait—not knowing that it was the man-eater, (who did not care

Major Radclyffe Dugmore

A GROUP OF HARTEBEESTS GO DOWN TO THE WATER-HOLE AT MIDNIGHT AND DRINK IN COMPANY

Despite the apparent stillness that comes over the jungle when darkness falls, there is nevertheless much movement among the animals by night. They are continually travelling to and fro between their sleeping haunts and the water-holes where they drink. Yet only the keenest human ear can detect signs of movement. One moment there may be no animal at the water and a minute or two later a whole herd may be drinking. The upper picture shows a group of hartebeests arriving at the water-hole, and in the lower photograph they are actually drinking.

From the great adventure film "Simba" by Mr. and Mrs. Martin Johnson

BUFFALO AND RHINOCEROS REVEALED BY THE CAMERA IN THE DEAD OF NIGHT

The jungle by night is full of risks and uncertainties for the lonely explorer, and even if he hears a beast approaching his hidden camera he can never be sure of the picture which the developed film or plate will reveal. Here, however, are two pictures which the photographer regarded as adequate rewards for his solitary vigil. The rhinoceros in the lower photograph continued to stand still, quite unconcerned at the sudden glare. The upper picture shows a buffalo drinking. This animal, the most vicious of jungle beasts, is far more dangerous than the lion or tiger.

From the film "Simba"

YOUNG LIONESS FEEDING IN THE HOURS OF DEEPEST DARKNESS

Though human beings generally sleep at night and work and eat in the day, in the jungle it is different, for there most of the animals, especially the beasts of prey, sleep by day and come forth at night to seek their food. In this picture, one of the finest and clearest night photographs of jungle life ever taken, we see a lioness standing by a zebra which she has slain. She seems quite unalarmed by the flashlight, possibly because vivid lightning is so frequent in tropical lands that a sudden glare seems a perfectly natural happening. A moment later and she had begun her meal.

for ox-flesh), that was about. But alas, there was no tree anywhere near. The only apology for a tree was a sort of pollard, the stump of which was too close to the ground to be of any use. So we fell on the expedient of borrowing from the nearest village a charpoy—a native bedstead—and thought that if this were dumped on the top of the small branches of the pollard, and lashed to the largest of them, it would support my weight.

I sat cautiously on it, my food-basket at my feet and my rifle between my knees, hardly breathing with excitement as the hour arrived at which my tiger should make his appearance. Suddenly the sleepy old ox made a rush to one side, and the dry jowari stalks, left as fodder, made quite a crashing noise.

It could be nothing but the tiger—at last! I leaned very cautiously and breathlessly a little to one side to get a better view, when without any warning whatever the main bough gave way, and the charpoy, myself, and the cold fowl descended with a crash upon the bullock and jowari! The heavy rifle barrel struck me on the forehead when I landed on my back, and dazed me for a moment, but the position was so ludicrous one could not take it seriously. Whether the tiger had come or not I shall never know. If he had, the sight of a charpoy, a man, and a dead fowl descending from the sky must have scared him as much as it did me and the ox.

I got one of the man-eaters eventually—for there turned out to be two—a fine tigress, but not by sitting up at night. The Government reward paid for the rifle with which I shot her, and her skin with the little double-barrel ·450, are here in my study where I am engaged on subjects so different from those which I have been tempted to recall.

A few years later I spent a night in the jungle in Nyasaland. I was travelling up the lake in a small launch, and we had moored for the night. I had landed and shot an eland. We took the meat we required, and as I was told that the place was noted for the number of lions, I decided to spend the night in the tree nearest to the carcase. We made a strong machan, and an African—a magnificent specimen of a man—sat beside me.

THE surroundings were different from the Indian jungle. Instead of the leafless teak trees, there was verdant forest. Instead of the melancholy sunset call of the pea-fowl, and the distant belling of a sambhur, there was the hardly audible sound of a distant lion. But there was the same indescribable feeling of intense isolation, of being in a strange world peopled by aggressive carnivora who had got all the odds on their side. And there was a difference from the dry Indian jungle of which I had omitted to take count. Clouds of mosquitoes

Major Radclyffe Dugmore

A LION AND HIS MATE PROWL THROUGH THE AFRICAN JUNGLE IN THE STILLNESS OF THE NIGHT

When darkness falls upon the jungle, and in tropical lands its descent is sudden, there comes a stillness that oppresses and appals. It is then, when every sight is blotted out, that man feels his utter helplessness. Only by an iron determination and a strong effort of will can the boldest explorer bring himself to spend a night away from his fellows, waiting long hours to bag a lion or a leopard with gun or camera. Fortunately, the camera is being used more than the gun nowadays. In the upper picture a lioness is coming back with stealthy tread to the animal she has killed the night before, and in the lower picture the lion is standing silently before the hidden camera, twelve yards away.

F. W. Champion

THE TIGER WALKS BY NIGHT AND FEASTS ON THE REMAINS OF HIS SUPPER

These pictures, automatically taken by flashlight in the Indian Jungle, show the tiger in two attitudes. In the upper one he is walking stealthily amid the tall grass of the jungle either in search of fresh prey or to visit the carcase of a previously slain animal. Below he is seen quietly devouring the remains of such a supper. As in the case of the photograph of a larger and older tiger in page 46 this picture was taken by the animal himself touching a wire that had been set beforehand to fire the flash and release the shutter of the camera.

Major Radclyffe Dugmore

THE SUDDEN FIRING OF THE FLASHLIGHT REVEALS A LIONESS COMING TO HER PREY

In the eerie stillness of the night the explorer of the African jungle who waits to get a flashlight picture of a lion or lioness soon finds that his nerves are overwrought. The mystery of the darkness and the fancied footfall of approaching beasts inflame his imagination and people the jungle with ferocious animals all approaching his hiding-place. When this fine picture of a lioness creeping through the undergrowth was taken by Major Dugmore in the Kenya jungle, the animal came within a few yards of the camera, and, as the light flashed, looked straight at it.

F. W. Champion

WHEN NIGHT COMES THE INDIAN LEOPARD SEEKS THE PREY HE HAS KILLED BY DAY AND DRAWN INTO THE JUNGLE

Contrary to popular supposition the leopard is a far bolder and more courageous animal than the tiger, and he shows little fear of man. To obtain a photograph of him in his native haunts by night involves an enormous risk, and requires a display of daring on the part of the photographer exceeding perhaps even that required for the taking of a lion picture in the African jungle. For the leopard can climb trees with ease and uses a tree as a coign of vantage from which to watch for his prey. At any moment, therefore, the photographer, waiting patiently for this picture in the dark, might have been pounced upon by the stealthy leopard and destroyed without warning or any possible chance of escape.

buzzed around, and there are few things better calculated to put an end to sentimental reverie! Before I had well appreciated the fact my face and neck and arms were smarting and itching desperately. The only cover I had was a waterproof sheet, and in the sweltering damp tropical heat it was not pleasant to smother one's face and neck and arms in such an air-tight covering. We were too far from our boat to make it possible to return, so my African and I spent the night in misery.

There was hardly a half-moon, and we could barely distinguish ghostlike forms around the dead eland, and, of course, it was impossible in the shadow of the tree to see even the barrel, to say nothing of the sights, of one's rifle. Modern aids to night shooting were not then in vogue. A rather ingenious idea occurred to me. I captured one of the fire-flies which danced around us, and with some sticky gum from the tree I stuck it on its back on my fore-sight, so that its luminous tail flickered constantly in the effort to get free. But it was impossible to make out what the forms round the carcase were. I suggested to my companion that we should get down and haul the carcase nearer. He failed I think to see anything very attractive in the idea, but Africans are brave fellows and will rarely refuse to follow a white man's lead.

A PROWLING LYNX FACES THE CAMERA

The Canadian lynx dwells in those deep forests of North America that correspond to the jungles of hotter lands, and when he moves about it is generally in a hurried gallop like that of the hare. He preys on the smaller mammals and on birds and has been known to devour pigs, lambs, and young fawns. Like most of the wild cats, he is bold, and here faces the flashlight without a flinch.

It was desperate hard work. An eland is a very large animal. An old bull will, I believe, stand nineteen hands at the shoulder. Grasping the horns our united strength could only move his head and shoulders a few inches at a time. Then we transferred our efforts to the other end of him, and by repeating the performance again and again we very slowly, with the perspiration pouring off us, gradually got the beast a little nearer. Meanwhile, my rifle lay handy in case of need and I kept a sharp look-out all round, for we had reason to think a lion had already visited the kill.

Shortly after we had got back to our tree the moon went down, and there was only dim starlight left. A stampede of the forms moving in the faint light—hyenas, jackals, or what not—told us a lion had approached, and presently I could clearly make out his shape as he moved off towards the high grass carrying some of the eland's entrails. I fired a wild shot, but it did not take effect. It seemed somehow an unnatural thing to hear the report of a rifle, and its echoes through the still night air, at such a time and place—as though one had let off a gun in a cathedral!

It got darker and darker, and there was no doubt now that one or more lions had returned. We could hear the crunching of the bones, but I did not fire again though I think I saw a lioness pass under the outlying branches of our tree. I was too tormented by the mosquitoes to care even about lions, and we were both heartily glad when the dawn broke and enabled us to descend and find our way back to our boat. I had no time to try for better luck, for we were engaged at the time in fighting the Slave-raiders at Karonga's at the North End of the lake, a place which during the Great War was to be the scene of a notable exploit by our troops.

THOSE were days when we travelled with very few extras. It had not as yet become fashionable to photograph animals coming to drink, and to reproduce the scene on a cinema film in London. Shooting big game by sitting up over a kill, or over water, is at best a poor form of sport ; for the game has not a fair chance, and I have never bagged anything in that way. It has its discomforts, no doubt, but with proper arrangements they can be minimised and the sportsman can sit in his tree and describe his impressions of the jungle by night with as much word-painting as he likes.

But it is a different story if your acquaintance with the jungle by night arises from the fact that you have lost your way and are alone. That most terrifying of all experiences has happened to me more than once. The recollection of such a misadventure in Burmah is as vivid as a nightmare to me even now.

It was in the interminable bamboo forest which stretches from Kyenyat to Sagardoung, north of Mandalay. Nothing grows under the great bamboo clumps, so that the forest, unlike other jungles, is practically pathless, and as the fronds meet overhead you can see no landmarks and rarely even the sky. I found later that following cart-tracks which I thought were those of the British force to which I belonged, I had nearly blundered into the camp of our enemy the Shans, who were reputed to have an extremely unpleasant custom of torturing captives by driving bamboo splinters between their finger nails and fingers, and finally splitting them open and pegging the unfortunate captive down on a white-ants' nest.

The feeling of utter and complete helplessness in such circumstances is one which has no parallel except in the Arctic ice-fields or in a nightmare. Should you go forward or backward, or to right or left ? Have you reached your objective or not yet reached it ? Which is forward and which is backward ? Your reasoning faculty cannot help you, and your best course is to sit down where you are till daylight—or rather twilight under the bamboos—with such philosophy as you can command. You will I imagine be more engaged in considering how empty you are inside, and remembering that there is nothing whatever to eat than in moralising over what the jungle looks like at night ! It is curious how vivid memories such as these remain when many serious and important incidents of life have passed into oblivion.

Major Radclyffe Dugmore

CROCODILE RESTING ON THE BANK OF AN AFRICAN RIVER BY NIGHT

While the large carnivores hunt their food by night and the feebler folk go to water-holes to drink, the crocodile does neither, and if in the glare of a flashlight he is seen at all it is usually, as shown in this photograph, resting on a bank. When he needs food he simply submerges his body and lies in wait for some unwary animal or human that may come down to drink or bathe. Then, with a sudden snap, he seizes his prey and drags it under the water to drown. There is no escape from the jaws of this powerful reptile.

Major Radclyffe Dugmore

From the film "Simba"

SPOTTED HYENA CAUGHT IN THE FLASHLIGHT AS HE STANDS BY A WATER-HOLE

The spotted hyena of Africa is essentially a creature of the night, and where a party of explorers is encamped in the darkness he will creep in silently among the tents and attack the tethered mules, ponies, cattle, or goats without warning. He is much fiercer than his Indian relative, and so powerful are his teeth that he can as easily crunch in his jaws the shinbone of an ox as a dog can crunch up the leg-bone of a chicken. He visits the water-holes at night, partly to drink and partly in search of food, and these photographs were taken during his nightly prowl.

Ostrich

Adjutant Stork

Secretary Bird

Curassow

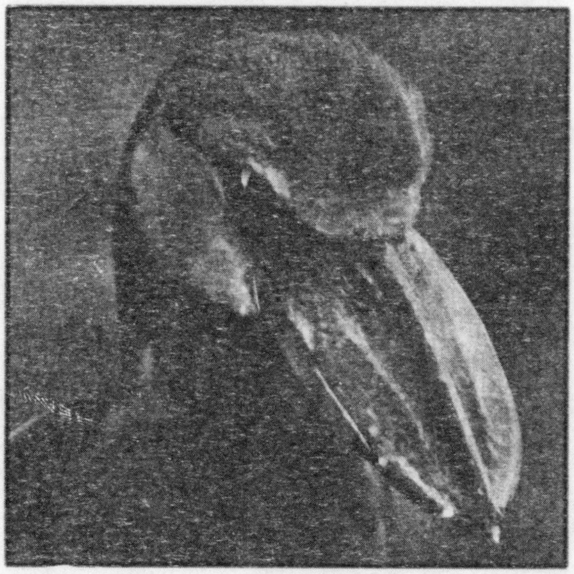

Boatbill

Spoonbill

Neville Kingston

BEAKS CUNNINGLY ADAPTED TO VARIOUS MODES OF LIFE

The boatbill's flat beak is well adapted to catch fish, while the spoonbill's with its broad flattened tip is used for sweeping from side to side in the mud and water for vegetable and animal food. The secretary bird, shown here in an angry mood, has a beak like an eagle's, but that of the curassow is short, stout, and often enlarged at the base. It is interesting to note that the ostrich's beak, flat, broad, and blunt, with nostrils in the middle, is the most primitive bill carried by any modern bird. The adjutant stork's enormous beak is thick and wedge-shaped.

Chapter VII

Beaks of Infinite Variety and Uses

By Frank Finn

Author of "The World's Birds"

THERE is a well-known scientific saying that in the course of its development every animal climbs up its own genealogical tree; that is to say, that the young stages in its development show what its ancestors were like.

Judging from this, as every bird is hatched with a beak, but some of them, the common sparrow for instance, come into the world without a trace of feathers, one would infer that birds developed beaks before they had feathers. This, as they evolved from reptiles, would make them comparable to tortoises, which have horny jaws or beaks; in one of the sea-turtles, in fact, the beak is so like that of a bird that the reptile is known popularly as the hawk's bill turtle.

The above statement about creatures' genealogical gymnastics is, however, only generally true, and the case of the birds' beaks furnishes one of the exceptions to it; for the earliest bird-fossils show us creatures with quite normally-developed feathers, but with jaws bearing teeth, which must have been more like the muzzle of a lizard than the beak of any bird we know.

Teeth were possessed by birds long after they had separated into very different forms. The first birds we find were evidently tree-livers, adapted for perching and with short rounded wings which were suitable for easy flights, from tree to tree or from glade to glade, a pattern of bird still very numerous in the tropics at the present day, as anyone may see who visits the Bird House at the Zoo. But the next fossils show us gigantic divers with little bits of wings, and strong-winged flyers with wings as powerful as those of our modern gulls—and all still had the reptilian teeth in their jaws, so that teeth must have been universally in fashion for ages.

In all modern birds the true teeth have so completely disappeared that no trace of them can be found even in the unhatched young; but false teeth have been developed in a good many birds, as in the merganser, a fish-eating duck. Such false teeth are mere projecting points on the horny edges of the jaws, and are quite unlike real ivory teeth such as mammals possess which are separate growths and are shed.

It is likely that the jaws of the earliest birds were covered with skin and had, as those of lizards now have, large scales at the tip and along the edges, and, though true teeth have so long disappeared, we have, perhaps, a trace of this covering in the beaks of some birds of the present day. Generally each jaw is covered with a continuous sheath of horn, like that which covers the claws; but in the duck family and the flamingoes the beak is only horny at the edges and at the extreme tip, where it forms what is called the nail, the rest being clothed with skin. It is upon this skin that are made the cuts on swans' beaks which form the swan-marks formerly so much in use, and still inflicted locally.

Then in many birds, especially birds of prey, though most of the beak is horn-cased, the part surrounding the nostrils is clothed in a skin called the cere, from the Latin word "cera," meaning wax, which the surface of this skin very much resembles in some cases.

Owls have the cere as well as day birds of prey, but in their case it is so buried in feathery whiskers that it is not generally noticed. Parrots also have the cere, and the crow tribe have feather-covered skin at the root of the beak, which in the rook becomes bare and exposed at about a year old as the result of an hereditary disposition to baldness, not through digging, as used to be supposed. In the snipes and woodcocks the end of the beak is soft-skinned and sensitive, so that they can feel worms when boring in mud.

Nevile Kingston

THE POWERFUL BEAK OF THE MACAW

Macaws are very showy birds but poor talkers, and their nasty habit of screaming almost incessantly makes them undesirable pets. They have a very large and powerful beak, and the upper jaw, owing to a peculiar joint, can be thrust straight out.

In many birds, too, although the beak is completely sheathed in horn, the horny casing is in several separate pieces, evidently another reminiscence of ancient arrangements. This is the case with all the ancient loose-plumaged running birds or ratites, from the ostrich to the kiwi or apteryx, and also in many of the flying birds, such as the frigate-bird and pelican and their kin, and the petrels and albatrosses.

The last are the only birds which have real noses, their nostrils being prolonged into tubes; in the albatross the nose is split, for there are two tubes, separated by the bridge of the beak. False unpierced noses have been developed in many birds, however, such as the knob which adds dignity to the swan's beak, and the combs of the condor and the Indian comb-duck, while the turkey sports an elastic nose which lengthens or shortens according to the wearer's frame of mind.

BIRDS' nostrils have generally been shifted back towards the forehead, where they are out of the way; or, rather, the beak has tended to develop in front of them. But many birds still have them about the middle, such as geese, gulls, and the ostrich tribe, among which the kiwi goes farther, and has them at the tip, protected by a flange. Nostrils being usually at the end of a nose, the forward position is no doubt the ancient one, though they need not have been, and probably were not, at the actual end, since some of the monitor lizards have them some way back on the snout.

Taking it all round, the beak of the ostrich, flat, broad and blunt, with nostrils in the middle, a covering of horn in separate plates, and a deep mouth reaching back under the eye, is the most primitive and muzzle-like beak carried by any modern bird.

The deep mouth is certainly a reptilian point, and in few birds except the ratites and the pelican tribe is it found; but the morepork shows it very well, and with its broad, blunt, very short beak, looks particularly reptilian; indeed, it belongs to a family known as frog-mouths.

Generally the corner of the bird's mouth reaches about half-way to the eye, and in some birds the contraction of the mouth has gone so far that it does not reach further back than the forehead; this is the case with parrots and with the duck tribe, and with all the group of mud-probing birds, such as the snipe, dunlin, godwit, whimbrel, and curlew. This last family shows an extraordinary variety of beak; it may be quite short, as in plovers, and turned the opposite way to the curlew's, as in the avocet; but the narrow mouth makes the faces of the whole clan remarkably alike and very silly-looking.

In other birds one pattern of beak has to serve for a whole group; for instance, the beaks of the game-birds are very little different, whether they feed on berries in the tops of tropical trees, like the American guans, on the ground on all sorts of things, like the fowl, pheasant, and turkey, or on the buds of stunted herbage under the snow, like the Arctic grouse.

Their natural enemies, the birds of prey, also show a very uniform type of bill, with a curving hook at the end, though here there is more variety; the great bill of the eared vulture, which is one of the master-vultures, is stronger than the golden eagle's, and contrasts strikingly with the weak bills of the smallest vultures, which are not unlike those of the large crowned pigeons.

Pigeons, as a family, have remarkably weak bills, though the fruit-eating kinds have stronger beaks than the seed-eaters, the beak in one of these being quite as strong for the bird's size as that of the condor. Fruit often takes a strong pull to detach it, and in any case fruit-eating creatures often have to make shift with buds, for even in the tropics, where perpetual summer reigns, fruit is not always on hand just when and where feathered or furred fruitarians may happen to want it.

So, what with the resemblance between some pigeons' bills and vultures', and other pigeons' bills and those of the worm-eating plovers, to say nothing of the likeness between parrots' bills and those of birds of prey, we often find animal-feeding birds and vegetable feeders also, managing to get along with very much the same type of bill.

The outstanding peculiarity of the parrot's bill is the attachment of the upper jaw by a joint; owing to this arrangement the parrot can poke its upper jaw straight out, and a macaw will do this when trying to smile, producing a weirdly comical expression, enhanced by the fact that the corners of the bird's mouth are soft and elastic like ours.

The somewhat human expression of the parrot's face, and its thick tongue and short, hollow beak, by the way, have nothing to do with the bird's power of imitating our speech, for the vocal organ of birds is situated nowhere near the mouth, but at the base of the neck, and birds with tongues and beaks quite different from those of parrots will learn to speak, as everyone knows.

Among such are the crow tribe, which have what may be called the standard or ordinary beak among birds, neither particularly long, short, thick, nor thin as a rule, though we get length and thinness in the chough's beak, and a decided increase in thickness in that of the thick-billed raven of Africa. Crows put their handy beaks to all sorts of uses, being eminently birds of all trades, and the beaks of thrushes, starlings, and a vast number of other birds differ but little from the crow type of beak, except in being smaller.

THE birds known as barbets have beaks very much like those of crows, and, though little known to the public, they are particularly interesting in forming a link between the woodpeckers and the toucans. Barbets peck out their nesting-holes with their crow-like beaks, but woodpeckers are always carpentering, since their chief food consists of grubs which they dig out of rotten wood, and so the slight curve of the barbet's bill is in them straightened out; the end of the bill is squared, and it becomes a very powerful chisel.

The woodpecker has been pitied for its life of toil, but it is as happy with its chisel-bill as a boy with a new pocket-knife, and quite recently a woodpecker in the Brent Valley bird sanctuary got itself into disgrace by its enthusiastic cutting operations on the nesting-boxes provided for other birds. On the other side, the barbets have evolved into the toucans, which are Roman-nosed to a degree, and have the biggest bills for their size of any birds. This, however, applies only to the larger species; in the smaller

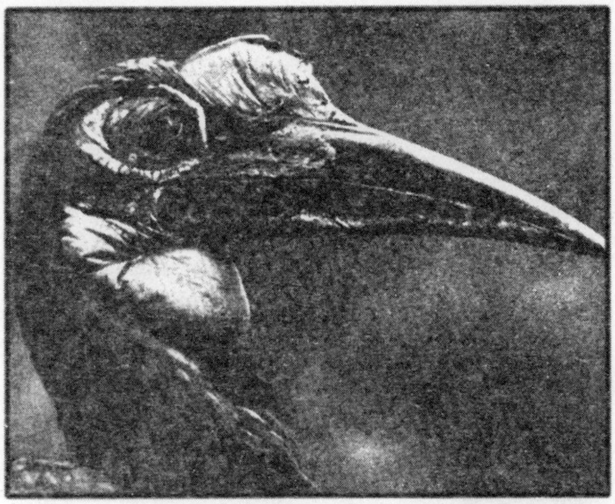

Ground Hornbill

Toucan

Black Hornbill

Thick-Billed Raven

Common Raven

Whale-Headed Stork

Neville Kingston

THE GIANT BILLS CARRIED BY BIRDS OF DIFFERENT SPECIES

The raven, once common in Britain but now rare, has a stout strong bill, arched towards the point, and sharp at the edges. while its relation the thick-billed raven has the tips of its beak hardened somewhat in the way that a gold fountain pen-nib is hardened by being iridium-tipped. Very different is the beak of the whale-headed or shoe-billed stork, which is broad, concave in profile, with a strong ridge, and the tip extended into a bold hook. The bills of toucans and hornbills are so huge as to be like caricatures. They are, however, not as heavy as they look.

toucans the bills are not quite so exaggerated, and in size of bill there is little to choose between the smallest toucan and the largest barbet, the chain of links being very complete.

The big beak of the toucan is not such a practical affair as the smaller ones of its middle-class and industrial relatives, and toucans find their nesting-holes instead of digging them, though no doubt the out-sized bill comes in handy in defending the entrance, as well as in reaching out to pick the fruit on which toucans mainly feed.

The only other birds in which the bill is as grotesquely exaggerated are the hornbills, which represent the toucans in the Old World, and generally have very similar habits, so that here we have a case of evolutionary history repeating itself. History, however, never repeats itself exactly, and the hornbills have seldom developed the brilliant colours which so often adorn toucans' bills, but instead, usually show a curious top-storey arrangement, varying much in form.

Moreover, the opening chapter of the history of hornbills is lost to us, for though the hornbills are undoubtedly related to the hoopoes, and more distantly to the kingfishers, and though the smaller hornbills have proportionately slighter bills than the larger ones, and usually lack the top-storey, the family does not grade off into any other as the toucans do into the barbets.

BOTH toucans and hornbills have the interior bony core of the bill very spongy or cellular in structure, which lightens it greatly; but nevertheless it is decidedly heavy, and it is remarkable that its weight does not inconvenience the birds, which are as active as if their bills were of the ordinary size.

Apart from the toucans and hornbills, most of the birds with eccentric or exaggerated beaks are waders or swimmers, and some of them have beaks so specialised that they are practically tied down to one particular way of living. One very well-known instance of this is afforded by the pelicans, which use their long pouched bills as a fishing-net; the branches of the lower jaw are united only at the tip, and will expand freely, forming a skin-floored scoop which shovels up water and fish together, the water spilling over the sides as the bill contracts again.

The opposite formation is seen in the even more specialised scissor-bills, which belong to the tern group, members of the gull family which usually have the ordinary or crow type of beak. In the scissor-bill the branches of the lower jaw are joined for so long a distance up that when detached from the skull it looks like a pitchfork, and when in position it projects as a thin, vertical blade far in front of the upper jaw. Thus food cannot be picked up in the ordinary way, and the bird feeds by skimming over the water with the end of the lower jaw immersed, and snapping down the upper one on any prey that is touched.

W. S. Berridge

A FALSE BEAK WORN FOR COURTING

One of the most remarkable of all the beaks is that of the puffin, which grows a brilliant or temporary, beak at the breeding season, as seen in this photograph. In course of time the false beak flakes off, and when winter comes the puffin has a plain black bill.

The spoonbill is so closely related to the ibis, which has a beak almost exactly like the curlew's, and uses it in much the same way for picking and probing, that a spoonbill-ibis hybrid was once bred in the Berlin Zoo; yet its beak is remarkably different, and is used in sweeping from side to side in the mud and water, securing both vegetable and animal food between the broad flattened tips.

The avocet, belonging to a quite different family of waders, the snipe and plover group, uses its thin, tapering and upturned beak in a very similar way, but at the surface of the water, its habit being to devour duck-weed as well as small animal life.

STORKS and herons have, as a rule, a very uniform type of bill of the spear pattern, but in the adjutant this is greatly exaggerated in thickness, this bird being largely a carrion-feeder, and needing a carver, while the shoe-bill, whose beak looks like the pelican's much shortened and broadened, is said also to use the hook of its bill in tearing carcases, though usually, at all events, it is a fisher.

The crossbill furnishes an example of a peculiar specialised bill among the small perching birds; except for its beak it would be a quite ordinary finch, and indeed looks very like one when it leaves the nest. But the bill soon develops the crossing hooks on the upper and lower jaws, which form an admirable pair of pliers for prising open the cones of fir and pine-trees, on the seeds of which the bird feeds; but it can be adjusted to pick up seeds in the ordinary way and to take insects, while a crossbill will also do much execution, parrot-fashion, on the woodwork of a cage, so that its deformed-looking beak is really a whole tool-box in itself.

Similar varied use of a specialised beak is seen in the common duck, the beak of which is furnished with rows of horny sifting-plates for straining small

Eared Vulture

Golden Eagle

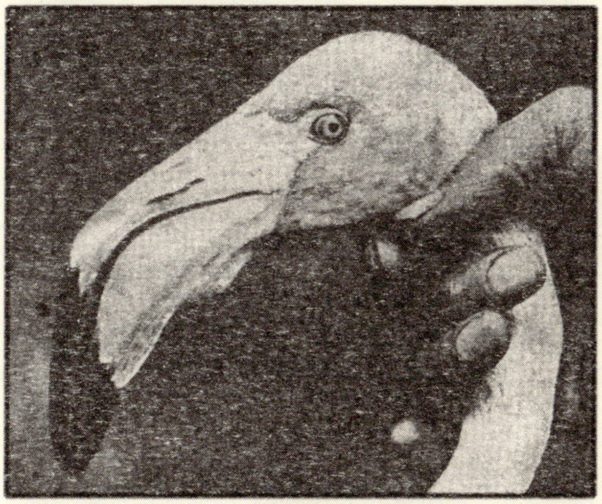

Flamingo

Sacred Ibis

Sheathbill

Morepork

Neville Kingston

SOME STRIKING EXAMPLES OF THE CURIOUSLY VARIED FORMS OF BEAKS

The sheathbill, which feeds on other birds' eggs, has its beak sheathed at the base to prevent the liquid from penetrating the nostrils. The morepork, or frogmouth, has a short, blunt beak, very reptilian in appearance. The flamingoes feed like ducks with the bill reversed, the upper jaw, which is very mobile, acting as the lower one. The ibis is closely related to the spoonbill, but its bill is very different, being adapted for picking and probing. Birds of prey always have powerful hooked beaks, and the eared vulture's is stronger than the golden eagle's.

specialised for food-getting, they are not so as nest-making tools. A bird will contrive to make almost any sort of nest with almost any sort of beak; the weaver-birds construct their wonderful plaited nests with beaks much like those of our ordinary finches; the kingfisher, with its long strong bill, and the sand-martin, with its tiny weak one, both dig out an underground home.

Neither are birds' beaks, at any rate as a rule, specialised as weapons. They are very handy in that capacity, it is true, and are generally so used in conflict both among birds themselves and with other enemies. But it is difficult to find a beak that is specialised as a weapon, though this may be the case with the toothed beaks of the male saw-billed humming-birds, humming-birds being excessively quarrelsome, and given to beak-clinching in a fight.

In many cases, however, the beak does seem to be specialised for ornament; the top-storey of the beak of the hornbills—which is sometimes different in the two sexes—the fleshy appendages of some birds we mentioned at the beginning, the horny "saddle" on the bill of the saddle-billed stork, and the bright colours on the bills of many birds, the toucans especially, may be thus accounted for, if it be ever proved that birds do select their mates for appearance.

The puffin goes the farthest of all in this direction, for it grows a gaily-coloured false beak in the breeding-season; this flakes off in time, and "Sea-Punch," as the Italians call him, and his Judy, go off to the open sea for the winter in plain black beaks.

animal life, seeds, and so on, from mud and water; yet the duck, as everybody knows, easily picks up grain and browses on vegetables on land, besides hunting small prey of all sorts.

In the shoveller-duck the sifting-plates are so much developed that they can easily be seen from the outside, and look like whale-bone on a small scale, while the beak is broadened into a shoe-horn shape. Thus it is a most perfect sifter, and the shoveller is the most frugal of ducks; give him a puddle with a few gallons of dirty water, and he will contrive to dredge a dinner out of it. But he can still feed on land, which the flamingoes, rivalling him as water-strainers, can hardly do, for they feed like ducks with the bill reversed, the upper jaw, which is very narrow and movable, acting as the lower one. Here again, then, we have a beak which ties down its owner to a certain method of living, and flamingoes are only found where large expanses of calm, shallow water exist, where they can wade and dredge.

It is curious that, though birds' beaks are so often

Neville Kingston

THE PELICAN'S BILL WITH ITS WONDERFUL FISHING NET

Some birds, like the pelican, have beaks so specialised that they are tied down to one particular way of life. This bird has a big pouch attached to the bill, which it uses as a fishing net, scooping up water and fish together and allowing the water to spill over the sides as the beak is closed. The bird spreads the pouch over its chest to dry it, as in the upper picture.

Chapter VIII

How Animals Express Their Feelings

By Frances Pitt

Author of "The Animal Mind," "Waterside Creatures"

ANIMALS have keen emotions, as is soon apparent when you watch the expression of their feelings, though they vary much in the manner they display them, from the angry spit of an enraged cat to the weeping of a frightened seal. Hate, anger, love, fear, boredom, and anticipation of good things to come are all expressed each in its various ways by the different creatures.

Seals are among the few animals that share with us the distinction of finding an emotional outlet in weeping. I have seen a young grey seal—a pup of the great grey seal that comes ashore in the autumn, choosing some retired nook upon the wildest coasts as a nursery for its solitary baby—cry pitifully because I was between it and the sea, and it could not escape to join its mother, who was floating in the sea a little way off the rocks, her dark head showing just above the surface of the waves. Tears of fear and anger ran down the young seal's face, making rivulets through its velvety fur, until they melted my heart, and I stepped out of its way, to let it heave itself over the shining seaweed-covered rocks and away into the green water.

No creatures display anger more effectively than the members of the cat tribe, from the stately tiger, the leopard, the lynx and caracal, down to our homely puss. In all of them anger is shown in more or less the same way, by spasmodic twitching of the tail in the long-tailed species, by flattened ears, ruffled fur, and explosive spits, varied with growls and menacing sounds. Only the other morning I was watching two cats, common household ones, purring happily side by side, when suddenly one cat stepped back, with ears flat, tail twitching, and spat open mouthed at her friend. What the cause of offence had been I cannot say, but next instant the two were fighting as only cats can, in a continuous storm of growls, hisses, and furiously scratching claws.

But for sheer temper one must turn to the wild cats. One of the worst is the Scottish wild cat, *Felis silvestris*, not only a distinct species from the domestic, but differing from it in temperament so much as to be quite untamable. Fear and hate gleam from its half-closed green eyes, and woe to the man or dog who attempts to interfere with the fury.

A cat's whiskers are a good indication of its feelings, whether that cat be a tiger, leopard, or something smaller, for when the owner's attention is fixed upon anything they bristle forward, only to relax as its interest wanes, and lie almost flat as it becomes sleepy or bored.

Boredom in the animal world is unmistakable, a wide-mouthed yawn being its sign among all creatures, from ourselves, through the apes, monkeys, dogs, wolves, and cats, down to the birds. I have seen a weary falcon yawn repeatedly, likewise a bullfinch that was tired of sitting on her nest brooding her eggs, a horse waiting in the stable with nothing to do, and many an animal in zoological gardens.

THE GIRAFFE "REGISTERS" HOPE

A giraffe has this advantage over the other animals at the Zoo, that he need not always see the world through the bars. He can look over them as this one did when he heard his keeper coming perhaps with the next meal. Hope is strongly expressed in the pricked ears and intent gaze

But there is one point about the yawn of boredom which should not be overlooked, and that is the bored animal does not lift its lips so as to exhibit its teeth as does the angry one. An enraged baboon, dog, or cat displays its whole dental outfit in a snarling grin. Note the photograph of two baboons shown in page 67, one rather bored; and the wild cat in page 75 very annoyed—and the difference is obvious.

Some creatures, however, do not open their mouths or lift their lips even when really angry: such are the members of the weasel tribe, stoats, martins, polecats, otters, and badgers, likewise the skunks, which are contented to bristle up and give a warning hiss when

C. Reid

WHISKERS WHICH REVEAL INQUIRY

Watch a cat's whiskers to discover its feelings, whether that cat be the domestic sort or a tiger or a leopard. The intent expression is always marked by a slight bristling forward of the whiskers, and pricked ears and wide-open eyes help to emphasise this cat's expression of inquiry.

they are prepared to do battle. They do not ever indulge in superfluous snarling.

Different birds have peculiar ways of displaying anger and indignation. The angry secretary bird, for instance, is a good study in irate expression, while the owls in particular leave no doubt about their feelings, putting their feathers on end, drooping their wings, and glaring furiously at the offender. The eagle and long-eared owls, with their magnificent orange eyes, which seem to glare hate and rage, are particularly impressive when in a temper; but for weird antics commend me to an annoyed barn owl.

THE barn owl is the so-called white owl—it is pale buff in reality, but looks white when on the wing—which is widely distributed throughout the northern hemisphere. It varies a little in different parts of its range, but one barn owl is much like another, and all behave in the same way when really upset. An angry white owl half closes its eyes, droops its wings, stands as high as it can and moves its head round in a circle, at the same time making a most extraordinary snoring sound, sometimes interspersed with a little beak snapping. One may sometimes find the bird engaged in this display, which seems to express the combined emotions of fear and anger, and serves the purpose of bluffing an enemy into thinking the owl an awful and dangerous creature.

In most cases the displays of temper indulged in by birds and beasts have a useful object, namely that of intimidating a foe. There is no doubt that the snarling and growling of an angry dog, and the spitting of an enraged cat, are not only outlets for emotion, but tell the enemy these animals really are furious and should not be lightly attacked.

But to turn from the emotions of fear and anger, how do animals express pleasure? The most familiar examples are of course the purring of the cat as she rubs against you, and the delighted bark of a dog greeting his returning master, when he also displays his joy in every gesture of his body from his wagging tail to his shining eyes. The horse gives a little contented whinny as he gets what he wants, but the cow's means of expressing pleasurable feeling are poor, and limited to a general look of peace and contentment; unless, that is, she is so happy that she indulges in a little play and pretends to horn her neighbour in a practical joking spirit. I have never seen a fox wag its brush, but I have seen a tame vixen, when very pleased to see a friend, open her mouth in a wide grin, and with ears laid flat back run to meet her. The badger shows pleasurable excitement through its fur. I had two pet females once, that used to romp with the dogs—what mad games they all had together!—and little ripples of excitement could be seen running through their rough grey jackets, at one moment the fur of their shoulders standing on end, next that on the back, and as this flattened again the tail was fluffed out.

Autotype

THE DOG'S WAY OF LOOKING EXPECTANT

Dogs express their feelings much more effectively than cats. In this case the unusual procedure of being set upon a cushion and photographed has brought out the familiar twist of the head and the pricked ears which mean interested observation.

MONKEY FACES AS AN INDEX TO MONKEY MINDS

Nothing could better express the languor of a warm afternoon and a temporary lack of interest in the scheme of things than the colossal yawn of the baboon here (bottom) on the Monkey Hill at the Zoo. A wide yawn in this case means the exhibition of a long oval of darkness beneath a snout that appears rather pig-like at this angle. The lip-less mouth is also very effective in the roloway monkey (top left), who is letting out a scream of indignation. Our remaining expressionist is a chimpanzee.

F. W. Bond

CHIMPANZEES CONTENT IN A MUTUAL EMBRACE

Of all the larger apes the chimpanzee is the easiest to tame and train for it takes kindly to human company and the opportunity of novelty and diversion which humans bring. Performing chimpanzees are common and people are apt to forget that this animal, which is so often made into a cruel caricature of human nature, has a real ape personality of its own quite apart from training. The attitude of affectionate companionship and complete content shown by the animals in the photograph is very striking.

Many birds, especially the hawks, show contentment by fluffing forward the soft little whisker feathers about their beaks. Nearly all birds when quite happy puff their feathers out a little, particularly owls, which then become a feathery ball. The brown owl has a most charming cooing call, (quite different from the loud penetrating hoot) which it uses when happy and pleased. It is one of the most caressing sounds I know, being even more so than the soft coo of the dove.

At this point the reader may inquire if animals ever feel amusement, and if so how they display their feeling? It is commonly assumed that laughter is purely human and one of the proud distinctions of our race, marking the gulf that separates us from "the mere brute."

WELL, first, before considering the display of the feeling of amusement, is there any evidence that animals have the least sense of humour? The chimpanzees that put out bait, in the shape of breadcrumbs, to entice fowls near their cages so that they could poke them with sticks, and exhibited symptoms of impish glee at startling the unfortunate hens, as Professor Kohler tells us in his book, "The Mentality of Apes," would seem to have been animated by the same practical joking spirit as many a mischievous child.

Then take the case of a dog, excellent friends with a cat, who took puss by surprise, by springing out at her from some grass, startling her so much that she bolted, raced to a post, jumped on to it, turned round and spat furiously at the dog, when the latter stood and grinned at her, looking hugely pleased. Or again take an instance of two otters at play in a pool. The female broke off the game and swam for the shore, when the male came quietly behind her, slyly nipping the extreme tip of her tail as she climbed up the bank, and in the same instant flung himself backwards out of her reach.

All these three episodes illustrate a spirit of fun, and as an eye-witness of the latter two, I can say that an expression of mischief was written plainly upon the features of dog and otter—which brings us back to the question, how do animals show amusement? Except in the cases of the highest apes, which sometimes contort their faces in grinlike grimaces and utter sounds not unlike laughter, obvious mirth of the human kind is unknown among birds and beasts. Yet the dog that chased the cat

Neville Kingston.

Natural History. N.Y.

F. W. Bond.

QUARTET OF QUAINT FACES FROM THE SIMIAN WORLD

The fascination of monkey expressions can be judged by the crowds that will stand for hours round the cages where these creatures are kept. It is not only the marvellous gymnastic displays that the smaller monkeys sometimes give which attract the crowd but undoubtedly their wealth of expression. Above we have some excellent examples of monkey faces: Humboldt's monkey from South America (bottom right), orang-utan from Borneo (top left), Red-faced ouakari (bottom left), and Proboscis monkey (top right)

W. Davis

FRIGHTFUL FANGS OF THE LION AND THE TIGER EXPRESS THE MENACE OF DANGER

The lion and the tiger, the largest of cats, leave no doubt as to their intentions when they wish to show anger. The bristling whiskers (see p. 66) the ears laid back, and those terrible rows of deadly white fangs constitute nature's most effective reading of the word "menace." In spite of traditions which make the lion the king of the beasts and a synonym of bravery, the tiger is undoubtedly the first in ferocity and is also more dangerous. It can beat the lion in agility, and the way in which it uses its frightful claws gives it an added advantage. Also, it should be remembered that a tiger can break the neck of an ox at one blow of its paw. These two beasts are certainly lords of their respective jungles.

Mr. & Mrs. E. H. Baynes

HOW THE COYOTE LOOKS WHEN HE HOWLS HIS EVENING HYMN

To point his nose to a star, lay back the head, open the fanged jaws to their utmost, fill the lungs and then howl and howl into the evening sky seems to fulfil a burning need in the coyote or prairie wolf of North America. The fur is much longer than that of the timber wolf and the tail much more bushy. The coyote flourishes in Mexico and in Texas, and other of the southern states of the U.S.A. It is harmless to man unless, perhaps, when cornered or with its young but is a great raider of chicken runs.

did look immensely amused, as did the otter that had teased his mate; their expression, however, lay not in grimace, but in the tense attention of attitude and sparkling eye. I remember a fox-cub which also delighted in teasing a cat, and the same joyous mischief was apparent in the cub's bearing.

Thoughtful attention is more easily deciphered, the pricked ears and steady stare of an attentive dog, likewise the pricked ears of the horse, tell the story of attention fixed on some object. The rabbit, hare, fox and wolf also betray their thoughtful study of anything by pricked ears, sniffing nose, and eyes directed towards it. The ears of wild animals are wonderfully expressive. Watch rabbits feeding at the covertside in an evening, and note those long, sensitive ears, now pricked in eager attention directed towards other rabbits, anon cocked to listen for danger, and then laid back in relaxed ease, all bespeaking the stream of rapid emotion.

PERHAPS the horse's ears are really the most eloquent. Watch the way they move, now pointing ahead, pricked in eager interest at what is coming, then laid back, now one forward, one back, then relaxed into indifference, only to be suddenly laid right back, obviously in response to a feeling of quick annoyance because his comrade has touched him unexpectedly. The great ears of the elephant are also eloquent in expressing their owner's feelings, and one might multiply instances of expressive ears almost indefinitely, but there are many creatures whose ears are far from sensitive registers of the emotions. Their ears do not tell us much about the feelings of rats and mice, but these latter show nervousness in a peculiar way, namely by washing their faces. The dainty, sleek-coated, slim, dark-eyed fieldmouse always cleans itself after an alarm, passing its tiny handlike paws over head and ears with lightning rapidity.

Fear is "registered," as they say in the cinema, in a variety of ways. Monkeys pull piteous faces, and try with deprecatory gestures to ward off punishment, dogs crouch and cringe, while other creatures betray apprehension by their furtive, slinking gait.

It is a problem for the student of comparative psychology to determine whether animals can have any idea of right and wrong, but I have often seen moorhens, those handsome black, white and grey water birds, acting as if they knew they were doing wrong and feared the consequences. In the early spring each pair of moorhens selects some area of pool or marsh on which to nest, and trespassers are prosecuted, not with the rigour of the law, but the rigour of beak and claw. I have often watched invading strange moorhens and noted their guilty, frightened air, as if they were well aware they had no business to be there, and knew they were likely to suffer the full penalties of trespassing. And when detected the intruders did not fight with anything appoaching the vim and determination of the owners of the pool, who appeared to be animated by feelings of righteous indignation.

That chimpanzees are aware when they have done wrong is testified to by Professor Kohler, who tells us that the guilty air worn by his apes, with their deprecatory manner, was often the first indication they had been in mischief. I have several times known a dog give himself away by his guilty manner, coming cringing to his master, completely betraying himself before the latter had any idea the retriever had been off hunting with another dog. Of course, in the foregoing paragraphs, I have been referring to pure fear undiluted with anger, but fear and rage mixed form the emotional background of

Autotype

NOBLE SOLEMNITY OF THE "KING OF BEASTS" IN CAPTIVITY

Curiously enough it is the caged lion which grows the largest mane and the mane is the lion's glory. Thus framed the head expresses perfect dignity as the animal, which may weigh as much as five hundred pounds, gazes at us through the bars of his prison—kingly even in captivity. But even Homer was said to nod, and this great beast, which a moment ago turned on us a royal gaze, will suddenly emit a vast yawn so like a cat's as to seem a little undignified. But the dignity is soon resumed again.

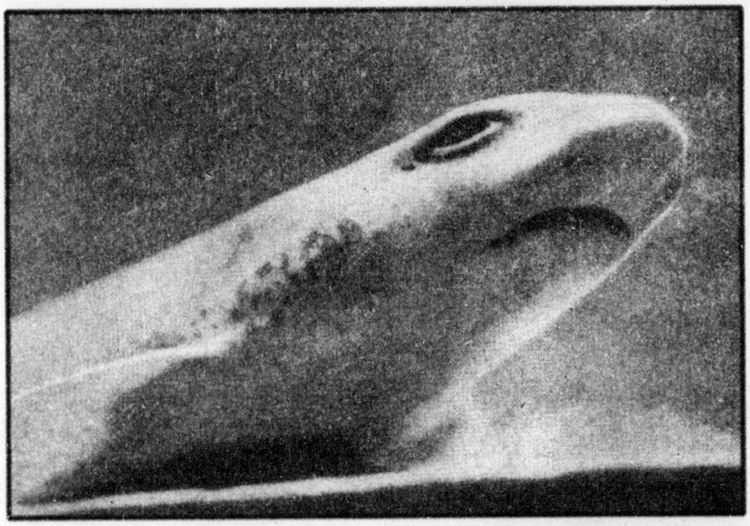

W. S. Berridge

FACES WHICH EXPRESS THE LIVES OF THEIR OWNERS
One would hardly go to the dogfish (top) for emotion as expressed by the face. But this cold eye that never blinks and the mouth that only opens to breathe and feed are adequate expressions of life in the dim waters of the sea. The tortoise opens its mouth in anger but otherwise is little more lively His face matches his life

some of the most ferocious displays, such as the savage exhibitions of various wild cats already mentioned. It is fear which moves them to anger.

Turning to a different type of feeling, sadness and low spirits are always apparent, but one sees them only among captive creatures which, with nothing to do, and perhaps not in the best of health, have time to mope and be sad. Healthy, busy wild animals, employed in getting their own living and caring for their young, never suffer from depressed feelings; they have no time for sorrows!

I am referring here to adults; young creatures awaiting the mother's return, or temporarily separated from her, are often quite frantic with anxiety. Watch the calf bleating for its dam, or a lamb that has lost the ewe, or, again, a young hedgerow bird chirping for the old one, and it is obvious that their whole being is one great anxiety. "Mother! Mother! Oh, where is mother?" Thus in our words we may epitomize their feelings. Is there anything more pitiful than the grief of a baby creature taken from its parent? Its sorrow may quickly pass, but in the meantime how the poor thing suffers, crying incessantly for her, its whole appearance betokening woe and anxiety.

SEPARATION from a well-loved comrade is nearly as bad. Monkey friends grieve greatly when parted, their sorrow depicted in doleful expression and loud lamentation; but the most enduring grief I have met with among animals was displayed by Madame Moses, my pet otter, when her sister ran away and she was left alone. The two had been inseparable and the most devoted of companions, going everywhere and doing everything together, from getting into all sorts of mischief and romping madly together, to sleeping in each other's arms in the most loving embrace. Then Miss Aaron ran off with a wild otter, and poor Moses was left to fret miserably for her. She whimpered and cried, she sought the truant far and wide, she came to me and climbed into my arms, there whimpering herself to sleep, only to wake up and resume the hunt for Aaron. For days she was inconsolable, and it was some time before she was her old lighthearted self. Poor thing, she expressed her feelings clearly enough!

Expectation, especially anxiety for food, is usually so plainly expressed as to be unmistakable. The open-beaked demands of a young bird are such that all the world knows its needs, whether it be a young cockatoo shrieking its demands or a nestling cuckoo urging with insistent squeaks its poor little foster parents to greater efforts on its greedy behalf. The expression of eager anticipation in young birds is not only depicted by the open beak, but by the fluttering of wings which seems to add insistence to their demands.

This fluttering of the wings is a sure token of expectation. I have seen an old raven, who thought he was going to secure a tit-bit, flutter his sable pinions like a nestling; and likewise a female blue-tit wanting to feed her young in the nest, and delayed by her mate who was delivering his supplies, flutter her wings in eager anxiety to get on with her work.

Natural History, N. Y.

F. W. Bond

American Museum of Natural History

BIRDS WHICH STRIKE TERROR BY THEIR APPEARANCE: JAMACIAN, BARN, AND EAGLE OWLS

While just sitting on a branch the eagle owl (bottom left) looks terrifying enough, but when disturbed (bottom right) the bird takes on an appearance that is positively startling in its combination of the horrifying and the grotesque. There is something about it which suggests the weird imaginings of those medieval craftsmen who devised gargoyles. Above are a Jamacian owl (top left) and an English barn or screech owl which is so often seen like a dim white ghost, flapping in ominous silence over the evening fields.

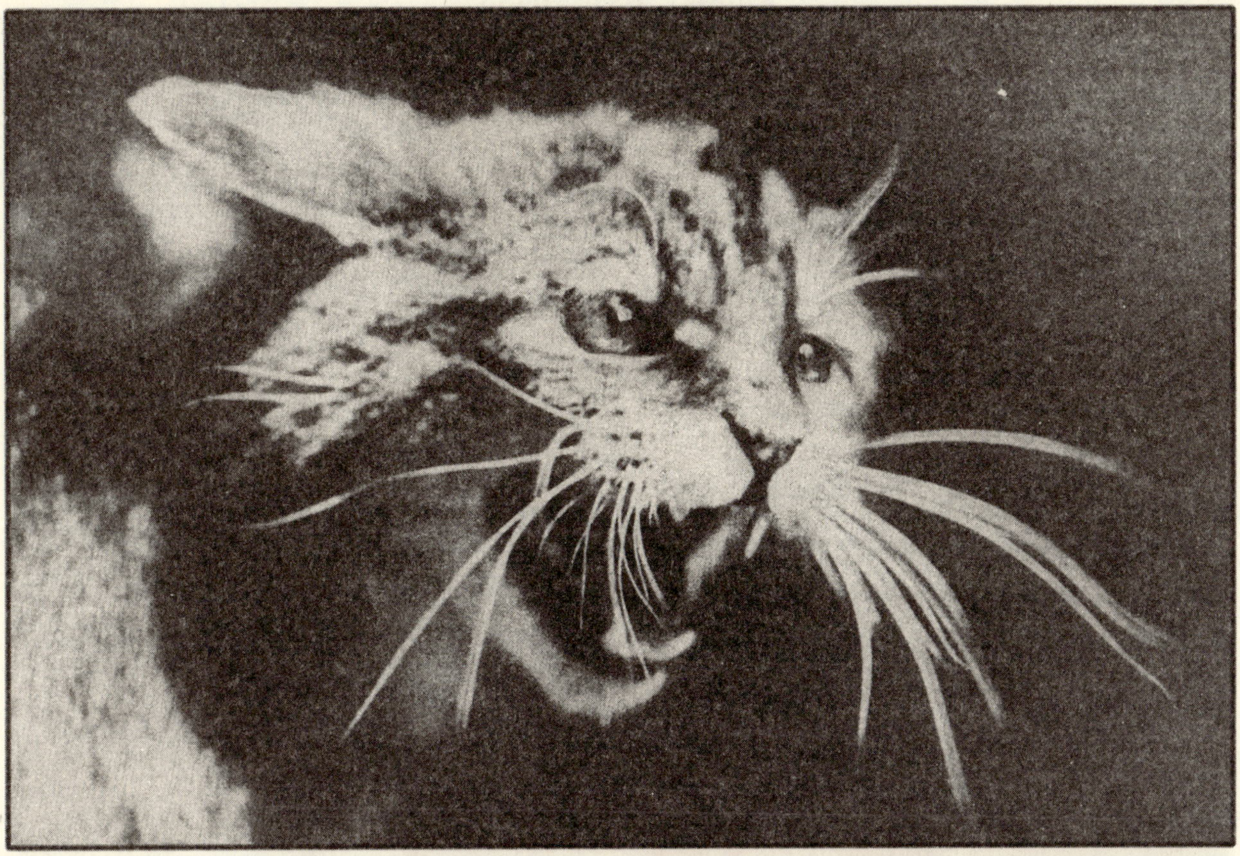

Neville Kingston

SPIT-FIRE FEROCITY AS THE WILD CATS SHOW IT

For sheer savage hatred the cat family is hard to beat. The lower photograph shows that rather rare specimen, the caracal, whose name is a French corruption of the Turkish Kara Kulak, " black ear." The animal is related to the lynx and is found in Southern Asia and in Africa. The Scottish wild cat (top) is the only member of the cat tribe left wild in Britain. It seems to have existed in North Wales and the Lake District until the nineteenth century but is now found only in the wild mountains of Scotland

Natural History, N.Y.

POMPOSITY HIGHLY INDIGNANT: THE FURIOUS COCKATOO

For a study in self-important exasperation we need go no further than this photograph of an enraged cockatoo. The family to which it belongs is native to Australia and the adjacent islands, and a feature distinguishing the species is the handsome crest which ordinarily lies back on the head, but, under stress of anger, resembles the head-dress of a Red Indian.

Wing fluttering is a sign of both expectancy and anxiety. It is nearly as eloquent as the wide-open beak, which it usually accompanies, as one may so often see in the case of pelicans expecting their dinner at the Zoo—the great beak open in mute appeal, and the eager wings enhancing the effect of anxious expectancy. Nearly as eloquent in the display of anxious feelings is the open-mouthed attitude of a hippopotamus begging for offerings. That displays expectancy as clearly as anything can.

Now, longing of a different sort—namely, to meet with a mate—is depicted in many ways, usually very striking, whether vocal or visual, for in courtship and love-making animal emotion reaches its highest pitch. The wonderful displays of many gaily plumaged male birds, from the cocks of the different magnificent birds of paradise, the argus pheasant, and the peacock, to that of the humble blackbird, are all the outcome of the intense excitement which thrills their being. Their feelings are so great they must give vent to them. Emotion wells within them until they strut in ecstasy. Watch a peacock displaying his wondrous fan, and note how he sets it a-quivering as waves of passion thrill through him; it is not a display of vain self-conscious pride but a display of passionate emotion, just as the songster is lost to all thought of self when he pours forth his paean of joy.

SONG, too, is an expression of emotion—the joyous excitement of the spring that possesses the bird to the exclusion of all else. Even mammals have their love songs, from the wolf howling in the forest, the coyote on the plains, to the dog in the backyard baying at the moon. And, as in birds, they lift up their voices to express their feelings and give vent to the surging emotion that wells within them. The tom cat screeching beneath our window at night is expressing his feelings, just as the fox out in the woodlands gives vent to his in a little, short, gruff bark—and so one could go on, giving many examples of the weird ways in which the most intense animal feelings, namely the emotional outpourings connected with courtship and mating, are displayed in beautiful posturing, extraordinary antics, and vocal outbursts, both impressive, awe inspiring, and charming.

Most wild creatures live in the present, time for them being limited, for they do not look far back nor yet far ahead. Hence the rapid stream of their emotions is one of fleeting impressions, as fleeting as cloud shadows racing along a hillside, and the expression of them as quickly variable. They fling their all into each passing phase, there is no posing, make believe, or acting about them; so in the expressions of animals we see depicted real emotion, and let us not blind ourselves to the intensity of the feelings thus expressed.

Chapter IX

Skeletons: & Some that are Worn Outside

By W. P. Pycraft

Author of "The Seashore,' "The Courtship of Animals"

THE very mention of the word skeleton suggests to most people something gruesome—an idea begotten of the fact that a skeleton is never seen except after the dissolution of the body. We have a feeling of sympathy with Ezekiel, who, when standing in the Valley of Dry Bones, was asked: "Can these bones live?" For it seems impossible that anything of interest can ever be said of them.

Look at a human skeleton, mark the fine lines of the frame-work on which our glorious bodies are built up; and then ask—whence comes this frame-work?

To find the answer to this question we have to go back to the simplest of the Vertebrates. Let us take that tiny, translucent little creature the amphioxus, a creature even more primitive than the lowliest fishes. It reveals to us the simplest form of skeleton to be found among the Vertebrates. The function of that skeleton, it should be remarked, is to furnish attachments for the muscles which affect the movements of the body. These must have some fixed point to work from, and this is furnished by a long, slender, unjointed, fibrous rod running from one end of the body to the other, and is known as the notochord.

Above it runs the spinal nerve-cord supplying the nerves which drive the muscles into action. Below it runs the main blood-vessel of the body. Such is the ground-plan of the Vertebrates, as distinct from the Invertebrates, wherein the skeleton is outside the body, and the nerve cord runs down the ventral surface instead of along the back, which is traversed by the main blood-vessel—an exactly opposite arrangement to that of the Vertebrates. But of this we shall see more presently.

The next stage in the evolution of the skeleton we find in the shark tribe, wherein the noto chord has become surrounded by a series of bony rings. Here we have the first vertebrae. The skull, at present. is a mere gristly or cartilaginous box, with special enlargements for the brain, eyes, and organs of smell and hearing. To its underside is hinged the lower jaw.

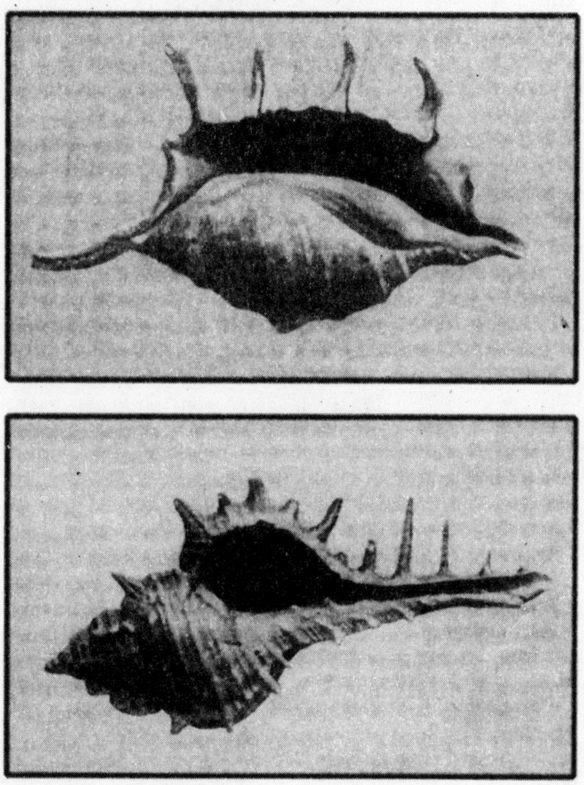

S. C. Johnson

SKELETONS OF WONDER

Protection has been sought by the mollusc known as the Venus shell (below) in the forming, out of what was originally its skeleton, of a beautiful covering for the otherwise defenceless creature. The scorpion shell (top) shows active defensive properties in its curved spikes

In the primitive land-vertebrate like the newt, for example, a bony skull has taken the place of the gristly box; bony hoops, forming the ribs, encircle the lungs and heart; and outside this cage we find the bony limb girdles and the limbs attached thereto.

Here we have a primitive Vertebrate, condemned to crawl on all fours.

Man alone walks always upright. His fore-legs have become glorified into arms and hands, ready to carry out the behests of his brain. Superb in the exquisite poise and beauty of his body, almost God-like in his knowledge, lord of "the beasts that perish," he is yet, all too commonly, the most brutal, and the biggest "beast" that the world has yet known, or is likely to know!

When we come to survey the Vertebrates, group by group, what an immense range of form and size we find. What have been the moulding forces which have resulted in this bewildering variety? We must reply the "shifts for a living," in the struggle for existence. In the scramble for food fresh sources of supply have had constantly to be tapped. And these have acquired constant adjustments of existing structures in response to the new conditions of capture, or of consuming and digesting the new type of diet.

These "winners in Life's race" we see in "the fowls of the air, and the beasts of the field, and the creatures under the earth," as well as in those under the waters. Fins have become legs, legs have become wings. And there are legs for every possible service; walking and running legs; clawing and digging legs; climbing and swimming legs. And all these have come into being only

As a consequence the muscles of the back, having less and less work to do, gradually dwindled away, at the same time lowering the back shield on to the ribs and spine. But matters did not end here. The sinking process went on till at last the great back shield and the ribs became welded together to form the shell of the tortoise as we see it in specimens great and small to-day.

It should be carefully examined ; for it presents some interesting features. The bony skin-plates have become beautifully interlocked with the ribs, while down the middle of the shell roof may be seen the tops of the spines of the vertebrae. But further, the horny plates have an arrangement of their own ; and along their edges the bony shield is deeply scored by grooves, forming a pattern superimposed on that of the bony shell itself.

There is yet another strange thing about this shell. In all the other land-vertebrates the shoulder girdle lies over, outside, the ribs. In the tortoise it has

W. S. Berridge

PRAWNS AND SHRIMPS IN THEIR JOINTED ARMOUR

Like a miniature lobster the prawn (below) frequents pools among the rocks while the shrimp (above) swims in its millions forming food for innumerable fishes. An examination of one of these creatures, even after it has been boiled, will reveal the simple but extraordinarily effective armour which has been slowly evolved out of what was once an internal skeleton.

by slowly modifying the hand or foot of the moment. By slow degrees the webbed foot has become the flipper of the turtle ; or the whale. If we examine the records of the rocks we can see how, in the course of time, the five-fingered foot of that strange creature phenacodus became the one-toed foot of the horse.

Everywhere we find that the size of an organ, or any part thereof, increased as the work demanded of it ; and on the other hand we see how organs, or parts of organs, shrink in size, till they become mere vestiges, and finally disappear as a result of disuse.

Such are the factors which have given us one of the most remarkable of all the Vertebrates—the tortoise. Familiarity, we are told, breeds contempt. If the tortoise were an exceedingly rare animal we should have discovered long since what a wonderful creature it is. Now we merely say of it that it is a creature which lives in a shell. But how has that shell come into being ? Wonder of wonders, it is the skeleton which has worked itself out of its body !

This remarkable state of affairs began when the ancestral tortoise started to develop an armour-plated skin, formed of bony nodules covered with a sheath of horn, after the fashion of the back shield of the crocodile.

As that armour increased in weight and size it gradually restricted the movements of the backbone.

come to lie under them, and therefore inside, rather than outside the body !

The great, broad breast shield, in like manner, has come to lie outside the body ; for its outer surface is covered by no breast muscles, but simply by the horny scutes of the skin.

That this strange shell was developed as a protection against enemies there can be no doubt ; for the creature, when alarmed, will withdraw both head and limbs within it, and thus defy all comers. But the extinct giant tortoise of Abingdon Island had the good fortune to live where there were no enemies to guard against. And so, as a response, the anterior aperture of the shell opened out, to form a great wide

W. S. Berridge

F. W. Bond

TORTOISES PROTECTED BY THEIR ADAPTED SKELETONS

By modifying the physical structure to new needs certain races of creatures have survived. Those who could not so adapt themselves perished. Witness the Abingdon Island Tortoise (bottom), which has a remarkably long neck and a much thinner shell than is usual with tortoises. It inhabits Abingdon Island, one of the Galapagos group (known also as the Tortoise Islands), which lies in the Pacific some 695 miles west of the coast of Ecuador. The upper photograph shows an Elephant Tortoise with a Greek tortoise placed on the shell.

Stone-Crab

Edible-Crab

King-Crab

Land-Crab

Spider-Crab

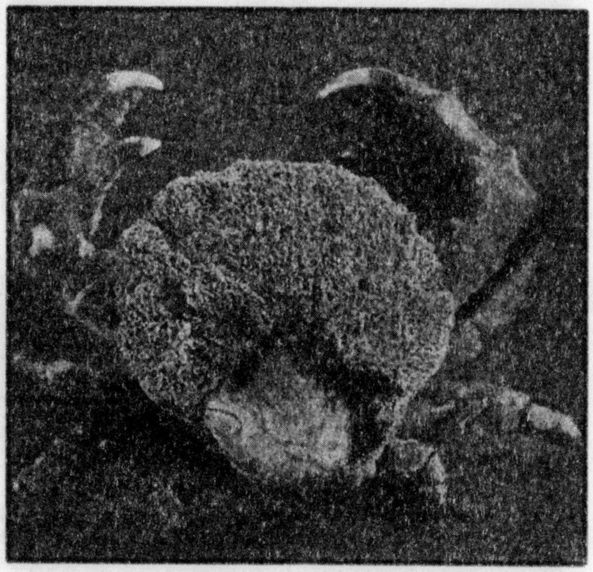

Sponge-Crab

HOW THE CRAB SOLVED THE SKELETON PROBLEM

A few examples of that group in the animal world which is called Crustacea are familiar enough on fishmongers' slabs, but there are many other representatives which the public never see. There is a great variety among the crabs alone which is apparent from the above photographs. But all have this common feature that the limbs are jointed and the skin has become hardened to form at once a protection and a skeleton or basis from which the body can be built up. The Photographs are by W. S. Berridge & E. Step.

Neville Kingston

SIMILAR PROTECTIVE DEVELOPMENT OF CRAWFISH AND LOBSTER

Here we see a truly marvellous development of the skeleton into something far more protective than in the case of the shrimps (see page 78). The intensely hard plates have not become welded into an immovable mass, as in the case of the tortoise (page 79), but are flexible like the suits of armour man devised in the age of chivalry. The crawfish (bottom) which is seen standing erect, must not be confused with the fresh-water crayfish. The lobster (top) is seen walking with bent legs on the floor of its tank. Both photographs were taken through the water.

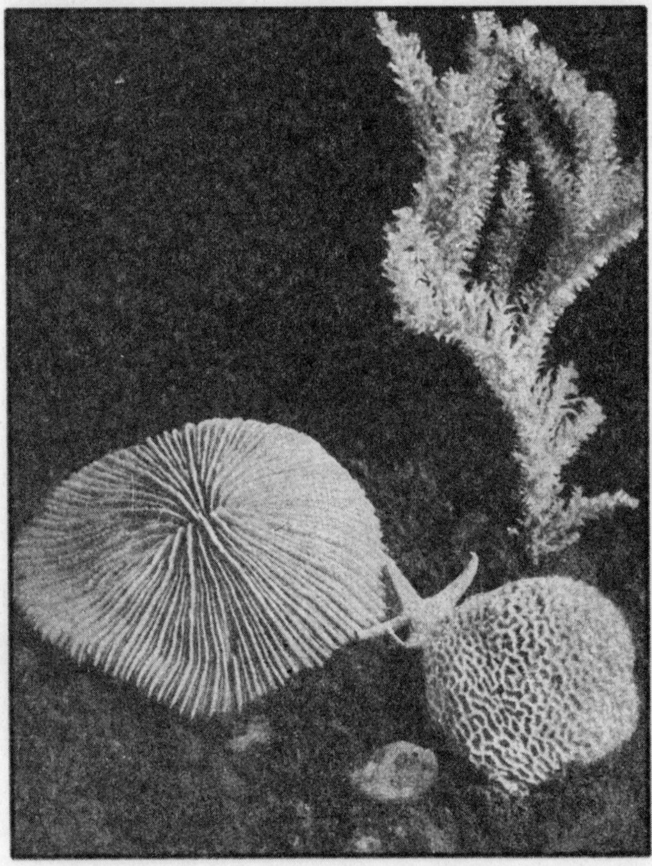

MARVELLOUS HABITATIONS OF THE CORAL

The lower photographs of species of Indian Coral and the upper of some from the China Seas, show the extraordinary variety of this miracle of the sea. These communal skeletons may resemble the under side of a mushroom, or a sponge while some seem to imitate frost formations.

doorway. Though this left the heart and lungs protected by no more than a sheet of soft skin this was a matter of no importance, since there was nothing on the island that could hurt it.

In some of the water-tortoises of the genus *Trionyx*, again, the need for a heavy shell has passed, and so it has become almost entirely replaced by a great leathery shield. Cause and effect are very well shown in the tortoises.

WHEN we turn to that other great group of the animal kingdom, the Invertebrates, we find an external skeleton to be the rule, not the exception. No better example of this type can be found than that furnished by the lobster, which is encased in what we may call a stony shell. And like the armour of ancient warriors, to afford freedom of movement for the body and limbs, that armour is wonderfully jointed. The muscles run from the walls of this shell to the parts which have to be moved, thus exactly reversing the order seen when the skeleton is internal.

If the Invertebrates had been limited to lobsters and crabs, prawns and shrimps, we should have said that only by hardening the outer wall could an efficient hold for muscles be obtained. But Nature is always achieving the impossible. And so we find that soft-bodied caterpillars are able to move about quite as easily as the hide-bound lobster.

The molluscs have an external skeleton, often of wondrous beauty, as witness the cabinets of the shell collector. But here that skeleton is solely for the protection of the body; a

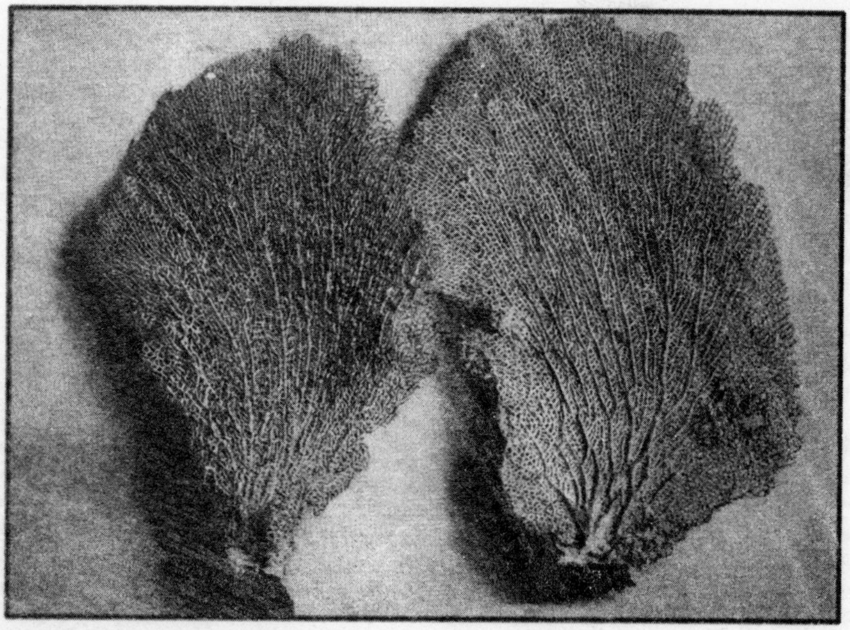

defensive armour. The body within it has a quite soft exterior. But there are a number of species which have contrived to discard the shell, as in the case of the nudibranch mollusca. Here the protection is afforded against enemies, either by warning or protective coloration. Some, however, like the slug and the squid or cuttle-fish have withdrawn the shell within the body like the Vertebrates.

In some of the cuttle-fish this shell takes the form of a long, thin, horny, blade-like plate, known as the pen; in others it is of a calcareous character, a long oval, and of considerable thickness. This furnishes the cuttle-fish bone hung so commonly in the cages of small birds to enable them to keep their beaks in good order. The so-called thunderbolts found so commonly in fossiliferous deposits are the pens of ancient and long extinct cuttle-fish.

E. Step

THE COMMUNAL SKELETON OF THE CORAL

Here we have one of Nature's greatest marvels. Minute, soft-bodied creatures, beautiful in form and colour, have contrived to win in the fight for life by building up, from the sea and the organisms that swarm in it, community skeletons to such an extent that a considerable portion of the world's surface is composed of them.

Though an external skeleton representing but a single individual is the rule among the Invertebrates, there are one or two groups which have a complex and much-branched skeleton shared by a large number of individuals. These are to be found among the great companies of creatures known collectively as the polyzoa, hydrozoa and anthozoa.

Everyone, when at the seaside, must have examined with some curiosity pieces of seaweed of horny texture sometimes beautifully branched, sometimes looking something like a bottle brush. These are not really seaweeds but the final relics of what was once a flourishing colony of polyzoa animals so soft-bodied that but for their ability to build up this common dwelling, which we might liken roughly to a series of flats, they would never be able to rise above the sea floor. A branch of one of these colonies, seen under the microscope, would reveal numbers of tiny bodies protruding half out of a delicate crystal cup projecting from a tubular stem, each little body surrounded by a crown of waving, glassy tentacles. Here the skeleton is outside the body.

The hydrozoa include not merely the familiar jelly-fish, which very emphatically has no skeleton, but also a large number of types, such as the horny-corals, and stone-corals, which have a very remarkable skeleton, sometimes of stony hardness.

The horny-corals and the stone-corals are creatures closely related to the sea-anemones, and very similar in shape, but forming colonies, building up internal skeletons of rare beauty. Such skeletons, it is to be noted, do not belong to the individual, but are formed by the whole colony as it grows. Their bodies form a common fleshy investment. Here, then, we have an entirely new kind of skeleton, and once more an internal skeleton.

Such skeletons have played, and are playing, a great part in the history of the world. A large part of its surface is made up of their fossilised bodies. They have formed, and are forming, islands in mid ocean, and vast "reefs," like the Great Barrier Reef of Australia, hundreds of miles long.

An immense amount of knowledge has been gained as to the habits and structure of these world builders; but we still seek in vain for an explanation such as will account for the bewildering variety of the shapes their stony masses assume. Some branch like trees; some assume the form of mushrooms; some form huge boulder-like masses with the surface covered with meandering ridges, reminding one of the mountain chains on a map.

The soft bodies which contrive to build up from the sea-water, or the food contained therein, these protean forms are strangely beautiful in their form, and varied in the brilliancy of their coloration. They seem to set the tone, so to speak, for the fishes, and other free-moving creatures which surround them. More than this, many of the fishes have become structurally modified, as to their jaws, for the purpose of feeding on them.

Though in British waters there are no coral reefs there is at any rate one species of coral in British seas. This is a species of *Caryophyllum*, which is to be found attached to shells near the Eddystone Lighthouse, and other places in the English Channel, as well as between tidemarks in the Scilly Islands and off the Shetlands.

One of the most highly-prized skeletons in the world is that of the red-coral of the Mediterranean. Deep down, from forty to a hundred fathoms, its crimson branches spread out, starred with little flower-like bodies. These are the coral builders. Their tiny bodies, all intercommunicating one with another, slowly transform carbonate of lime drawn from the sea water into the stony tissue we know as the red-coral. When this is first brought to the surface the "bark" formed by these jelly-like bodies is stripped off, and the outermost layer of the branch is filed away. Afterwards it is ground with emery-powder and finally polished with steel to form the beautiful beads and other ornaments looking rather as though made of wax than of a substance as hard as stone.

Though we can dissect and classify these singularly diverse types of skeleton, and the polyps or bodies which build them up, we are yet unable to discover the secret of their being. Each of these separate polyps is to all intents and purposes a sea-anemone. When and why did the first corals begin to anchor their bodies down to the ocean floor by means of a central core of stony hardness? Why did others go on budding out into new individuals attached by a common base, and sharing a common stomach, to break out, so to speak, into the innumerable types which form the stone-corals and the horny-corals and sea-pens of to-day? All alike are living in the sea, and all alike feed on the same kind of food—minute microscopic organisms. It is clear that there is an inherent difference in the qualities of their tissues, a difference of subtle physiological processes whereby, as in a chemist's laboratory, different substances are built up by different combinations of the same elements.

The red-coral, we have remarked, furnishes one of the most precious skeletons in the world, because of its extreme beauty after it has been suitably prepared by human hands. But there are other skeletons which run it very close, though we value them, not for their beauty, but for their usefulness. These are the skeletons of sponges. What should we do without our bath-sponge?

I need not enlarge upon the different types of sponges; we all know them well. But a knowledge of their nature is by no means so general. Those who would see for themselves what a living sponge is like have only to search the edges of slow-moving streams for small, more or less oblong patches looking rather like green felt. Gently remove such a patch to a glass bottle, and watch it through a magnifying glass. Minute particles of solid matter will be seen streaming into small holes in the surface. Much stronger currents will be seen streaming out of the large holes. The addition of a little colouring matter, dropped just over the patch, will make these movements more clearly visible.

The solid particles going in are food particles, and they are drawn into specially modified digestive cells to be converted, presently, into the tissue of the sponge. The emerging particles are waste products.

But the fresh-water sponge has no lasting skeleton. With the marine species this is quite otherwise, for most of these have a skeleton of horny fibres, or of horny fibres stiffened with simple, or branching, rods known as "spicules," microscopic in size, and as hard as flint. Many are very brightly coloured during life.

The living bath-sponge is not very attractive-looking, being of a uniform black, or slate colour. It is taken by divers, or harpooned, and when brought ashore is macerated in sea-water till the soft tissue, or flesh, rots away when the horny skeleton is hung up to dry.

Some of the sponges—of no commercial value—are of considerable size, and some are of great beauty, as for example the glass-rope sponge, which forms a long stalk of strands looking like spun glass. This stalk is thrust down into the mud, leaving the beautiful cup-shaped body well above the sea floor.

We began by discussing such skeletons as serve as points of attachment for muscles, which send out, so to speak, contractile bands to the several parts to be moved. These muscles, save in the case of the tortoise, invest the skeleton. In the Invertebrates, on the other hand, the skeleton invests the muscles; in either case the hard parts are intimately associated with movement.

There are exceptions to every rule. In the snails, and other univalve molluscs, the skeleton is but loosely attached to the body, and serves only as a coat of mail to protect an otherwise defenceless creature. What are the factors which have brought about

AWE-INSPIRING SKELETON OF THE GIANT DINOSAUR, TYRANNOSAURUS

Dug from the soil of Montana this colossal frame which the Tyrannosaurus developed is in the American Museum of Natural History. A man, standing beside one of its legs, gives us a vivid idea of the gigantic size which this pre-historic animal attained. **This is a case of a normal skeleton developed to titanic proportions by the species—the Dinosaurs—which once were the most powerful beings on the earth. The little** mollusc (page 77) the Venus shell, adapted itself to changing conditions. The Dinosaur failed—and perished.

the astonishing range of beauty in the form and coloration of their shells we have yet to discover.

Finally, we have to consider skeletons such as can only be seen under the microscope, but which are indescribably beautiful. Some are made of lime, some of silica, looking as though they were of cut-glass of exquisite workmanship. Minute though they be, their dead, fossilised bodies make up vast areas of the earth's surface; and their descendants are still at work. These are the skeletons of the foraminifera, and the radiolaria which exhibit an amazing variety of form.

THE foraminifera of which there are hundreds of species, number some giants among their ranks. Parts of the Egyptian desert are strewn so thickly with their disc-shaped bodies, nearly two inches across, as to make it difficult to walk over them, because they slide about under the feet. These, and the smaller species, form enormous areas of limestone in various parts of the world. And this is largely used for building purposes. They bear witness, also, to stupendous changes in the earth's surface, as we may gather from the fact that this limestone forms part of the mighty Himalayas, 19,000 feet above the sea level. They once covered the sea floor. The chalk cliffs of Dover are built up of their frail bodies! Microscopically examined these shells are seen to be perforated with minute holes. Through these are thrust delicate strands of protoplasm, the stuff of which the living tissue is made, and which forms the shell. This protoplasm, in the form of long, delicate threads, at one and the same time serves as oars and hands to capture food.

The jelly-like substance, or protoplasm, of the radiolarians is in all essentials like that of the foraminifera. Yet it possesses qualities we cannot detect; qualities which make possible the formation, from the sea-water, of fragile, translucent skeletons of flint-like silica; these shells are of marvellous beauty.

They swarm to-day in all the tropical areas of the ocean, and have been closely studied by men of science, who tell us that these shells are, for the most part, composed of a central capsule, enclosing the more vital part of the protoplasm, since it contains the nucleus and oil-globules which help to keep them afloat. Around this is an outer shell, the two being held together by radiating rods of silica. Over this outer shell is a layer of jelly, and from this proceed innumerable pseudopodia, or threads, for locomotion, and the capture of food. Moreover, during life this outer region of jelly is often most brilliantly coloured.

The spherical shells with their radiating rods recall the wonderful ivory spheres carved by the Chinese into a sort of filigree work. Their range of form is truly astounding.

John J. Ward

BEAUTIFUL SPIRAL CASING OF THE GREAT TRITON

Painters of mythological pictures were very fond of introducing this shell into their canvases as an instrument for the attendants of the sea-deities to blow. The shape and formation have a most beautiful design from the top of the cone to the ringed aperture. Some of the markings show successive stages of growth, the shell, the triton's adapted skeleton, becoming gradually thicker. It is interesting to note that the Polynesian islanders still use the triton shell as a trumpet for religious ceremonial.

Chapter X

What Comes Out of An Egg

By Dr. C. G. Patten

Professor of Anatomy, Sheffield University

"WHICH comes first, the hen or the egg?" Perhaps a poser for some of us, but certainly not for the student who possesses even an elementary knowledge of biology! He knows that the forces of evolution proceed always from the simple to the complex; from *homogeniety* to *heterogeniety*.

The egg, compared with the parent, is a very simple organism, composed in the main of thin gelatinous material called protoplasm, the basis of all living matter. Yet this egg possesses marvellous potentialities not only in the direction of growth and development, but also of heredity. When we consider, not only the structural uniformity of the egg, but also that embryos of various animals in their earlier stages are practically indistinguishable, we marvel at the *vis a tergo*, which, in the elaboration of varied and manifold processes, insists on like begetting like.

For the sake of argument we might possibly conceive of the earlier stages in pre-natal development being mechanical (seeing that all embryos are so alike); indeed we might, so to speak, conceive of them being "cast in the same mould." But in the later stages the conception of mechanism is ruled out of court. The exact impress of the particular parent, portrayed towards the termination of pre-natal existence, must have some other force behind it. It is impossible, for instance, to explain specialisation of the form of the limbs in different animals on mechanical grounds. All limbs arise alike: but compare the vast difference in the hoof of the horse, the flipper of the whale, and the hand of man. These are simple examples out of hundreds of others. This wonderful hereditary conservation, which insists on like begetting like, depends upon long associated habits of the cellular protoplasm of the embryo itself; in other words, upon memory processes which would appear to have a very definite physical basis.

There is reason to believe that memory has its place in the structural as well as in the temporary reaction of living organisms. It would be outside the scope of this article to follow the intricacies of embryological processes; albeit the broad principles may be indicated. Our bodies are composed of myriads of units, called cells. But the term is hardly appropriate, seeing that these cells are not hollow receptacles. They are, in the main, filled with protoplasm. True, some grow fibrous, cartilaginous, or even osseous, in order to subserve their particular wants; nevertheless constitutionally they remain definite body-units.

Our body-cells bear some analogy to the bricks of a building. Whence have they been derived? From that wonderful single cell we call the Egg, technically known as the ovum or germ-cell, after a special part of its protoplasm, called the nucleus, has fused with that of a much smaller cell, the spermatozoon or sperm-cell. The egg-cell proceeds from the female parent; the sperm-cell from the male parent. After the nucleus of the latter has fused with the nucleus of the egg we hear no more of its individuality. It finishes its career by acting as a fertiliser. Fertilisation awakens the egg into a wonderful state of activity. Carrying with it the combined hereditary factors present in the conjoined nuclei, it starts to divide actively and with great rapidity into daughter-cells, each of which in turn repeats the process, and hands on the stimulus to its descendants.

AS a result, myriads of cells, clustered together into a mass resembling a mulberry, are formed. The generic name of the fruit is *Morus*, hence the term *Morula* has been given to this stage of embryonic development. These cells, at first simple, form the raw material, the "bricks and mortar," so to speak, out of which the body is built up. The "bricks" arrange themselves in a wonderful manner to suit the architecture of the "edifice." Not only are walls formed and apartments partitioned off, but also, by a process of infolding and separating certain groups of bricks, the vital organs (already assuming their requisite contour) are laid down. From the embryo, in all cases limbless at first, simple buds sprout forth, which later on become differentiated into characteristic forms. As already mentioned, these buds all arise in like manner, whether they afterwards become a flipper of a whale, a hoof of a horse, or a human arm terminating in its free fingers and thumb, which can perform such exquisite, delicate, and skilled movements. Such then are the broad outlines which

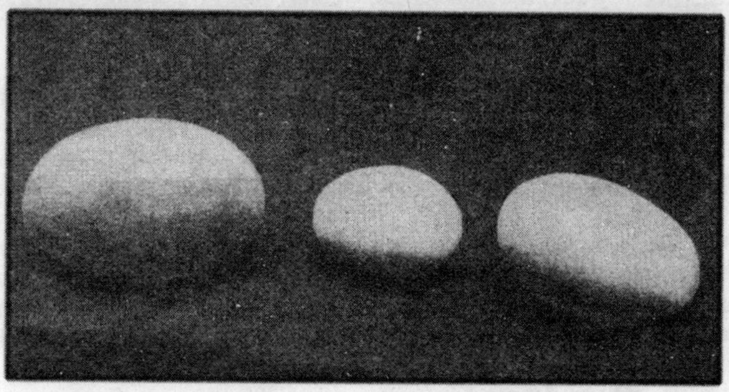

EGGS OF BIRD AND REPTILE COMPARED

The first egg here is that of a python, the second that of an ordinary barn-door fowl, and the third a crocodile's. In size, shape, and colour there is little difference, but a crocodile's egg placed under a hen might cause her some surprise when hatched out.

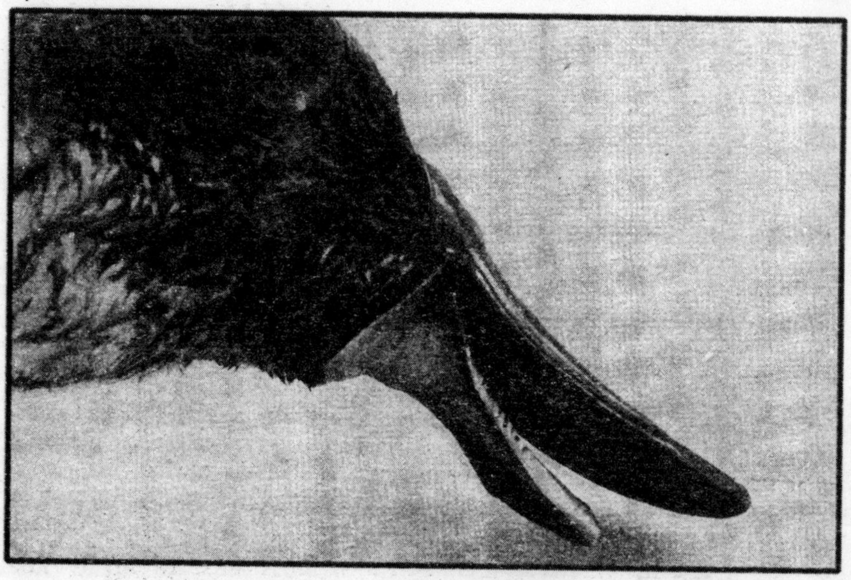

Let us now make a general survey of the characteristic features present in the eggs of various animals according to their position in the Animal Kingdom. Let us follow the way in which these features arose and adapted themselves to the wants of the individuals. Beginning with organisms which occupy the highest position in the Zoological Scale, namely, the Mammals, we find that the egg, with very few exceptions, is extremely small.

In Man, who we know is a mammal, it is barely visible to the naked eye, reaching only one 125th of an inch in diameter, and destitute of a shell. No calcareous or other tough protective encasement is necessary, seeing that this minute germ of life is " laid " within the uterus of the mother. Nay more, not remaining merely on the surface of the cavity which it first touches, it soon embeds itself in the actual substance of the uterine wall. In that way it shuts itself off from all possible dangers which might be caused by shock or injuries to the mother. Here, in its snug little excavation, and surrounded at an extremely early stage by a mantle, which forms a bag filled with fluid (technically called the amnion, and popularly the caul), it sends out thousands of fine branches with tiny blood-vessels, which take up nutriment from the mother's uterine circulation.

Zoological Society, N.Y.

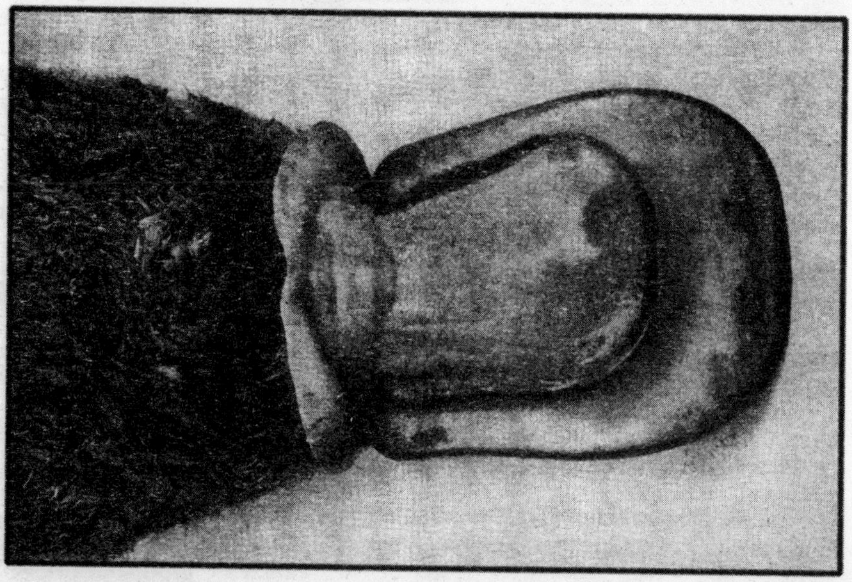

E. R. Sanborn

THE STRANGE, BILL-LIKE MOUTH OF THE PLATYPUS

This Australian mammal, with mouth like a flattened beak and webbed feet, seems to have much in common with the duck, and is popularly known as the duck-bill. It lives largely in the water, and finds its food—worms, insects, and small crustaceans—by probing in the mud. It is nearer the reptiles than the birds. Above is a side view of the bill and below, a top view.

mark developmental processes in the individual as yet unborn.

Whence can we trace the existence of the egg? In those far far away vistas of the past, those almost inconceivably remote ages when naught else of life but the egg existed; when by fission it formed two daughter eggs, each descendant in turn repeating the process, not clustering to form a body; but moving away independently; each a sole reproductive unit; *a physically immortal being!* Cells as they multiplied had not commenced to form tissues; there was no aggregation of " bricks and mortar "; no edifice was erected. In other words no body was appended to the eternal reproductive system; hence no corpse needed casting off. Descendants of this ancestral egg, marvellous to relate, still persist unchanged, while others have proceeded far ahead, growing more and more elaborate, until they acquired bodily organization which has culminated in the development of the stupendously complex vertebrate series.

FROM a single-celled microscopic organism, represented by the amoeba which has persisted to the present day (though it no doubt at the first dawn of life existed in a still more simple form), and comparable to the single-celled egg of existing creatures, all multicellular organisms have arisen, whose descendants in turn commence life as a single cell, the egg. So the cycle of life goes on, ever evolving from the simple to the complex; ever elaborating; ever adapting.

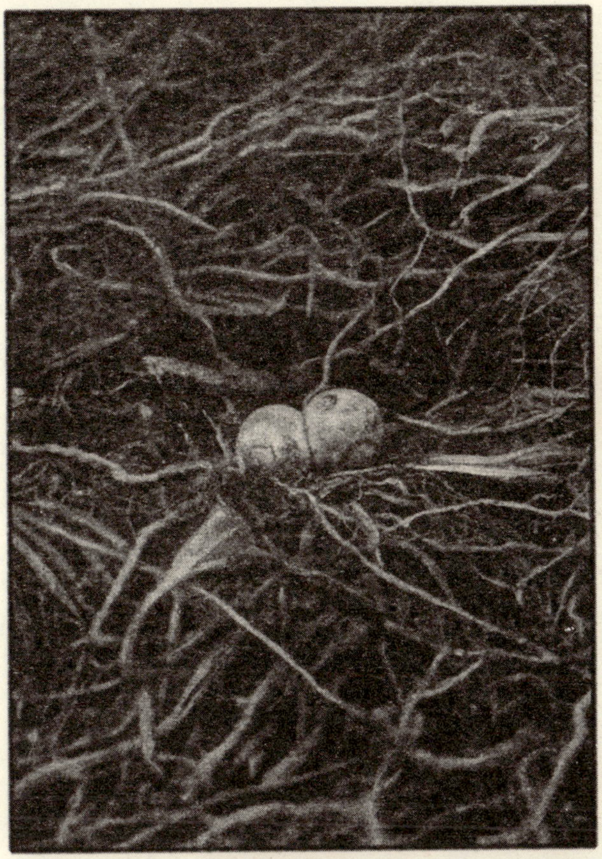

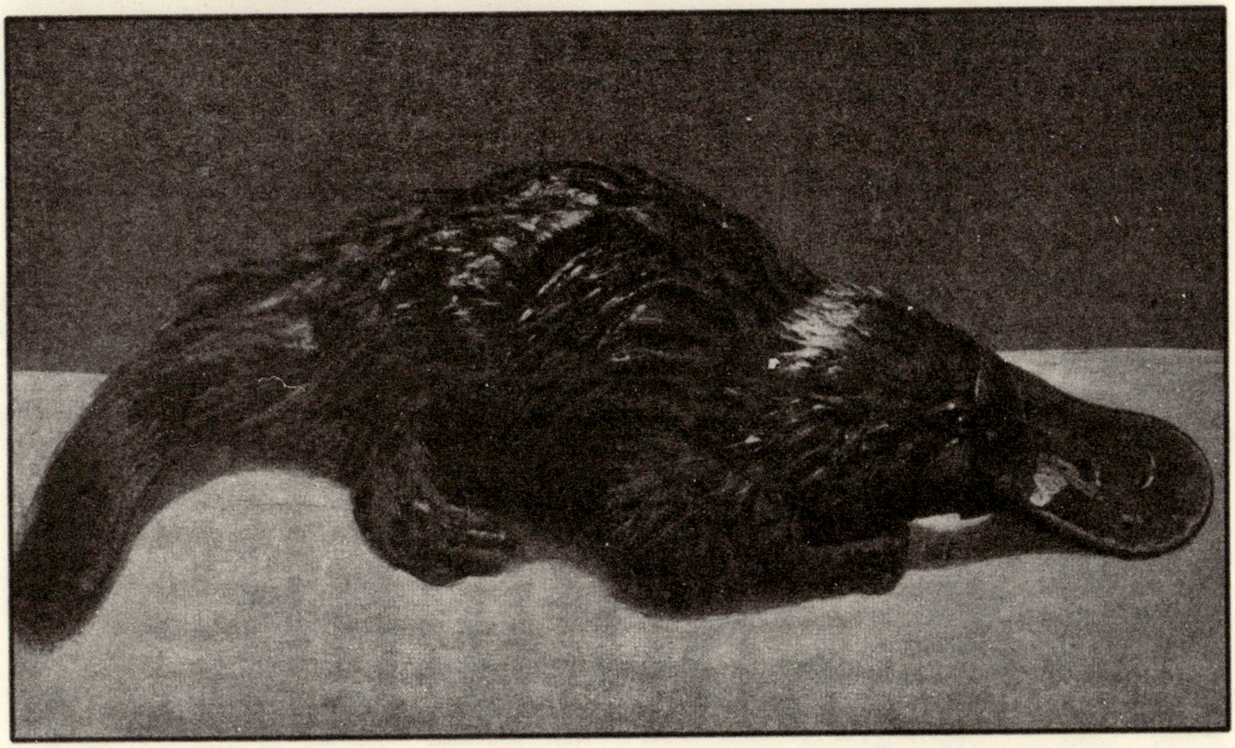

MAMMAL THAT LAYS AN EGG AND HATCHES OUT ITS YOUNG LIKE A BIRD

The platypus, or ornithorhyncus as scientists call it, is one of the strangest of living mammals, for its young are produced from eggs which the mother lays in a nest (top left) and sits on as a hen does on hers. There may be one, two, or three eggs in the nest, and when hatched (top right) the young are blind. They have little cheek teeth which soon drop out, and each jaw is then furnished with two pairs of horny plates. Full grown (bottom picture) the fur-covered platypus is about eighteen inches long, and it sleeps rolled up like a hedgehog. Its temperature is below that of other mammals. The upper photographs are by Mr. Harry Burrell and the lower one by Mr. Elwin R. Sanborn.

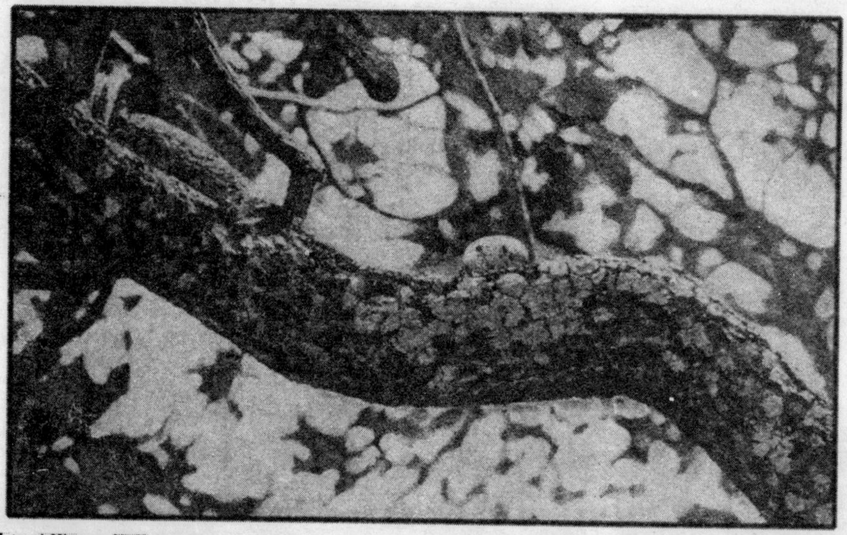

Natural History, N. Y.

down the gullet by a muscular mechanism in connection with the mammary gland. All living marsupials are indigenous to Australasia, with the exception of a few species of opossums which are found in America.

More aberrant still are the Monotremes, which include the duck-mole, or duck-billed platypus (*Ornithorhynchus*), and the spiny ant-eater (*Echidna*). They lay comparatively large eggs, measuring from half an inch to an inch long, invested with a white shell, tough yet flexible. The platypus excavates long serpentine burrows, with branching recesses.

EGGS OF TWO REMARKABLE BIRDS
Birds' eggs are generally laid in nests or in some safe place on the ground, but the tuamoke or fairy tern of America lays its solitary egg on the bough of a tree (top). Below is an ostrich egg and a young one just hatching out. It is fitting that a big bird should come from a big egg and the ostrich's weighs as much as two dozen hen's eggs.

We may compare the embedding of the mammalian egg and its fine rootlets to the germination of a tiny plant which, on sinking in the soil, sends out innumerable fine root-hairs. The caul usually ruptures and the fluid escapes just before birth, though not invariably. David Copperfield came into the world, caul intact. No doubt the sailors in the time of Dickens considered him a lucky infant! The minute mammalian egg is not heavily laden with yolk; moreover, the yolk-sac, which afterwards becomes demarcated from the rest of the embryo, shrinks almost to a vanishing point at a very early stage. As a nutritive organ for the embryo it is supplanted by a vascular spongy structure—the placenta—derived in the main from the wall of the mother's uterus. With this the embryo comes into intimate connection through the extremely fine vascular rootlets mentioned above. Such then is the typical way in which the minute egg of the placental mammal becomes connected with the mother. At birth the offspring reaches its full natal development, and gestation often covers a prolonged period.

In Marsupials, such as the kangaroo, that is to say animals provided with an abdominal pouch into which the embryo is born prematurely after a short period of gestation, the egg is also small; but it is provided with a considerable amount of yolk, and the sac remains large, enabling the unborn young to obtain much nourishment from it. The embryo is not intimately attached to the uterus; only in a small measure its connection with maternal tissues is made by fine rootlets from the yolk sac. The offspring, when born into the pouch, is far too premature to start to suck in the ordinary mammalian manner. Nature provides that when the teat has become engaged in the mouth, the milk is pumped

In one of these, well above high-water mark, the eggs are deposited, two forming a clutch. The echidna also burrows, but it would appear that the eggs from the beginning are hatched and carried in a pouch which develops as a temporary measure. Most of us are familiar with the curious form of the platypus, a creature about half a yard in length, clothed in dark brown, short, soft fur, and provided with protruding flattened, horny jaws, which bear a startling resemblance to the beak of a duck. The eyes are very small, and no external ears are visible. The animal is aquatic, living along the banks of lakes and rivers. Its front limbs are webbed and clawed, and it swims and dives with speed and alacrity.

The echidna, or spiny ant-eater, frequents drier and more elevated situations. It may be found in timbered districts, at a height of three thousand feet, provided ants are plentiful. It varies in size according to species, but on an average its dimensions are comparable to those of a large hedgehog. Like the latter, it can roll itself into a ball, its spiny coat protecting it from the enemy. Usually, however, it bolts for its burrow when suspicious

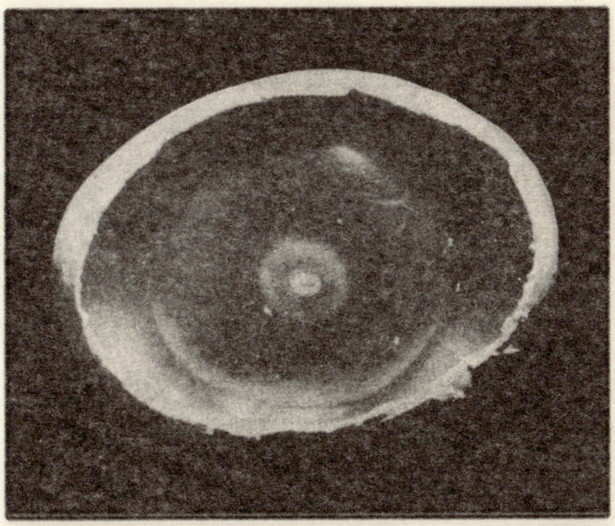

After twelve hours

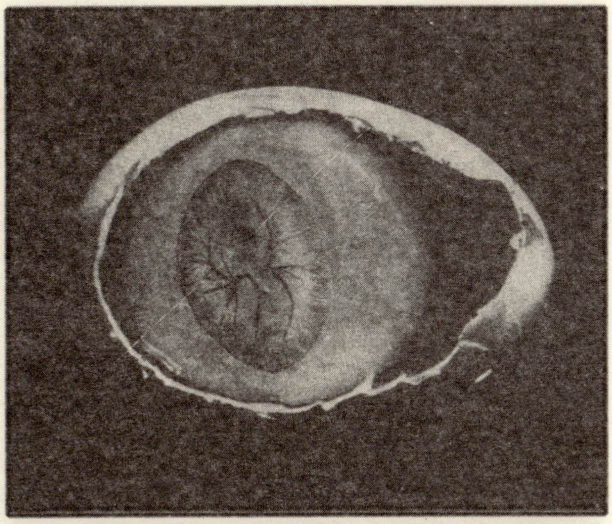

Third day

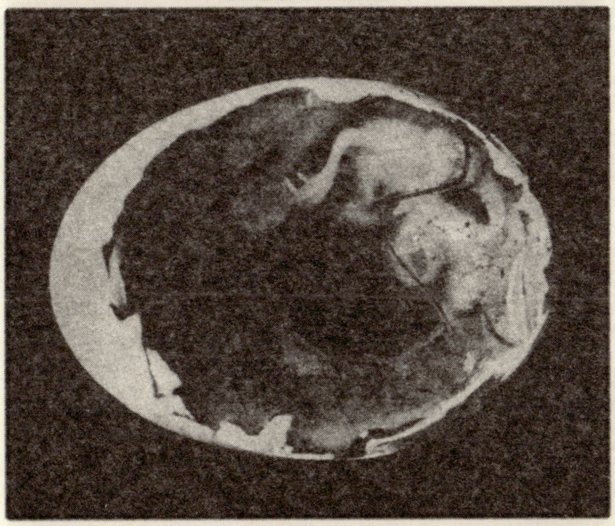

Eleventh day

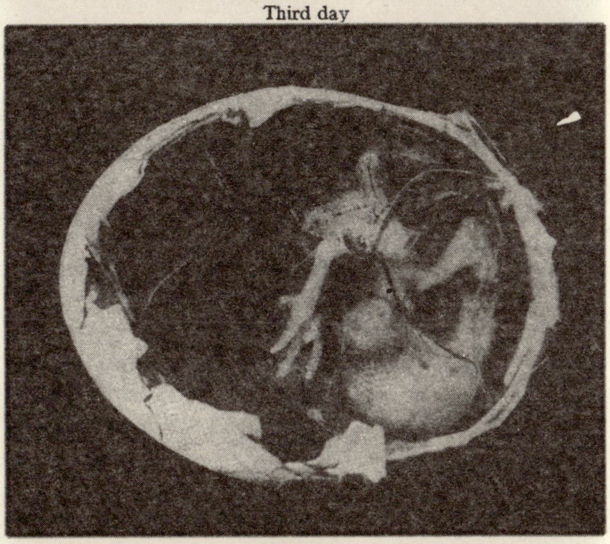

Fifteenth day

Twentieth day

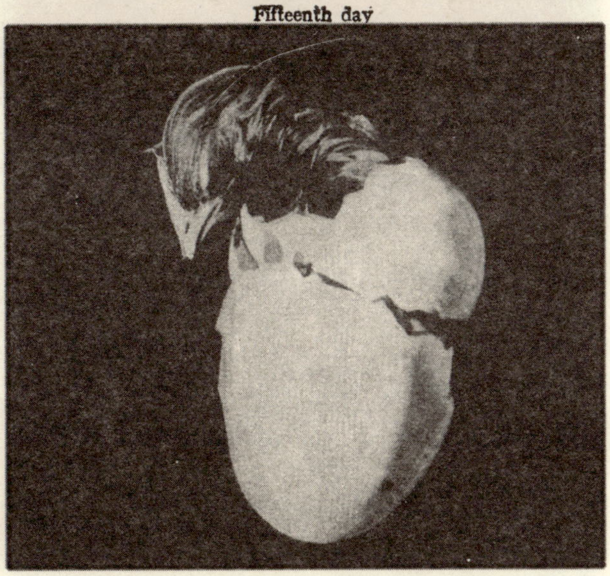

Chick emerging

THE EGG OF THE DOMESTIC FOWL AND THE CHICKEN THAT COMES OUT OF IT

If the fertile egg of a hen be broken open there will be noticed on top of the yellow yolk a small white spot. This represents the germ or protoplasm which will develop into the chick, and the yellow cushion of yolk on which it rests provides a store of food which is gradually absorbed as the bird develops in the shell. It is the germ and yolk which really constitute the egg. The albumen, or " white," and the shell are merely accessory structures. These remarkable photographs show six stages in the hatching out of a chicken from the egg.

A CROCODILE'S NEST WITH THE MOTHER GUARDING HER EGGS— G. P. Lewis

Crocodiles and alligators, giant reptiles that sometimes grow as long as eighteen feet, are hatched out of eggs with a hard white shell about the size of a goose egg. Some crocodiles lay their eggs, ranging from twenty to sixty in number, in a hollow of the sand by the river bank—where they bask, and others, like the marsh crocodiles of the Dutch East Indies, build a nest of leaves, twigs, and branches, as seen in these photographs, and there lay a clutch of eggs (bottom). The mother then retires to a shallow trench surrounding the nest (top) where she guards the eggs from marauding monkeys, and ten weeks later the young reptiles hatch out.

—ONE OF THE YOUNG CROCODILES EMERGING FROM THE SHELL

The actual birth of a young crocodile is shown in these remarkable photographs, all of which, except the fourth one, were taken by Mr. Felix Kopstein and are reproduced here by courtesy of " Asia " magazine, New York. When the young reptile is ready to emerge it makes some sound, and if the eggs are buried in the sand the mother crocodile uncovers them. The baby crocodile then cracks the shell and (top left) pokes the tip of its nose out. Then (top right) it pushes the whole of its clumsy head out. Gradually more and more of its body emerges (centre and bottom left) until at last (bottom right) it is clear of the shell. Even while hatching it shows signs of savagery.

W. S. Berridge

ENGLISH GRASS SNAKES COMING OUT OF THEIR EGGS

It is curious how frightened most people are when they find a grass snake and still greater is their horror if they come across a cluster of eggs with the young snakes just hatching out, as in this photograph. Yet the grass snake is quite harmless to human beings, does good to the farmers by devouring field mice, and is a very beautiful creature, exceedingly graceful in its movements. It makes an excellent pet, is easy to keep, and soon gets to know its owner. Grass snakes love the water and may often be seen swimming in lakes and brooks.

In both platypus and echidna, the young break loose from the egg-shell at a very imperfect stage of development. The skin is naked, the eyes closed, the beak very short and pliable in texture. The frail little offspring is carried about for a time in a recess of the skin studded with milk-glands, the ducts of which open on the surface without the intervention of teats or nipples. The young seize hold of the skin over a diffused area at the bottom of the transient pouch, and vigorously suck the milk, as a schoolboy in a hurry might deal with a juicy orange! The inception of temporary "brood-pouches" foreshadows the further development of those which have become permanent in the marsupials, thus affording an interesting link in the chain of evolution.

We naturally ask—why do these strange mammals lay large eggs after the fashion of birds and reptiles? Furthermore we ask—will they continue the practice? They lay eggs like birds and reptiles because their reproductive receptacles are built on exactly the same plan. They have no uterus to accommodate a growing embryo; no "soil" in which a minute egg could become embedded. They are provided with only comparatively thin-walled tubes—the oviducts—in which the eggs, in gathering up their yolk and shell, may tarry awhile, but no attachment ensues; the eggs are always on the move towards the exterior. Reaching a common chamber, called the cloaca, which also receives the excretory products, the egg is soon expelled from the body through a common outlet. This structural arrangement is found in reptiles and birds. These creatures we know are typically oviparous, and a shell protects the egg.

But it is fascinating to observe that a similar arrangement maintains also in the embryos of the placental mammals, provided with a uterus. It is an arrangement, however, which has only a passing phase. As development goes further forward, the simple cloacal clamber, with its single exit, is supplanted by the more elaborate arrangement of the external passages and sex-organ chambers, which is typical of the great Order of Mammals. It is obvious, then, that platypus and echidna will continue to lay eggs invested with a shell, as long as their sexual receptacles correspond structurally to those of birds and reptiles.

The duck-mole and spiny ant-eater have a limited geographical distribution. They are not found outside Australasia. In that respect they resemble in distribution the Marsupials which, with the exception of the American Opossums, are confined to Australia and Tasmania. All these animals belong to a very low Order, animals which have survived without further development, owing to insulation of their native soil before alien competitors could manage to invade them. Australia geographically thus became a sanctuary for her indigenous mammals. They were not forced to part with their primitive characteristics though in habits of life they specialised in all

HARMLESS AMERICAN SNAKE WHICH INCUBATES ITS EGGS

Although most snakes leave their eggs unattended to be hatched out by the heat of the sun or of the manure in which they are laid, there are some that incubate the eggs themselves, curling round them and assisting with the heat of their bodies. The python is a notable example of this rare maternal instinct, and another example is the pine or bull snake of America, shown in the photograph. This reptile is creamy white, blotched with brown, and it often grows to a length of six feet. It is pugnacious and malodorous, but not poisonous.

F. W. Bond

E. Step

TOAD AND CRAB CARRYING THEIR EGGS

The midwife toad in the upper photograph is a male, and when his mate lays her eggs threaded together by elastic filaments and gelatinous capsules the male attaches himself to them and carries them with him till they are hatched. The crab (below) is a female, the underside being shown with a mass of eggs attached to her body. These she takes about with her.

directions. Domestic tragedy in a large measure then became Nature's key-note; carnivorous marsupials preying upon herbiverous marsupials; Tasmanian wolves and devils dining off kangaroo and wallaby chops and steaks!

Every one knows that birds lay eggs. In some species the ground-colour of the shell is rendered very beautiful by delicate tints, enriched further by spots, streaks, and blotches of darker hue. The pattern of the markings is usually distinctive. In many cases the ground-colour remains an unspotted monochrome. The shell is, in all cases, composed of carbonate of lime, and is hard, though brittle. The comparative size of egg to bird is a very inconstant equation indeed. But even in the case of those birds which lay relatively small eggs (for instance, the cuckoo) the egg remains gigantic when compared with that of the typical mammal. Generally speaking, the independent, precociously-developed chick, which races hither and thither directly it is hatched, emanates from a large egg. This is particularly the case in birds whose clutches are small and hence capable of being covered by the sitting parent. The eggs of the mallee-fowl and brush turkeys are enormous proportionately to the size of the parent. The young are born fully feathered, and can fly almost immediately.

These birds are known as mound-builders, because they lay their eggs on substantial hillocks composed of sandy soil containing decomposing vegetable matter. The heat dissipated becomes sufficient to incubate the eggs. The parents display the reptilian habit of not brooding on their eggs: the young chicks have never known their parents. They must shift for themselves immediately they come into the world. Hence their unusually precocious development. What a striking contrast the infant pigeon presents: scarce able to lift its head, it requires the assistance of its parent who, engaging the little beak within its own, pumps softened regurgitated food down its throat.

The immense size of the bird's egg depends primarily upon the enormous aggregation of yolk, a necessary provision for the sustenance of the fast-

BIRTH OF A CROCODILE: PHOTOGRAPHED EMERGING FROM THE EGG

F. W. Bond

HOW THE YOUNG TORTOISE IS BORN AND THE MOTHER GUARDS HER EGGS

Tortoises like crocodiles lay eggs, but these vary much in size and shape. Most of them like those of the grooved or spurred tortoise of these photographs are spherical, and in the case of the giant species of Galapagos the eggs are as big as tennis balls. Those of the water terrapin are elliptical. The grooved tortoise is a native of the hot regions of Africa and the shell is often three feet long, measured across the curve. As the bottom photograph shows, the young at the moment of birth is a small replica of its parents.

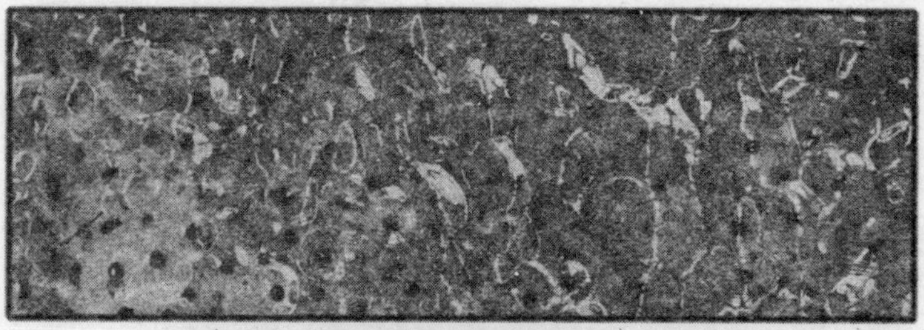

The spawn or egg cluster

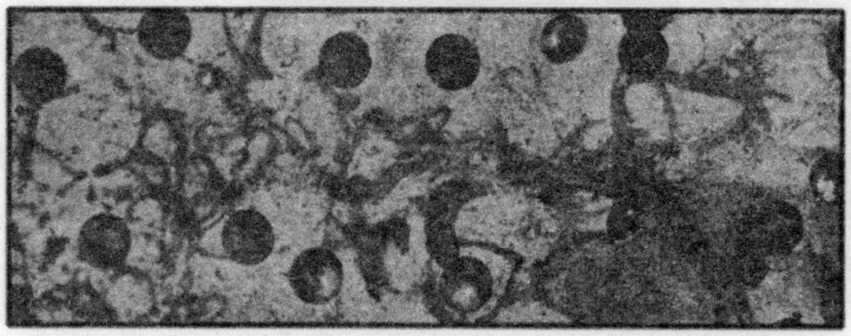

Tadpoles forming in the egg

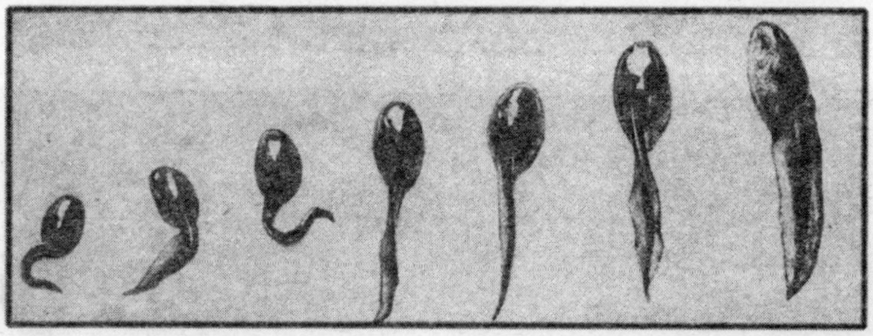

Stages of tadpole growth

The legs begin to form

Tail disappears and legs become perfect

THE FROG FROM EGG TO PERFECT AMPHIBIAN

The frog lays a number of eggs at the bottom of a pool or ditch and these, by absorbing water swell and rise to the surface, where they float as a gelatinous mass. After a time the tadpoles hatch out, and these grow rapidly, developing gills and a big tail, which later is absorbed. Then lungs and legs form, and the perfect frog comes to land. The photographs are by John Roberts and M. H. Crawford.

growing embryo during incubation. Birds are highly specialised creatures, but it is interesting to note that their specialisation bears a stamp of uniformity. The fore-limbs are highly specialised to subserve the function of flight, yet we cannot point to one single instance in which either these or the hind-limbs are wanting: nor can we point to any bird being viviparous. It is different with Mammals. Whales, porpoises, and dolphins, have lost their hind-limbs; and viviparity gives way to oviparity in the duck-mole and also in the spiny ant-eater.

LIKEWISE in the Reptiles, specialisation has not proceeded on uniform lines. The snake has departed still further from type in becoming quite limbless, and also in a minority of instances in being viviparous. A few species of lizards also are hatched before they leave the body of the mother. But reptiles, like birds, are typically egg-laying creatures. As in the case of birds, the eggs of reptiles are large and heavily laden with yolk. The shells, however, unlike those of the birds' eggs, can lay no claim to beauty. In those of snakes they are oblong in shape and leathery in consistency. In crocodiles and alligators, and most other classes of reptiles, they are calcareous. In some species, notably the common land tortoise (a familiar garden pet) the shell is so dense that it becomes quite a business to pierce it with a steel egg-drill.

Speaking generally, the eggs of reptiles are nearly circular in shape; unglazed in texture; and dull whitish in colour. They are laid in great numbers: a clutch ranging from fifty to two hundred. The eggs are usually deposited in hollows excavated for their reception. They are carefully covered up with the soil, and hatched by the heat of the sun's rays. It is easy to understand why so large a clutch is permissible. Reptiles do not brood; if they did and the eggs depended upon the heat derived from the area of the body which could cover them, the clutches, like those of the bird, might be composed of only about half-a-dozen eggs!

Here, however, we note an extremely interesting exception. The python, having carefully stacked her eggs so as to form a convenient pile, coils herself round them and, with maternal solicitude, broods over her numerous treasures for three whole months! Her length and girth reach such remarkable dimensions that she can gather in her coils actually her entire progeny! But a brooding tortoise or turtle could never cover her clutch. It should be noted, however, that the eggs of reptiles are generally proportionately smaller than those of birds. The egg of the crocodile, for instance, is comparable in size to that of the goose; the egg of the green turtle (a creature three feet long) to that of the domestic fowl.

Infant reptiles have to shift for themselves at a tender age. Mothers may defend the newly hatched (which at times include other than those of her clutch) against the onslaughts of a hungry adversary. Parental care, however, soon comes to an end as the youngsters begin to wander from her side and fend for themselves.

Below the Order of Mammals, vertebrate animals are typically oviparous. We have seen that no exceptions arise among the birds. Below that order, exceptions do occur among the reptiles, as in a few snakes and lizards; among the amphibians, as in the salamanders; and among the fishes, as in some sharks. It is difficult to account for these anomalies. Curiously enough, it is in the typical condition that instability may arise. Thus it has been observed that the oviparous grass-snake, and a few other non-poisonous species, may be induced in confinement, and under other unusual conditions of life, to become viviparous.

It would appear that the converse has not come under observation. Eggs of the viviparous British adder or of the rattle-snake of America have not been observed aggregated for purposes of incubation. In the vast domain of Invertebrates oviparity, or egg-laying, is the rule. We find only a few forms of insects are viviparous. But we are confronted with so many strange forms which issue forth from the egg, forms strikingly dissimilar to their parents, and forms which portray such a complicated embryonic life-history, that even a general survey of the eggs and progeny of invertebrate creatures in general, would take us too far afield.

The chain of eggs

Tadpoles hatching out

Tadpoles rising to the surface

Young toad ready to land

The full grown toad

THE LIFE STORY OF THE COMMON TOAD

The toad, when fully developed, is much more terrestrial in habit than the frog. Its eggs, however, like the frog's, are deposited in water, not in clusters, but in long double chains, and when hatched out into dark-coloured tadpoles, the creature's life, in its early stages, is very much like the frog's. It is slower in movement than its relation. The photographs are by W. S. Berridge and M. H. Crawford.

What Comes out of An Egg

F. W. Bond

HUGE SNAIL WITH ITS EGG AS BIG AS A PIGEON'S

The Brazilian giant snail, the largest of its kind, has a shell that often reaches a length of six inches, and it lays an egg about the size of that of a pigeon or ringdove. When the time of hatching comes the egg-shell breaks and a young snail emerges which is a miniature of its mother. Giant snails are found not only in South America and the West Indies, but also in South Africa.

What comes out of the egg is commonly called, in the insect world, a larva. We hardly think the expression appropriate when the young is an exact miniature replica of its parent. True, wings are suppressed until adult life ; but we know that there are insects which are wingless throughout their existence. It is among such forms that the newly-hatched egg may bring forth an absolute facsimile of its parent. Notable examples are the lice and springtails. Newly hatched earwigs, cockroaches, and locusts have no wings ; otherwise they resemble the adults. In mayflies and dragonflies there is a distinct difference between the aquatic and wingless larvae and the aerial adults, provided with beautiful lace-patterned wings. Nevertheless, the metamorphosis here is only partial.

In butterflies, moths, beetles, ants, bees, and several others, we have a very different story. The larvae are not only quite different in form from the adults, but they also differ markedly in habits of life. These larvae feed greedily, grow rapidly, moult their epidermis frequently, soon become motionless, and encase themselves within a firm chitinous shell or silken cocoon. The chrysalis or pupa stage is now reached in which the larval organs are wholly disintegrated. From the "debris" new "bricks and mortar" are manufactured which are utilised in building up the various organs, and so on, of the adult. The latter in due time sallies forth, an active winged-insect called the imago, leaving the empty husk behind. It should be noted that the caterpillar represents the typical and fully-developed larval form with the limbs and head developed. Grubs have a head but no limbs ; "maggots" are destitute of both. Larvae vary enormously in size, shape, and other particulars.

Many forms are exceedingly destructive, greedily devouring the living tissues of both vegetables and animals. Happily, in the Economy of Nature they have many enemies. Nevertheless, by means of strategy, of mimicry, and of protective coloration insect larvae manage to hold their own so tenaciously that at times they invoke the wrath of the agriculturist, fruit-grower, farmer and cattle-breeder. The wholesale raids made, on such provocation, by human agency are warmly supported by the community

We shall conclude by confining our attention to some salient points in regard to the eggs of insects and the behaviour of the progeny when hatched. It seems appropriate to say a few words about the eggs of insects, seeing that in form and structure they fall somewhat into line with the eggs of oviparous vertebrates in being rendered definitely opaque because they are encased in a firm, resisting shell.

On an average, insects' eggs measure in length a few millimetres. They differ from the eggs of oviparous vertebrates in their immense variety in form and shape. Even among the butterflies and moths alone we recognise oval, circular, barrel-shaped, and flask-shaped, forms, with their surfaces smoothed, embossed, pitted, ribbed, and reticulated.

Some insects deposit their eggs singly or in small groups ; this method is adopted by the house-fly. Others lay them in great numbers which are clustered together. The blue-bottle fly offers a familiar example. They are usually deposited on substances which provide food for the hatched offspring, and they are held together by adhesive material during the period of incubation, which is a matter often of but a few hours. Sometimes, however, the eggs, if laid in the autumn, behave like seeds in not "germinating" until the warm days come in the following spring.

Chapter XI

Solving the Secrets of Animal Life

The Naturalist and His Fascinating Task

By Prof. J. Arthur Thomson

Regius Professor of Natural History, Aberdeen University; Author of "The Study of Animal Life"

SOMETIMES we wonder far too much, oftener far too little. After a fine lecture on the Wonders of Astronomy, a member of the entranced audience was heard to remark that he thought the greatest wonder of all was that these men of science had been able to find out, not merely the distance and composition of the stars, but their actual names. That was pseudo-wonder. One also remembers the dear old lady who remarked that what seemed to her to be a very admirable wonder of the world was the way in which so many great rivers ran through great towns. That was another pseudo-wonder.

On the other hand, we often wonder too little, for we take scientific achievements for granted, and get no glimpse of the often consummate patience and ingenious device by which steps of importance have been made. Here I wish to give some illustrations of this from the field of Natural History.

At a very low estimate there are 25,000 named and known backboned animals, and ten times as many backboneless animals; and there is some reason for pride that they have been arranged in approximate order so as to show their relationships. We can usefully, but woodenly, arrange our books according to their sizes, or alphabetically according to their authors' names; but it is not this wooden kind of classification that has been worked out for the tens of thousands of different kinds of animals and plants. What may be called "blood-relations" are grouped together, and in many cases it is possible to draw a tentative genealogical tree. How has this been done?

More than two thousand years ago, Aristotle (384–322 B.C.), with his discerning brain, saw clearly that living creatures must be grouped according to their deep resemblances of structure. Unlike some of his successors, he knew that whales must be placed among mammals, not among fishes; and similarly that bats were flying mammals, not birds. He knew that the resemblance between a whale and a shark was quite superficial. Both are suited for cleaving the water, but a whale has a mammal's brain and skull, heart and lungs. No whale is quite without hair, and the mother gives milk to her young.

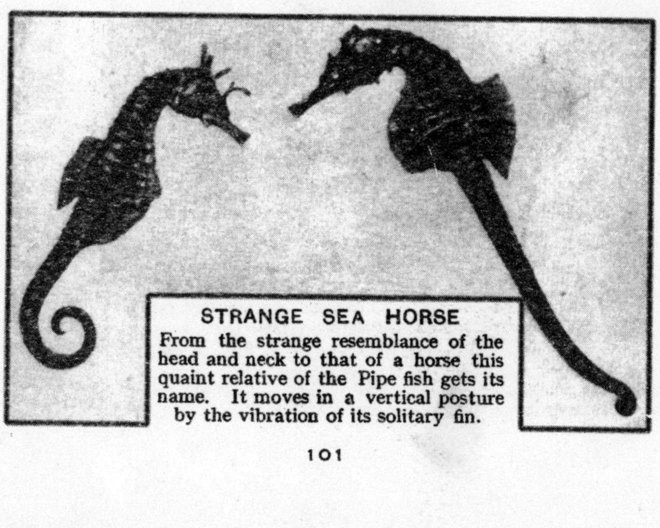

STRANGE SEA HORSE

From the strange resemblance of the head and neck to that of a horse this quaint relative of the Pipe fish gets its name. It moves in a vertical posture by the vibration of its solitary fin.

Classifying must be grounded upon deep resemblances of structure, taking the young stages into account, if possible. Everyone is familiar in the summer months with swallows, martins, and swifts. After looking carefully a few times, one says to oneself: "There is no confusing these three birds, though they fly about after insects in somewhat similar ways. The swallow, for instance, is marked by its continuously blue back, by chestnut and blue bands on its breast in front of the white, and by its long forked tail. The house-martin has a shorter tail, and it has a white rump splash as well as continuous white underneath. The swift is dusky all over and has much longer wings." This is good enough for a beginning, but a more important step is made if we are able to examine, let us say, the skulls and the toes of the three birds. For then it becomes plain that swallow and martin are "perching birds," or Passerines, and first cousins, while the swift belongs to a different group altogether, and is nearer the humming-birds.

ARISTOTLE'S resolute clearness of mind enabled him to discern that superficial likenesses are apt to be misleading; a true classification, that brings real relations together, must dig deep. The shape of an animal counts for little and the colour for nothing in classification; it is necessary to get down to the architecture of important parts like the skull and the backbone, the brain and the heart. The same resolute clearness of mind was displayed when Huxley showed that reptiles and amphibians should not be held as near allies, though a lizard is often superficially like a newt, and though a limbless reptile, such as a slow-worm or blind-worm, is superficially like a limbless amphibian—a Caecilian, also confusingly known as blind-worm.

Huxley peered into deep resemblances, and showed that backboned animals fall into three great groups: First, the Ichthyopsida, namely, Fishes and Amphibians; second, the Sauropsida, namely, Reptiles and Birds; and third, the Mammals by themselves. Cuvier, who was a very great anatomist, had not freed himself from the old idea that amphibians and reptiles were near one another. Huxley had insight and courage enough to say: "no, in spite of appearances, amphibians are nearer to the fishes, and reptiles are nearer to the birds."

One of the warnings that the history of science gives us is the story of the Dark Ages. The foundations of science were laid in a magnificent way in Greece three or four centuries B.C. When we name Hippocrates, Eudoxus, Aristotle, and Archimedes, we are selecting four very great men out of a brilliant aristocracy of intellect. They had their successors, but gradually the tradition became dim, and the end of progress, on the Natural History line, was with the genius of Galen. He was one of the greatest of biologists, who died about 200 A.D., obliged to flee from his practice in Rome because of the fierce jealousy of his fellow physicians, whose wilful ignorance was made uncomfortable in face of the science that Galen had built up by looking for himself at the structure of the human body.

But after 200 A.D. the darkness set in, and for twelve centuries or more, with no doubt a few luminous exceptions, the night lasted. Aristotle's biological works had not been translated into Latin, which was very unfortunate; but men were preoccupied with the practical tasks of war and peace, they were under the spell of tradition and authority, and somehow they had lost the desire to make new knowledge for themselves. It is an extraordinary fact that Galen found no successor until another foundation-layer, Vesalius, published in 1543 his "Structure of the Human Body," in the same year as the revolutionising work of Copernicus, "On the Revolutions of the Heavenly Bodies."

The darkness of the Middle Ages was not only retardation, it was relapse. Having ceased to look for themselves and face the facts, having apparently lost the desire to know in the Aristotelian and modern sense, men fell into the quagmire of magic and floundered after the will-o'-the-wisps of wild fancy. Although Galen had made great steps in elucidating the structure of the human body, men took it upon themselves to portray what they thought the interior of their bodies should be. And, similarly, in regard to the realm of animals, fabulous creatures acquired credit beside the familiar beasts of the fields; popular names, like sea-horse for a fish and sea-mouse for a worm, were taken literally, to the damage of sound classification. The moral is that degeneration follows the loss of the desire to know for oneself. The danger is not by any means absent to-day. The making of new knowledge is the test of scientific health; but how is the new knowledge reached? Take a few examples from Natural History. The great majority of the European eels spawn in a stretch of water towards the Bermudas in the North Atlantic, as described

M. H. Crawford & W. S. Berridge

SWIFT, SAND MARTIN AND SWALLOW OFTEN CONFUSED

When we see twenty or thirty birds swooping and wheeling fifty feet up in the air, all hard at work catching flies, we are apt to say "swallows" and leave it at that. But, at a distance, swifts and sand martins are easily confused with swallows. The swift is not related to the other two and all three differ in size, colouring or structure.

S. C. Johnson

F. W. Bond

SLOW-WORMS—SO CALLED

The slow-worm (top) is also known as the blind-worm. But its movements are by no means slow, it is not blind, and neither is it a worm. So much for the name. Further, the creature looks like a snake but is really a lizard. Below is a real snake, an adder.

in another chapter. How did Johann Schmidt find this out? By some seventeen years of patient observing. It was known that eels never spawn in fresh water; it was known that young eels, or elvers, come up European rivers from the sea, and that there is no return journey until the eels are five to eight years old. Then it was suspected that strange creatures of the open seas, like transparent knife-blades, that had been named Leptocephali, were the young stages of eels, long antecedent to the elvers. What Schmidt did was to collect, on a fishery investigation vessel, all the sizes and gradations of these Leptocephali, or glass-eels, till he had a complete series from very young creatures, not longer than half the breadth of one's little finger-nail, on to larvae the length of one's middle finger, and thence to elvers, with reduction of length to one's first finger, and with change of shape from penknife blade to slender knitting-needle form.

Then, year after year, with Darwin-like patience, he townetted in the Atlantic, carefully recorded where the glass-eels were common and where they were rare, and where they were large and where they were small, till he was able to map out their spawning waters and write their diary from the still unknown hatching of the eggs to the eel-fare of the elvers up the rivers, which they ascend when about two and a half to two and three-quarters years of age.

In the Dark Ages people repeated to one another many extraordinary stories about the life-histories and transformations of animals. Thus there was the story of the barnacle tree that grows by the sea-shore, whose fruit "if it falleth on land dieth, but if it falleth into the water it liveth, and becomes the familiar barnacle goose." The real story of ship barnacles is not less wonderful, and it has this great superiority—that it can be verified by anyone with good eyes and plenty of time. Yet the first discovering of the life-history is often a triumph of insight and patience. Let us take the story of Bilharzia, a peculiar little worm belonging to the class of flukes which is a painful parasite of man in some warm countries, such as Egypt. The bilharzias live in couples in the blood-vessels of the bowel and bladder, the half-inch male carrying the inch-long female. Each of the many microscopic eggs has a sharp spine which cuts into the walls of the blood-vessels and causes serious trouble, as well as severe pain. In some places every third child is infected with bilharzia, a very dreadful handicapping of life.

Now many naturalists had tried to clear up the life-story of this formidable little worm, and some useful facts had been established. But it was not till the War that the whole story was made clear, and largely by the thoroughness and resoluteness

Hinkins

EARTHWORMS, MAN'S GREATEST BENEFACTORS

It was left for one of the greatest scientists, Charles Darwin, to discover the true worth of the earthworm. All his life he accumulated facts about it, and finally reached the conclusion that there are about 53,000 worms in an average English acre, and that every year some ten tons of soil per acre are passed through their food canals thus enriching the soil.

Elephant

Camel

Horse

Hippopotamus

Llama

Giraffe

Hyrax

Pig

Sheep

WIDELY DIFFERING RELATIONS. ALL OF THE SAME GREAT FAMILY—

In previous pages we have seen examples of creatures which resembled each other superficially but were really separated by important differences. Here we have a group of animals whose appearance is, in each case, definitely distinctive and yet which are really related. It is the work of the scientist, equipped with knowledge and inspired by genius, to find truth amid what at first appears to be the bewilderment of Nature. Step by step, clear thinking and undeviating diligence have brought to mankind the marvellous truths of the animal world

Rhinoceros

Deer

Buffalo

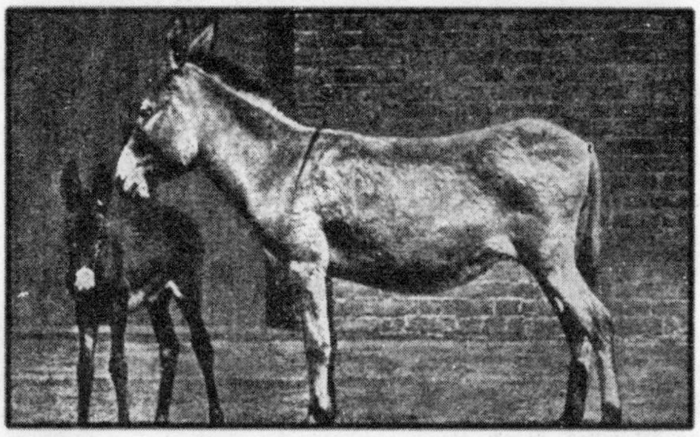

Ass

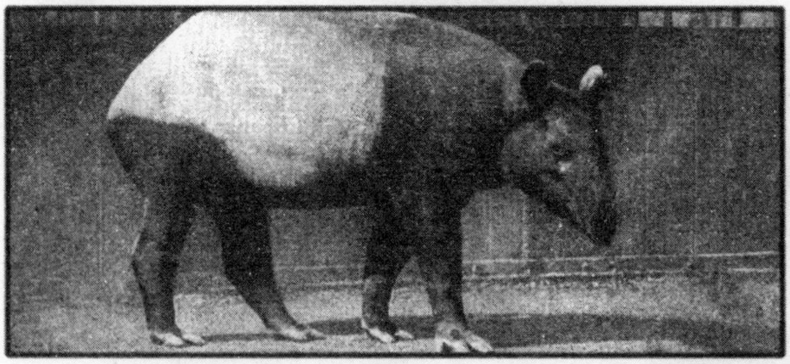

Tapir

Antelope

Ox

Zebra

—THE UNGULATES WHICH ARE MAMMALS EQUIPPED WITH HOOFS

Who would have thought to find a close relationship between the Rhinoceros and the Zebra or the Llama and the Pig before the naturalist solved the problems which creation has set,? The family of the Ungulates, or hoofed mammals, includes every animal present in this and the opposite page. The little hyrax, which looks something like a rabbit, is actually a development of the Ungulates, and related to the elephant. Thus have varying conditions and ages of time worked upon this amazingly varied stock of some remote common ancestor.

of one observer, Major Leiper, who remembered to great advantage what he had learned as a medical student in Glasgow University regarding the life-history of the common liver-fluke of sheep. It was this that gave him the clue which he followed.

If the microscopic eggs pass from man into pools of water they hatch into free-swimming larvae which find their way into water-snails, such as Planorbis. There they multiply and produce a second kind of larva with a bifid, or forked, tail. These, called Cercariae, leave the snail, swim in the water, and bore their way into the skin of children paddling in the pool, or of washerwomen busy with the clothes, or of gardeners watering the flowers with a hose, or of soldiers bathing out of bounds. In some places, as in Japan, the second host is not always man, but it may be a cow standing in the water; in some cases man is infected not through the skin of hands and feet, but by his mouth, as when he eats raw vegetables that have been soaked in contaminated water.

Now Major Leiper not only discovered the larvae in the water-snails and the free-swimming stages in the water, he also showed that the Cercariae die if the water is kept drawn for thirty-six hours, or if a little sulphate of soda is added when the lettuce or the like is washed. Thus, by his scientific thoroughness, he saved many lives.

Darwin was in the habit of saying: "It's dogged that does it." But that is true only of certain ways of making new knowledge. Thus, like Gilbert White before him, Darwin had the conviction that earthworms are the most useful animals in the world, because they have made and continue to make the fertile soil. He proceeded to prove this doggedly, and from his student days in Edinburgh, when he was trying to be a medical, on until he was an old man, he continued accumulating facts in regard to the agricultural work of earthworms. His book, "The Formation of Vegetable Mould through the Agency of Earthworms," was on the stocks for over forty years, and was not published till 1881, the year before his death. Patiently and by many measurements, Darwin showed that there are 53,000 worms in an average acre of English soil, that they pass ten tons of soil per acre per annum through

W. S. Berridge

their food-canals, that they bury the surface with their castings at the rate of three inches in fifteen years, and so on. With sublime doggedness he proved that earthworms have been the great soil-makers.

But discovery often means much more than doggedness; it implies a flash of insight that is afterwards put to the proof, or the use of some new method or instrument, such as statistics or the microscope, or the application of a new idea, like Darwin's idea of Nature's sifting.

Let me give a few instances. Bacteria, the extremely minute organisms (well called microbes, which means small life) which cause rotting and disease, but many changes that are beneficial, were first seen by the Dutch observer Leuwenhoek towards the end of the seventeenth

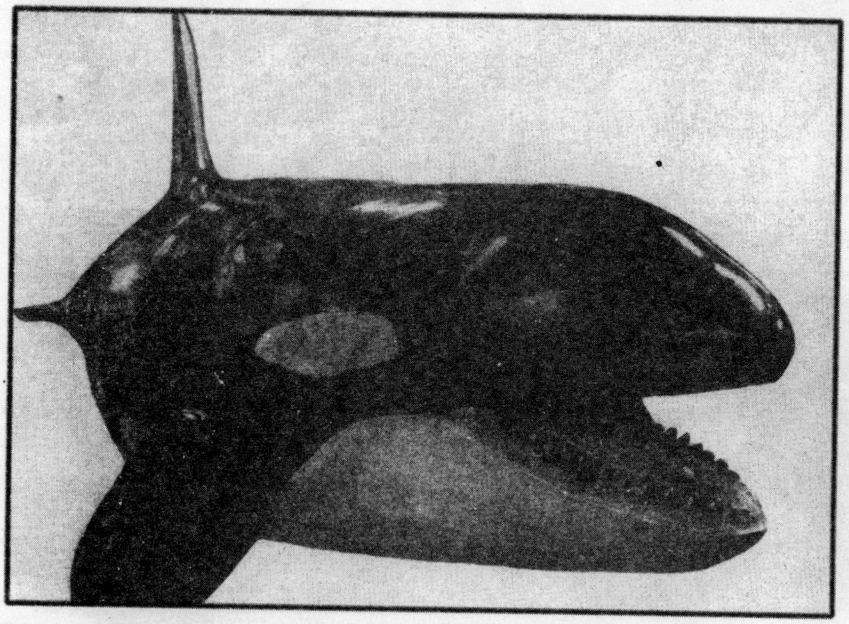

James

FISH AND MAMMAL THAT RESEMBLE EACH OTHER

If animals were classified by the unscientific according to their apparent resemblances most people would certainly place these two creatures in the same family. Both live in the sea, and their outward forms are much alike. But one (above) is a fish, the mackerel shark, and the other (below) is a mammal, the killer whale. Scientists are able to place them in their correct classes.

century, but a recognition of their importance is to the credit of Pasteur, who died in 1895. It was in a natural and logical way that he came to realise the many-sided rôle that bacteria play in the world by putrefying, fermenting, poisoning and digesting, but he reached his conclusions by insight long before he had patiently proved them. What a step it was in theory and in practice when Pasteur showed that many diseases, the causes of which had been entirely obscure, are due to the operations of minute living creatures. All over the world Pasteur's central idea made the visible intelligible in terms of the invisible.

John J. Ward, F.E.S.

SEA MOUSE THAT HAS NOTHING TO DO WITH MICE

From some rather imaginative resemblance to a common household pest this marine worm has been called sea-mouse by popular fancy. The worm is between three and five inches long and has an oval body. Its back is covered in broad plates and its underside with feet and bristles. Specimens are sometimes washed ashore round British coasts

SOMETIMES the new step has been the outcome of a certain resoluteness of mind, the discoverer saying to himself: "How can I prove this so that no one can doubt?" And the method of proof has often been nothing more than shrewd commonsense. Thus for a long time naturalists had discussed with one another how much of an animal's behaviour should be called instinctive and how much should be called intelligent, the point being that instincts are ready-made, inborn powers of doing apparently clever things, whereas intelligence means individual learning and judgment, putting two and two together, and controlling behaviour in the light of previous experience; which also means the use of memory.

One may argue about this for a long time and not get any further, but a definite step was taken when Lloyd Morgan and others began making the simple experiment of hatching birds' eggs in an incubator and seeing what the young creatures were able to do in isolation from their kind. If chicks incubated in the laboratory pay no heed to their unseen mother's cluck outside the door, this proves, for chicks at least, that a recognition of the mother's call is not instinctive. But if, in similar conditions, a newly-hatched peewit utters the characteristic call-note, this proves the instinctive nature of the peewit's simple effort at speech.

For a long time it has been known that if a hive-bee finds a nectar-treasure, such as a fine patch of white clover, she fills her honey-sac and makes a bee-line for home. But in a short time there is a little band of bees exploring and exploiting the honey patch. How does the news spread? To this it was customary to answer that the first discoverer, having unloaded her treasure-trove in the comb, proceeds to guide her sisters to the clover-patch. But by the simple device of marking individual bees, and by the neat arrangement of having an observatory hive with windows through which one can peer, Professor K. von Frisch was soon able to prove that the old answer was wrong, and that something quite different actually happens. The bee that makes the discovery is in no hurry; she is quite well-pleased with herself. She does not show her sisters the way; indeed, they find the treasure before she comes out again.

What happens is that the well-pleased bee executes a little, but very characteristic, "nectar-dance" on the honeycomb, and when she is seen dancing the bystander worker-bees, who have been resting near, come nosing about her, and get the scent of the clover, or whatever it was, from her body. With this as a clue, they hurry off on the search for flowers with that perfume. The bee-language is partly a dance and partly a fragrance. Von Frisch's story is more detailed and convincing than we can indicate here, but the point is that by resoluteness of method he was able to pass from what had previously been mere vague hearsay to verifiable science.

TILL a century ago the naturalist's knowledge of the migration of birds was very general and vague, but gradually the standard of bird-observing was raised. Precise records of arrivals and departures began to be kept, and thousands of facts were gathered from lighthouses and lightships, and other strategic stations. This was all very well, but a distinctive step was taken when the "ringing method" began to be widely used. That is to say, light aluminium rings with a stamped address were placed on the feet of young birds just before they set off on their autumnal migration to the South.

A variable percentage of these ringed birds was caught elsewhere—in France, perhaps, or South Africa—and if the capturer sent the ring, with due information, to the stamped address, it became possible to say: This stork, ringed at Dantzig on such and such a date, was captured at Lake Chad, in Africa, three weeks later. As these data accumulated and were registered on a map for each kind of bird, it began to be possible to make definite statements in regard to the paths that birds follow on their migratory journeys. Thus, too, it became possible to prove beyond all doubt that birds sometimes return from distant winter quarters to the place of their birth. A swift ringed in Ayrshire in 1914 was caught again at the same place, with the ring on its foot, in 1918. The bird in question had doubtless wintered in Africa four times between its 1914 ringing and its 1918 "homing."

ONE of the characteristics of the new natural history, as compared with the old, is the more frequent backing of observation by experiment. In the subterranean waters of Dalmatia and Carinthia there lives an interesting newt called Proteus. It is about six inches long, with no visible eyes, and with no pigment except where the red blood shines through the three pairs of external gills. It has been known for a long time in the darkness of its native haunts, a strange, wan, blind troglodyte. Now naturalists discussed with one another whether Proteus has lost the power of producing pigment in its skin, or whether the pigment-forming is simply hindered by the darkness of the caves. Dissection would show that there is a small eye beneath the skin, but one might ask whether the eye suffered from some intrinsic weakness, or whether the arrest of development was due to the absence of light. The discussion might continue for a long ti without leading to any certain result; the only w out is to experiment. When the Proteus is broug into a well-lighted laboratory it soon begins to g spotty, and after a while it becomes dark-colour like many a newt. This proves that it is the absence light that hinders the development of the pigme The power is by no means lost.

Similarly, if the young stages of Proteus a reared in a laboratory under red light, the eye beg again to develop, increases in size, reaches t surface, and becomes a seeing eye. The blind ne receives its sight. The reason for using red light simply that ordinary illumination causes a darkeni of the skin, which would shut off the light bef the re-awakened eye had had enough. This clear-c case may serve to illustrate the value of the app to experiment. We no longer suppose that Prote has lost the sense of sight; we *know* that it has not

People are sometimes sceptical about t statements naturalists make in regard to numbe There is a British starfish, Luidia by name, wh produces 200 million eggs, but who has coun them? We have so many millions of red bl corpuscles in our blood that their surface area about 3,300 square yards; but how is that know In the rind of our fore-brain we have 9,200 mill nerve-cells which form the home of some of mental processes. That is to say, if the population the globe is 1,750 millions, we have more than f times as many nerve-cells in our cerebral cort But how do we know? The answer is, by sampli In the case of the blood, for instance, we take a sn quantity, such as a cubic millimetre (a lineal m metre is about one-twenty-fi of an inch so that a cubic mi metre is about one 16,400th cubic inch); we easily disco how many drops there are this small quantity. Then put a single drop under microscope and count the nu ber of corpuscles. We do t several times till we have g reliable average; then we say that there are five mill red blood corpuscles in a cu millimetre and twenty-five t lion in an average human bei

This "blood-countin might seem at first sight waste of time, and yet it n be actually life-saving; fo may enable the physician detect the first hints of s disease. At every corner find that science begins v measurement; at every co we find that science stands the ending of ignorance and many evils, and the maint ance and amelioration of Li

M. H. Crawford

James

TWO CREATURES THAT LOOK ALIKE BUT ARE NOT RELATED

A lizard and a newt to a casual observer have very much the same form and might well be taken for first cousins. Men of science, however, know that they are not nearly related, for the lizard (above) is a reptile, and as such has kinship with the birds, while the newt (below) is an amphibian and is related to the fishes. Formerly even science was deceived and linked them together.

Chapter XII

Birds That Cannot Fly

By J. R. Ainsworth-Davis

Formerly Professor of Zoology, University of Wales

It is now universally admitted that the innumerable kinds or species of animals which exist at the present time, and the myriads of forms which once existed but are now extinct, were not specially created to suit their surroundings, but have arisen by a process of evolution from earlier types. Birds, for example, are a specialised branch of the reptilian stock, as proved by the " record of the rocks," and the most ancient bird known, archaeopteryx, which is Greek for "ancient bird" actually possessed teeth and a long jointed tail like that of a lizard. But it was an undoubted bird, with wings and feathers, and able to fly somewhat clumsily.

Improvements gradually took place, and an average modern bird, such as a pigeon or swallow, embodies an almost perfect solution of the problem of flight. Some of the wing-bones are firmly fused together, giving effective support to quill feathers that beat upon the air, and the tail has shortened, its end-joints uniting into a ploughshare bone for the attachment of a fan-like group of steering quills. The teeth have disappeared, though traces of them may still be found deeply imbedded in the jaws of a few forms, such as parrots. These are never "cut," and are simply reptilian vestiges or souvenirs of ages ago.

Autotype

RHEA OF SOUTH AMERICA

Although the Rhea cannot fly its wings are far from useless since, when alarmed, it spreads them and runs with the wind behind it, thus converting them into sails. Its very long legs give the bird great speed and its colour makes it very difficult to see at a distance.

A typical bird then is a wonderfully constructed flying machine, and yet we all know that some birds, such as the ostrich and penguin, are unable to fly. They possess wings but cannot fly with them. How is this to be explained? They have descended from birds that *could* fly, so the power of flight must have been given up, and the wings have become reduced in size.

In trying to account for the existence of flightless birds we must remember that animals are continually engaged in the search for food, and the vast majority of them are exposed to the attacks of carnivorous enemies, whose pressing attentions can only be evaded by active or passive defence, fighting power or swift retreat. Furthermore the surroundings or environment of an animal are continually changing, so that forms unable to adapt themselves to fresh conditions are liable to become extinct sooner or later.

The acquisition of powers of flight by birds had reference to both these primary necessities. It allowed escape from carnivorous foes only able to progress on the ground, and also rendered it possible to pursue the numerous flying insects which, long ages previously, had achieved the conquest of the air.

But animals always get their living in the easiest possible way, and in some parts of the world, under certain conditions, a number of birds have found it a practical policy to abandon flight, and resume a life on the ground or else become aquatic. It must not, of course, be supposed that such a change of habit was consciously adopted, as it might be in the case of human beings. One very interesting extinct bird, Hesperornis, which lived at a time when the chalk was accumulating as a limy mud at the bottom of the sea, may be taken as a first example. It possessed small pointed teeth and was between three and four feet high, but the wings were mere vestiges and quite useless for flight. Professor O. Marsh described this bird as "a carnivorous swimming ostrich," but later authorities consider it was remotely related to our modern divers. In any case it was entirely adapted to a fish diet.

There can be no doubt that hesperornis was a descendant of flying forms, but in the remote times when it flourished predaceous mammals had not come into existence, and the chief enemies to be feared were reptiles, which were no match for the more active and quicker-witted birds. The evolution of the latter involved not only the development of wings but a great improvement in the organs of circulation, the heart being divided into four chambers, thus enabling the impure and pure blood to be kept separate. This led to birds becoming one of the dominant races of animals, for it made them hot blooded, with better nourished bodies, and endowed them with the restless activity familiar to us in modern species. Such creatures would naturally explore the various ways of getting a living, and it is not surprising that some of them took to a fishing life, and became adapted to swimming, with the ultimate result that they became flightless, their wings being converted into paddles.

By the close of the chalk period hosts of reptilian types died out, including carnivorous forms that infested the seas, which were thus rendered safer for adventurous birds, while the rise of predaceous mammals at the same time made the land more unsafe. Many birds that became fishermen retained the power of flight, such as divers, gulls, and albatrosses, but some few abandoned it.

AMONG such flightless birds the great auk or garefowl (*Alca impennis*) once swarmed round the shores of Iceland, Scandinavia, the British Isles, and Newfoundland, but was exterminated last century by the agency of man, who has been responsible for the extinction of so many interesting forms. It was a large bird belonging to the family Alcidae, which includes the existing razor-bills, guillemots, and puffins, with small wings useless for flying, but serving as moderately efficient paddles for the pursuit of the fish which formed its food.

The last two living specimens were caught at Eldey Island, off Iceland, in 1844, while the latest known captures from other localities were Ireland 1834, St. Kilda 1821, and Orkney 1813. Great auks abounded most in the seas of Newfoundland and, speaking of the islands where they congregated, Professor Alfred Newton says: "English and French mariners alike resorted to these spots, driving the helpless and hapless birds on sails or planks into a boat, 'as many as shall lade her,' and salting them for provision." This ignorance and lack of foresight combined to deprive that part of the world of both an interesting bird and a source of emergency food supply.

Penguins (*Spheniscidae*) are remarkable among flightless birds as expert swimmers of the first rank, their wings serving as highly efficient paddles which enable them to dart through the water in arrow-like fashion, the legs being directed backward in line with the body. The feathers on the wings are scale-like, and quills are entirely absent. On land the body is kept vertical, and they present a comic resemblance to little old men afflicted with corns, waddling along in a somewhat deliberate way, though at feeding time the pace can be accelerated considerably. There are many species, varying considerably in size, the largest being about three and a half feet high.

Penguins are limited to the southern hemisphere, and are particularly numerous in Antarctic seas, where they have few enemies—except man. They range up the Pacific as far as the Galapagos Islands, are to be found on the south coast of Australia and the south and east coasts of New Zealand, round the Falkland Islands, and as far north in the South Atlantic as Tristan da Cunha. They also occur on the coasts of South Africa and some of the lonely islands in the Indian Ocean.

NEW ZEALAND is particularly rich in species, and it is not unlikely that penguins first came into existence in that Dominion, where an extinct fossil form nearly seven feet in height has been discovered. If so, they gradually spread from that original home until the existing very wide distribution was attained. In this connection it is important to realize that the relative position of land and sea areas has undergone many profound alterations during the vast period of time for which our planet has existed.

At an immensely remote epoch the East Indies, New Guinea, Australia, New Zealand, and the now intervening seas, formed a continuous land surface projecting from the continent of Asia. By a gradual sinking of the land this area was broken up into islands, and New Zealand was the first to be isolated, Australia the second. The various orders of mammals were meanwhile coming into existence in the main landmass of the Old World, and migrating in all directions until held up by sea barriers. New Zealand became isolated before any of them could get there, and Australia was severed from the main land-mass after receiving a certain proportion of some of the more primitive mammalian forms.

THE ocean barriers which prevented the immigration of mammals other than bats into New Zealand and checked that immigration into Australia after the ancestors of the egg-laying types (duckbilled platypus and spiny ant-eater) and pouched forms (kangaroos, wombats, and so on) had gained a footing there, were crossed by a considerable number of flying birds. Some of these, in the absence of powerful enemies, found flying no longer a necessity, and in course of time became flightless. That this really happened is rendered probable by the fact that birds which cannot fly are particularly numerous in both New Zealand and Australia. Penguins have been mentioned already, but before considering the other flightless birds of the Antipodes, the influence of isolation and absence of predaceous enemies will be illustrated by reference to another part of the world where this isolation reached an ideal state.

Réunion, Mauritius, and Rodriguez, are volcanic islands in the Indian Ocean, respectively 320, 500 and 844 miles from the east coast of Madagascar, and devoid of any native ground mammals. Mauritius was formerly the home of a well-known flightless bird, the dodo (*Didus ineptus*), immortalised by the

Neville Kingston

PENGUINS WHOSE WINGS HAVE LEARNT TO DO THE WORK OF FINS

Only in the southern hemisphere will you find the penguin in its wild state, and the chief home of this quaint-looking bird is the Antarctic. One of the many strange things about this bird is that its offspring often grows nearly as big as itself before being able to feed without parental help (lower photograph). The King penguin (top left) is the largest of the species, and the remaining photograph shows a Zoo penguin gazing in a worried way at the hole through which his swimming pool has been drained away because of frosty weather.

Neville Kingston

F. W. Bond

POWERFUL LEGS OF THE FLIGHTLESS OSTRICH IN ITS STANDING AND SITTING POSTURES

For the lack of flight the ostrich has compensated itself and thus survived by developing a very powerful pair of legs upon which it is said to run faster than any horse. The feet are more specialised than those of any other running bird, the toes having been reduced in number to two, the third and fourth, with their undersides equipped with pads rather like those of the camel. The bird defends itself with a tremendous side-kick, which is very formidable. The breast-bone is strikingly different from that found in flying birds, which possess a keel to which the wing muscles are attached. Such a keel can be seen when carving game or poultry. But the ostrich has no keel to its breast-bone. The plumage, too, is markedly different in that the feathers are not interlocked.

expression "as extinct as a dodo," and Belloc's description in the "Bad Child's Book of Beasts":

The Dodo used to walk around
  And take the sun and air,
The Sun yet warms his native ground—
  The Dodo is not there!
The voice that used to squawk and squeak
  Is now for ever dumb—
Yet may you see his bones and beak
  All in the Mu-se-um.

It was a clumsy creature, larger than a turkey, and distantly related to the pigeons, which had a large blackish hooked beak, and an apology for a tail in the form of a curly tuft. It was endowed with a goose-like voice, and laid a single large white egg. First observed by the Dutch in 1598 it had become extinct by 1681, as a result of the introduction of pigs, cats, and dogs, to say nothing of its ruthless slaughter by human beings. The ancestors of this unfortunate bird found plenty of food in the forests, and became flightless, while in the absence of enemies they did not acquire the power of rapid locomotion on the ground, or other means of effective defence. It may also be mentioned that flight may be actually dangerous to the inhabitants of islands where strong winds are prevalent, so that the assumption of a ground habit avoids the danger of being blown out to sea and so perishing.

Another species of dodo (*Didus borboni*) once lived in Réunion, but this also was exterminated in similar fashion. The same fate befell a related form, the solitaire (*Pezophaps solitarius*) of Rodriguez, a flightless bird somewhat larger than a swan.

New Zealand, to which we will now return, is notable for the number of flightless ground birds, extinct or still living, which have made it their home. Among them are species of the cosmopolitan family of rails (*Rallidae*) which include our own corn-crake and moor-hen. Though most members of the family can fly it is noteworthy that they spend much of their time on the ground or, in the case of moor-hens, in the water. It may be mentioned, in passing, that flightless cousins of the latter are found in the islands of Tristan da Cunha, Gough, and Gilolo.

In ground-rails the body is flattened from side to side, which facilitates rapid progression through close-growing vegetation, and baffles pursuit by predaceous mammals or birds of prey. New Zealand's extinct forms include a gigantic flightless rail the Aptornis, of which near relatives inhabited Mauritius and Chatham Island in comparatively recent times. A smaller bird of the kind, the takahe (*Notornis*), also unable to fly, one of the world's rarest birds, was last recorded in 1898, but is possibly still in existence. The weka rails or wood hens (*Ocydromus*), small

Autotype

CURIOUSLY CRESTED CASSOWARY, HANDSOMEST OF RUNNING BIRDS

Despite the well-known rhymes about the missionary and the cassowary that lived "on the plains of Timbuctoo," this bird is not found at all in Africa, but is a native of New Guinea. The cassowary is the most handsome of the running birds, the neck and head, bare of feathers, being very brightly coloured. The wings are small and the plumage hairy in appearance.

Autotype

GRACEFUL EMU OF THE AUSTRALIAN PLAINS

Two species of Emu, a bird confined in Australia and some of the neighbouring islands, are found, the one in the east and the other the west of the continent. The birds live on the plain, or in the more open wooded country, and are able to run very fast. Like the ostrich, to which they are next in size of the running birds, they defend themselves with powerful kicks, but backwards as well as sideways. The wings are entirely useless, and the neck and head are covered in feathers. A full-grown bird stands over five feet high.

brown flightless birds, are represented by three or four living species.

The kakapo or owl parrot (*Stringops*) is another existing New Zealand type devoid of powers of flight, and among extinct forms in similar case were a kind of goose (*Cnemiornis*); a gigantic bird of prey (*Harpagornis*); and the moas (*Dinornithidae*), representatives of the running birds which will now have to receive our consideration.

RUNNING or ostrich-like birds make up a somewhat miscellaneous assemblage of flightless forms characteristic of the southern hemisphere, though true ostriches range north of the equator. In all of them the wings are either very small or practically absent, and the breast-bone is a curved plate devoid of the laterally flattened projection or keel to which the muscles of the wings are attached in ordinary flying birds. Anyone who has carved a fowl must have noticed this keel when cutting slices from the breast, really the muscles of flight. The shape of the breast-bone has suggested a somewhat fanciful resemblance to a raft or flat-bottomed boat, for which the Latin name is *ratis*. Hence the scientific name *Ratitae* has been coined for this group, as opposed to the term *Carinatae*, which is given to the flying birds with reference to the presence of a keel, the Latin for which is *carina*. But it should be noted that in such forms as the flightless rails and owl parrot of New Zealand the breast-bone has also lost its keel, or nearly so, but this does not indicate relationship to ostriches, being simply an adaptation to habit.

The running birds have soft or even hair-like plumage, and any quill feathers that may be present differ in structure from those of a flying bird in one very important particular. Examination of such a feather taken from, say, a pigeon will show a central axis bearing flattened branches or barbs, provided in their turn with branchlets or barbules that interlock by means of minute hooks. The combination of strength and lightness thus secured adapts the feather to its function of rowing or steering in the air. There is no such interlocking in the quills of running birds, where the barbules are disunited, as may be seen in the elegant ornamental plumes of the ostrich. In an ordinary flying bird, again, some of the end-joints of the short tail are fused into a ploughshare bone for the support of a fan-like group of tail quills used in steering the flight. There is no need for such an arrangement in running birds, and the end-joints of the tail remain distinct, with rare exceptions.

Running birds are divided into the following six divisions, which will be considered successively: first, moas; second, kiwis; third, cassowaries and emus; four, rocs; five, American ostriches or nandus; six, African ostriches.

MOAS (*Dinornithidae*) include about twenty species of remarkable extinct birds which formerly abounded in New Zealand, and were finally exterminated by the Maoris three or four hundred years ago. Native traditions credit them with having been somewhat slow and clumsy. They had mere vestiges of wings or none at all. There were three spreading toes, directed forwards, and in some cases a small great toe directed backwards. Some species were no larger than a turkey, while others were gigantic, attaining a maximum height of over ten feet, as against the eight feet of an African ostrich. In the remote past, before human beings made their way to New Zealand, that country passed through a period during which the climate was rigorous, and in all probability this ice age brought about the extinction of most of the moas, the remainder being doomed to extermination at the hands of man. Not only bones, but eggs, feathers (resembling those of emus), and mummified remains have been found.

Kiwis (*Apterygidae*), of which several species exist in New Zealand, are four-toed birds with greatly reduced wings and tail, hidden in the hair-like plumage. The nostrils are in an unusual position, being close to the tip of the long slightly curved bill, thus helping them to detect the presence of the earthworms which constitute their food. They live in wooded country, are nocturnal in habit, and are able to run very rapidly when alarmed. Their cry is a sort of whistle, to which the native name of kiwi has reference. The egg, about five inches long and three broad, is enormous considering the size of the bird, which is no bigger than a hen belonging to one of the heavy breeds.

Cassowaries (*Casuariidae*) and emus (*Dromaeidae*) are long-necked three-toed running birds with greatly reduced wings and no obvious tail. The plumage is of hairy texture and the feathers appear to be double, which is intelligible when we remember that in an ordinary flying bird there is often a small branch or aftershaft springing from the base of the main expansion or vane. If this aftershaft were to grow to the size of the vane we should naturally get a double feather.

The cassowaries include about ten species of large active birds with a curious projection or helmet on the top of the head. Both head and neck are bare and brightly coloured, and fleshy wattles are often present. Were a beauty competition set up for running birds, the cassowaries would undoubtedly take first prize, for the shining bluish-black plumage makes a striking contrast to the bright blue, red, and green of the naked head and neck. They are forest dwellers, very swift of foot, and defend themselves by kicking forwards with their powerful legs. The small wings, in which the quill feathers are reduced to spines, appear to aid progression.

The well-known doggerel which locates the cassowary on "the plains of Timbuctoo" cannot have been perpetrated by a naturalist, for these birds do not live in Africa. The largest species is native to north-east Australia and attains a height of about five feet. The other kinds are indigenous to New Guinea and some of the other islands north of Australia.

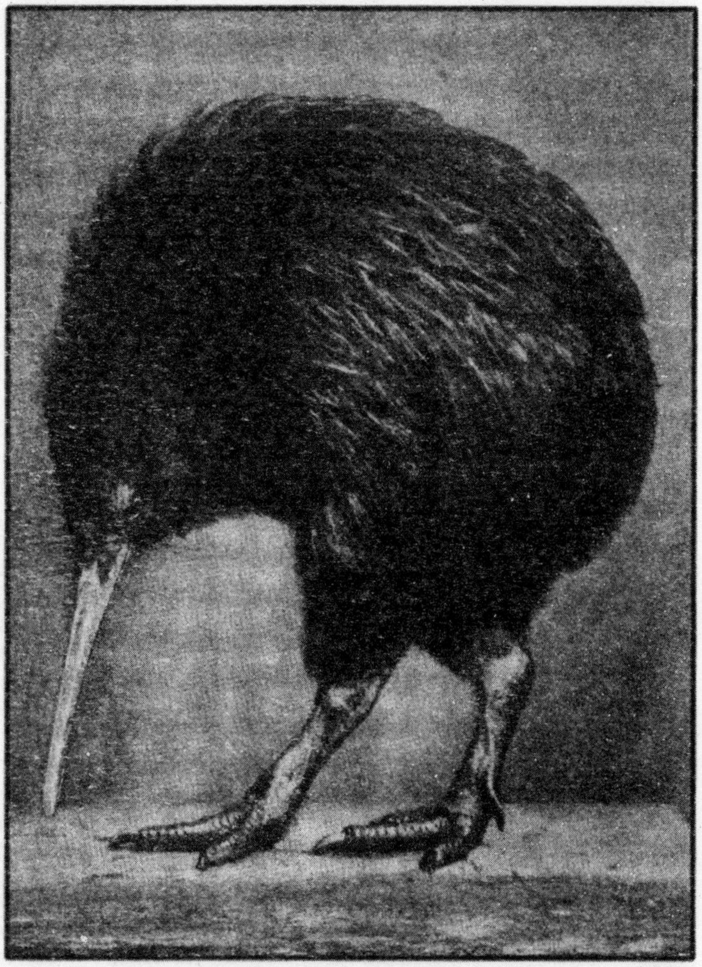

Autotype

THE QUEER KIWI OF NEW ZEALAND

There are several species of kiwi or Apteryx in New Zealand, which was cut off from adjacent land masses by the sea before any animals likely to be dangerous to this bird had migrated thither. The nostrils are near the tip of the beak, with which it captures earthworms. It is nocturnal.

Birds That Cannot Fly

The emus of Australia include two species, one eastern and the other western, and are larger than cassowaries, being over five feet high. There is no helmet, both head and neck are feathered, and spines are absent from the much reduced and apparently useless wings. These birds live on plains and in open wooded country, are swift runners, and defend themselves vigorously by kicking outwards and backwards.

ROCS (*Aepyornidae*) included several species of four-toed running birds with much reduced wings which once inhabited Madagascar, and appear to have been distant relatives of the moas, and some of them were probably larger than the biggest of these. One or more of the smaller kinds appear to have lived on into the period of human occupation, to meet the usual fate of extermination at the hands of the natives. Exaggerated accounts of these creatures probably gave rise to various stories of a gigantic bird, the roc or rukh, to be found in the "Arabian Nights," the travels of Marco Polo, and elsewhere. Writing of Madagascar towards the end of the thirteenth century Marco Polo says:

> The people of the island report that at a certain season of the year, an extraordinary kind of bird, which they call a rukh, makes its appearance from the southern region. In form it is said to resemble the eagle, but it is incomparably greater in size; being so large and strong as to seize an elephant with its talons, and to lift it into the air, from whence it lets it fall to the gound, in order that when dead it may prey upon the carcase. Persons who have seen this bird assert that when the wings are spread they measure sixteen paces in extent, from point to point; and that the feathers are eight paces in length, and thick in proportion.

A French work of fiction, "Furteriana," published in 1696, says that the natives of Madagascar were obliged to walk about with tame tigers, to protect them from enormous birds that preyed on sheep and human beings. One of H. G. Wells's most delightful stories, "Aepyornis Island," deals with this fascinating extinct type, which is at any rate unsurpassed among birds with regard to size of eggs, some of these being about thirteen inches long and nine and a half inches broad, with cubic contents of about two gallons.

American ostriches or nandus (*Rhaeidae*) include three species of three-toed running birds which live on the pampas of South America, from Patagonia to Bolivia and South Brazil. The wings are fairly well developed, and though useless for flight can be employed as sails to aid progression before the wind. These birds are much smaller than African ostriches, and do not possess the well-known ornamental plumes of the latter. Furthermore, the feathers have no aftershafts.

SOUTH AMERICA was an island-continent at the time when predaceous mammals were being evolved on the northern land-masses, so that but few of these are among its inhabitants. Like Australia and New Zealand, therefore, it has presented conditions favourable to birds abandoning flight and taking to a ground life. Little is known of the geological history of American ostriches, but in the remote past a considerable number of flightless forms existed in Patagonia, and these were often of large size, one of them *Phororhacos longissimus*, for example, possessing a massive skull two feet long. The body, however, was relatively small. There were four toes.

African ostriches (*Struthionidae*) include three existing species, one in East Africa and another in South Africa, while the third and more familiar kind, the common ostrich (*Struthio camelus*) or camel bird ranges north into Arabia, Syria, and Mesopotamia, and formerly existed in Central Asia. It is about eight feet high, and runs far more swiftly than any other African animal, taking 25-foot strides, and aiding progression by spreading its small wings. Safety is promoted by the social habit, for ostriches are associated in small troops; and also by keen hearing and sight, which make it easy to detect approaching enemies, especially as these birds live in deserts or open country. When brought to bay they defend themselves with beak and legs, kicking sideways with great force.

African ostriches possess more specialised feet than any other running birds, for their toes have been reduced to two, the third and fourth, of which the former is much larger. The under sides of these toes are provided with elastic pads, as in camels.

It remains to enquire whether any more flightless birds are likely to be evolved in future. As regards ostrich-like types, the answer is distinctly in the negative, for they have no flying relatives to undergo such a transformation. It is not impossible that some of the existing rails which fly but little may ultimately become flightless, but this is unlikely. As we have seen, such adaptation to life on the ground has only taken place in isolated areas like Mauritius or New Zealand, in the absence of predaceous mammals; but pigs, dogs, cats, and stoats have now been introduced almost everywhere by human agency, thus doing away with the favourable conditions that formerly existed.

SHOULD future generations be able to record new flightless birds it is most probable that these will belong to the duck family (*Anatidae*), for aquatic forms are less exposed to enemy attacks than those which live on land. Many members of this family, such as swans, geese, ducks, and flamingoes, actually lose the power of flight for part of the year, for the wing quills are all shed at the same time, but they conceal themselves with great skill when in this comparatively helpless condition. One very interesting species, the steamer duck (*Tachyeres cinereus*), a form nearly as large as a goose and native to the Falkland Islands and the Straits of Magellan, is unique in the fact that it can fly when young, but cannot do so when adult. The Auckland duck (*Nesonetta aucklandica*) is also noteworthy in this connection. It is a flightless form living in the Auckland Islands, a small group about 290 miles south of New Zealand, and closely resembles a duck (*Anas chlorotis*) native to that Dominion.

Chapter XIII

Vampire Bats & Their Harmless Relatives

By Frank Finn

Author of "Ornithological and Other Oddities"

One of our leading publicists once said that no matter what remarkable tale one told, facts would presently come along to corroborate it. Certainly this has been the case with regard to bats. Man had long ago made up his mind that these harmless and useful little creatures were nasty, ill-omened things, when evidence turned up that bats really could be very objectionable, as the world and its animal inhabitants became better known. Moreover, the vampire legend of creatures far larger and more important than fleas, which practised blood-letting at nights, found a parallel in fact.

The original vampire legend was of east European origin, and dealt with ghouls, generally supposed to be the ghosts of suicides and sorcerers, which left the grave to suck the blood of the living at night—generally those of their nearest and dearest—and these had to be duly exorcized to render them harmless, and the corpse, buried at a cross-roads for preference, kept quiet by a stake thrust through it.

But when America was discovered it was soon found that there were living corporeal creatures which practised wholesale blood-letting, and that these were bats. But centuries passed before the right bats were brought to book. As late an author as Linnaeus, whose "Systema Naturae," classifying all the animals and plants then known, was published about the middle of the eighteenth century, mixed up the blood-sucking vampire-bat with the kalong, one of the East Indian fruit-bats known as flying-foxes. His description of *Vespertilio vampyrus* credits it with sucking "the combs of cocks, the blood of sleeping slaves, and the sap of palms." As the kalong is the biggest of bats, reaching five feet in span of wings, and has a head and fangs as big as a ferret's, its attentions to sleeping slaves would have been calculated to give these unfortunates a very rude awakening; while, as a matter of fact, the vampire was already known not to disturb the repose of its victims, and the East Indian locality was wrong for the real blood-sucker.

Later on the charge was fixed on one of the vampire-bat's family, but not the right one, the accused animal being the spectre bat (*Vampyrus spectrum*), an ugly-looking creature enough, it is true, and large as bats go, but not half the size of the kalong, though a fruit-eater like it. Ultimately Darwin, who was just as great as a field observer and collector as he was as a philosophical theorist, succeeded in getting the real offender, his servant having actually captured a vampire on the withers of a horse as Darwin's party was bivouacking near Coquimbo, in Chile. This bat is the *Desmodus rufus*, and is not at all sensational in appearance, being only a little larger than our noctule or great bat, which is big as European bats go, but of about average size if the bats of the world are taken into consideration; while the only noticeable points about the blood-sucker's external appearance are the presence of a "nose-leaf" or flap of skin on the snout, and the absence of the tail and of most of the web that usually, in bats, connects this with the hind limbs.

This true vampire's teeth are, however, very peculiar. In bats generally the incisors are small and the fangs or canines large, as in carnivores; but in the blood-sucker the upper incisors and canines are both large and very sharp-edged, while the grinders, not being required by reason of the bat's liquid food, are reduced and unimportant. Thus the vampire is able to make a horizontal razor-cut, as it were, on the skin which severs numerous capillary blood-vessels and lets plenty of blood with no pain such as a vertical cut or puncture would inflict. Then, as the vampire's meals are uncertain, the stomach is prolonged into a long, tubular pouch so that the creature can gorge itself and then fly away to digest its meal at leisure. The bat's intestine, by the way, is shorter in proportion than that of any other beast.

W. S. Berridge

THE BAT SLEEPS

This Australian fruit-bat, like the rest of the great family, hangs itself upside down upon a branch by its toes. The bat therefore needs no nest or home of any kind and has a ready "take off" in case of sudden danger.

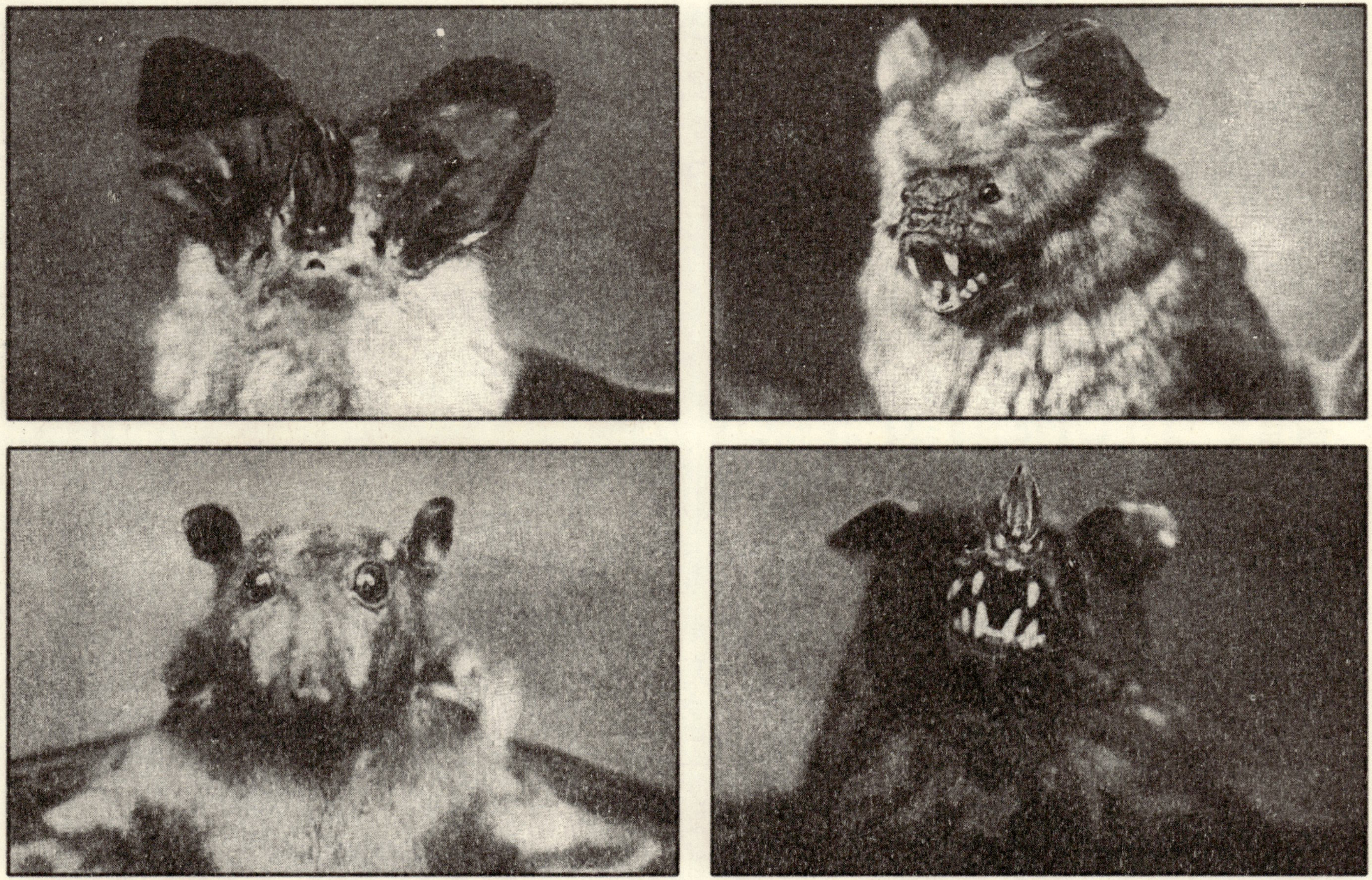

W. S. Berridge

WINGED GROTESQUES: HIDEOUS BAT FACES LIKE THE GOBLINS OF A NIGHTMARE

Of all the mammals the bats are the most highly gifted by Nature. They have developed a wonderful power of flight with wings which, for their size, are far more effective than those of birds; and besides this, they are equipped with a kind of "sixth sense" which enables them to avoid collisions in the dark. The membranes of their wings and, in the case of the Leaf-nosed bats (top right), the strange flap of skin covering much of the face, seem to be the seats of this strange power of sensation. The Vampire bats, of which we have a specimen here (bottom right), is confined to America and the West Indies. The other photographs show (top left) the false vampire, and (bottom left) the African epauletted bat.

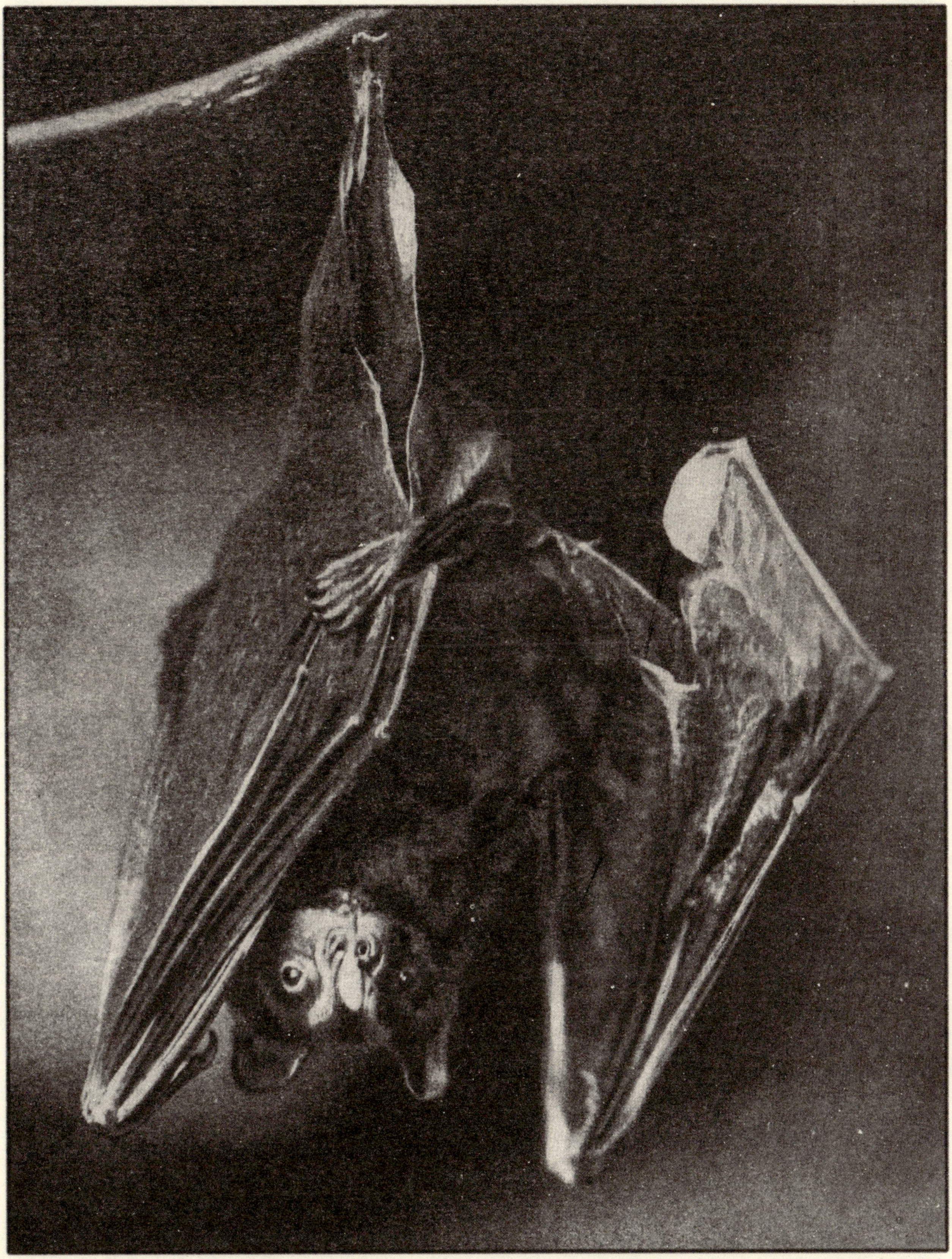

JAVELIN VAMPIRE OF BRAZIL HOOKED TO A TREE

Trunks of trees, especially if they be hollow, are favourite resting places for the javelin vampire which is believed to have a taste for blood. The javelin is distinguished from the other vampires by its short, broad muzzle, and the fact that it has two instead of three pre-molar teeth on either side of the lower jaw. In size this bat is only three to four inches long in the body, which is usually dark brown on the upper parts and pale brown below. It spends the hours of daylight in this posture.

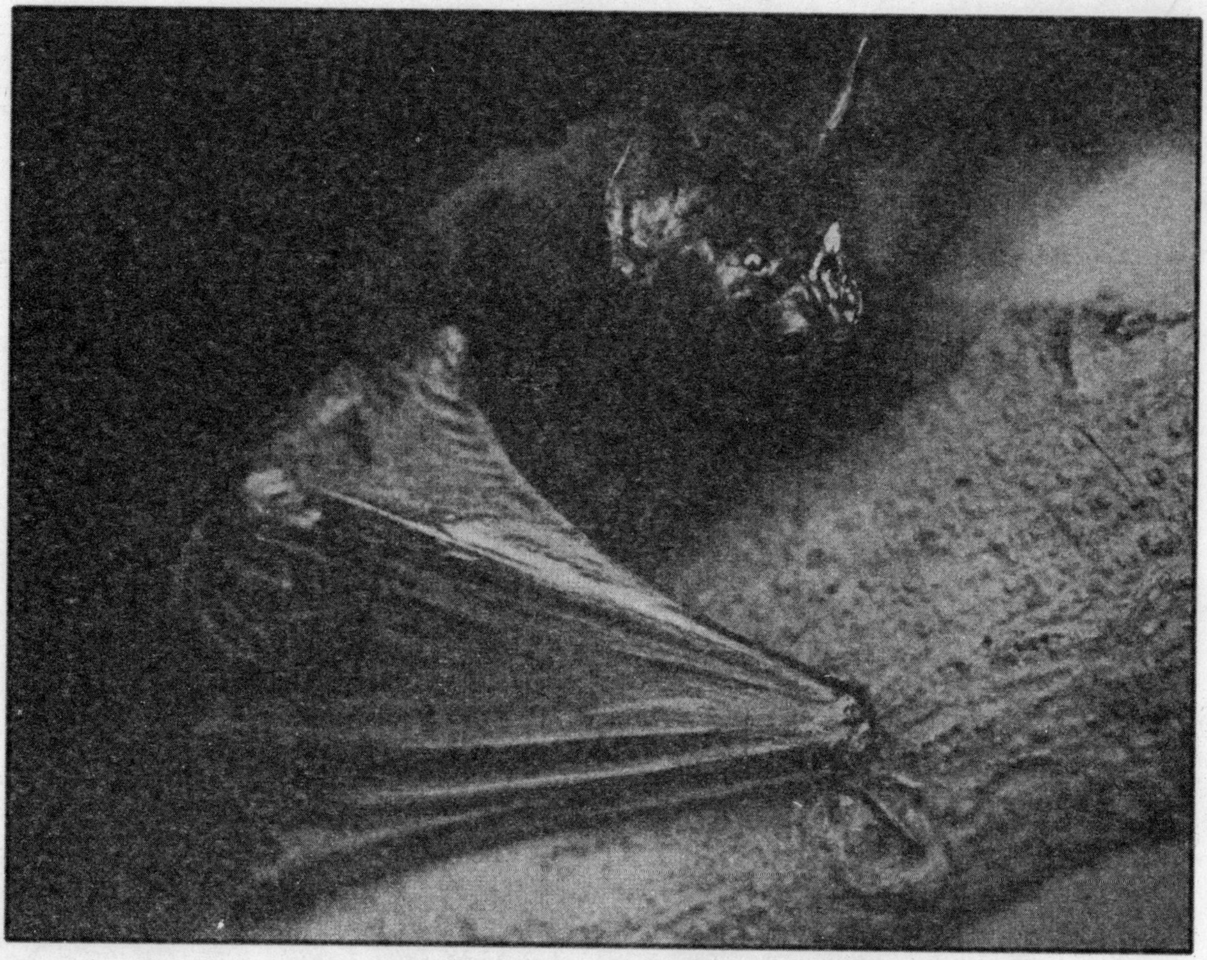

W. S. Berridge

VAMPIRE RESTS BY DAY FROM ITS GRIM NIGHT'S WORK

In former times when superstition was preferred to truth, men told grisly tales of a demon which came by night and sucked the blood of its victim. In South America the tale has come true and there is nothing more demoniac in Nature than the face of the blood-sucking vampire. The big toe is a favourite place for the gentle bite of those razor-sharp teeth which never wakes the sleeper. It is thought that, unless disturbed, the vampire's saliva helps to staunch the wound when its blood-thirst is quenched.

The vampire's victim is usually left bleeding, but a recent observer has stated that this is because the bat is usually brushed off at last, even if unconsciously, and that if it be allowed to have its own way it will fill the wound with its saliva, which coagulates quickly and acts as a styptic to stop the flow of blood, and also as a disinfectant. However this may be, the vampire's bite is very troublesome, if not dangerous, to people who are specially favoured by bats, while fowls succumb outright and horses and cattle are much weakened; the trouble in horses being aggravated by the fact that they are bitten just where the saddle is placed, so that a sore back is the consequence.

Light is said to keep the vampire away, and clear glass bottles, filled with water to make them heavier and suspended above beasts, are a deterrent, as the bats strike against them in the dark. Netting is the best preventive, and for travellers it should surely be possible to find some " dope " which could be applied to the portions of man and beast most liable to vampire attack and make them distasteful. In human beings the big toe is the usual point attacked, as it is likely to project from the bed-clothes, but the vampire can make shift with the nose if the toes are inaccessible.

ONLY two other blood-sucking vampires are known, but the common species is found throughout the warm parts of America, so that bat-bites are likely to occur anywhere in this part of the world ; and so enterprising are the creatures that they even invade the guano islands off Peru, where they must look to the sea-lions and sea-fowl for a livelihood.

Incidentally, they have given a bad name to an innocent family, for the vampires generally are insectivorous or fruit-eaters, though one at least, Waterhouse's vampire, is a semi-cannibal, feeding on other bats smaller than itself. In this, as in some other points, it resembles the Indian fake vampire, or megaderm, a bat of another family, which was first convicted of being carnivorous by being found sucking the blood of a smaller bat. This is a thorough carnivore, preying on birds and lizards as well as

Otho Webb

A TREE IN AN AUSTRALIAN "BAT CAMP" BEARING A STRANGE CROP

In Australia the fruit-bats or "flying-foxes" congregate in "camps"—districts of woodland to which they always return to sleep. This particular "camp" in Southern Queensland covered about 25 acres and, as this is a photograph of only one tree, the number of bats in the whole "camp" can be imagined. In the evening the bats wake up and depart in search of food, darkening the sky with their swarms and filling the evening with the noise of their million beating wings. Woe betide the orchard which such a swarm may find in the picking season!

W. S. Berridge

BATS BEHIND BARS: A MUSTER OF DOLEFUL FACES

The bat always sleeps in this inverted position, with wings folded about the body like a cloak. To get the full effect of these six faces (the seventh bat shows only half a face on the extreme left) and six pairs of watching eyes and expectant ears as the shutter of the camera goes "click," turn the photograph upside down. Then we have a picture which might illustrate a scene from a story on the lines of "Dracula." The imagination of a Bram Stoker or an Edgar Allen Poe might well place this group discovered at the bedside by an awakened sleeper.

smaller bats; it is a bone-cruncher more than a blood-sucker, devouring its prey in a wholesale hyena-like fashion. It also eats large insects, however, and an allied African species has been seen hunting insects by day and, what is more remarkable, making short flights after them and returning to its perch like a flycatcher, whereas most bats, as everyone knows, resemble swallows in their hunting habits, and remain for a long time hunting about on the wing.

One does not hear complaints of the fruit-eating vampire's depredations, but the great fruit-bats or flying-foxes are very troublesome in this way; in India the one local species of flying-fox, which is the next largest bat to the kalong, does a great deal of harm to fruit, and Australia suffers from no fewer than five species of flying-foxes, all enthusiasts for the slogan "Eat more fruit." They assemble in thousands in roosting places, or "camps" as the Australians call them, and an Australian scientist one year sent out an S. O. S. asking for suggestions for their destruction, especially for a "biological check." But such a check would be hard to find, for bats as a group are singularly free from enemies, as is shown by their great numbers in the tropics.

A small insectivorous species in Burma, the wrinkled-lipped bat, comes out of the caves in which it shelters in masses which look at a distance like clouds of smoke, and further east a flight of flying-foxes has been seen which darkened the sun, and was estimated to number half a million individuals—and this in spite of the fact that bats are not prolific, usually having only one or two young at a time, and that only once a year.

Even destructive man has so far been powerless against bats, though in some parts of Africa and the East they are much hunted by him for food; and bats were eaten in ancient times, for it is recorded that the citizens of the old town of Borsippa in Mesopotamia ate salted bats; while the prohibition of the bat as food in the Mosaic law shows that the lawgiver looked on bat-eating as a possibility.

As the Indian flying-fox at any rate does drink the sap of palms, when it can find the pots in which the natives collect sap for toddy, and gets incapably drunk on it when, in the hot Indian night, the juice

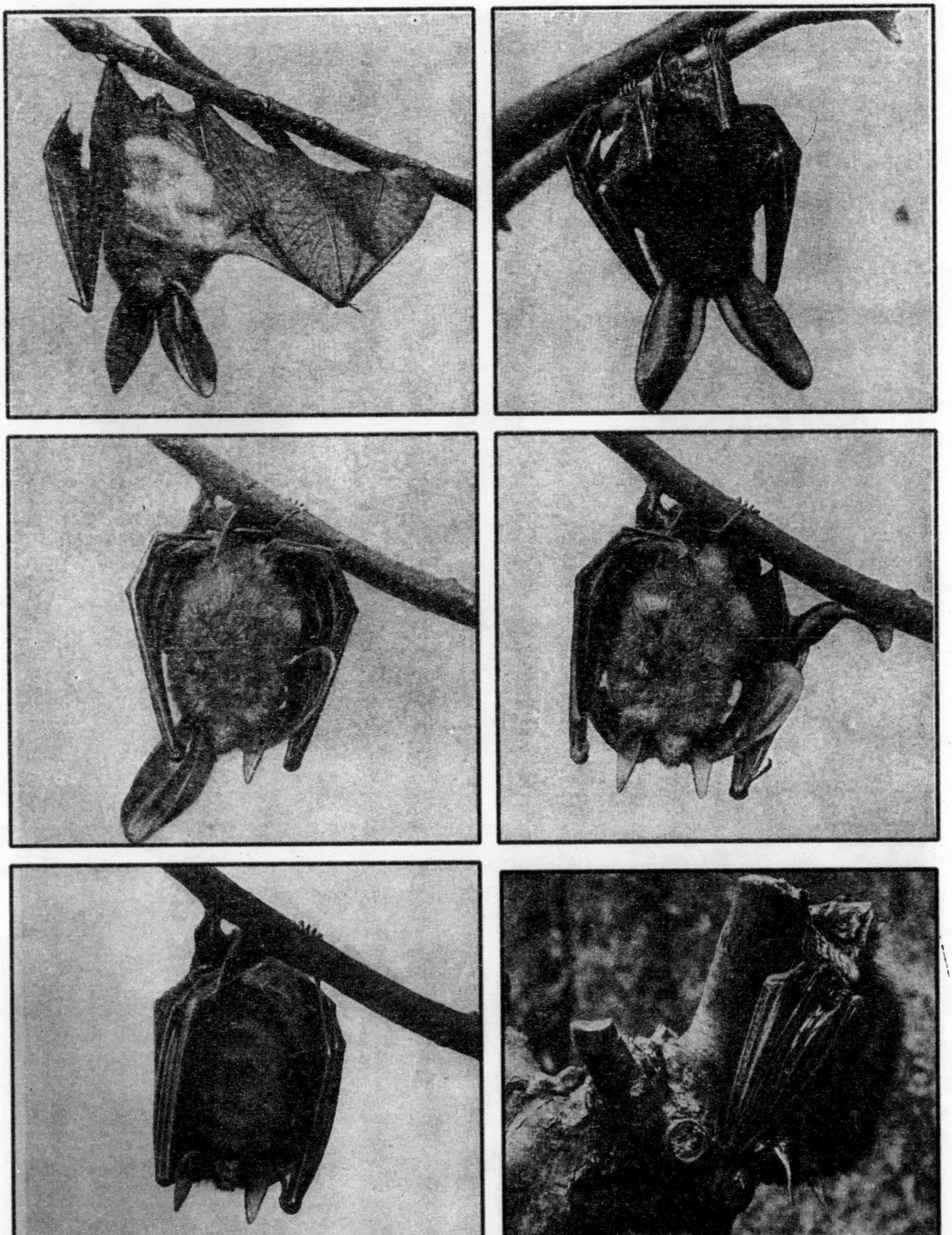

J. J. Ward and W. S. Berridge

HOW THE LONG-EARED BAT PREPARES FOR BED

Among the bats of Britain is this species which is remarkable for its ears, so huge in proportion to its body. The bat is commonly about two inches long and it has ears one and a half inches long. When it decides to sleep after its nightly flight for food it hangs itself up, folds up first one ear and then the other under its wings and so, warm and comfortable, it spends the day. The colour of this species is brown-grey above with lighter under parts, the shade of colour varying to some extent with the individual.

Otho Webb

"CLOSE-UPS" OF THE FRUIT-DESTROYING "FLYING-FOX"

So devastating have the ravages of the fruit-bat or "flying-fox" become in Australia that in 1920 the Queensland Department of Agriculture experimented with that hideous engine, the flame-thrower, to check the pests. The lower photograph gives the proportions of the animal and above (top left) we see the sleeping position and the way in which the thumb is separated from the fingers, which support the wing-membrane, and is used for climbing and hanging. The other photograph shows the bat's resemblance to a fox.

W. S. Berridge

PHILIPPINE FLYING-FOX AND THE NOCTULE OF BRITAIN

A species of flying-fox or fox-bat (bottom) is found in the Philippine Islands and, as can be seen by a glance at its long muzzle, the term is a very suitable one. The contrast between the face of this fruit-eating type and that of the vampire and insect-eater is very marked. The noctule (top) is the most familiar of the bats seen in Britain and is also known as the great bat. Its wing-spread is usually about thirteen or fourteen inches. It inhabits trees and is particularly fond of cockchafers, its teeth being specially suited for crunching them.

W. S. Berridge

THE SEROTINE, MOST WIDELY DISTRIBUTED OF BATS

Both the Old and the New World are inhabited by the serotine, the only bat indigenous to the two hemispheres. It is found in the southern counties of England and can be known by its slow and fluttering way of flying. But specimens in England are rather rare. The usual colour is chestnut brown on the back and the hair is long and of a silky texture.

has fermented into toddy on the tree, it seems as if a good plan would be to establish a free canteen in every bat-camp, when the debauched delinquents could be dealt with at leisure. It ought to be possible to put them to some practical use, and the writer is inclined to think that their broad, naked wings would make a very useful fine leather; he fears it would be of no use to suggest bat-eating to white Australia!

It is a pity that any bats need to be put out of the way for conflicting with human interests; for their race is in many ways one of the most wonderful and perfect products of evolution, and we ought to have some fellow-feeling for them, since of all animal aviators they are the nearest in structure to ourselves, and they have solved the problem of existence admirably, as their abundance shows.

Though sociable, bats are not in the least socialistic—in fact, they are decidedly quarrelsome; yet, more than any other animals, they have freed themselves from the ties of property. Other beasts and birds need some sort of den or nest, or have lively straggling youngsters to look after; but all the bat needs is something to hitch his toe-nails on to. His flexible wings, wrapped round him, serve him as bed-clothes, and his mate carries the batling clinging to her breast even when she flies out to forage. The feeding habits of bats, also, are very wide; though most are useful insect eaters, many, as we have seen, are fruitarians and a few carnivorous. One or two, in tropical America, even catch fish, snatching them up with their hind claws like a fishing hawk; and even the fruit-eating flying-fox has been once seen to do this in India; while a smaller fruit-bat in Burma has been found feeding on shell-fish when the tide was out.

Thus, although they came into existence ages after birds had won their wings, bird competition seems not to have troubled them, and they have almost as varied a diet as birds have, while in some respects they beat birds as flyers; if none can fly so fast or so far as some birds can, no birds but the humming-birds can beat them at dexterity in evolutions in a small space. Even the comparatively clumsy fruit-bats are difficult to tire out in a room, where almost any bird soon succumbs; the reason of this being that a bat is much better at the turn, for its wings embrace a far larger amount of air, although its provision of muscular power is ridiculously small in comparison. A bird with breast-muscles no larger than a bat's is the poorest of flyers; but the skin of the bat's wing extends all down the flanks and legs to the ankle joint, in addition to the web which joins the long wire-like fingers.

Fragile as the bat's wing looks, it has great resisting power; the flying-fox slogs its way across the sky with a slow sweeping stroke which makes its flight far more impressive than any bird's, and the sudden doubles and wrenches of the ordinary little flitter-mouse look as if the filmy wings ought to snap under the strain. The bat's wing must be, indeed, in some cases, easily thrown out of gear. One may often see a bird flying with a great gap in one or both wings which re-growing quills will soon repair; but one never sees a damaged bat abroad.

Probably a broken finger-bone or a slit in the wing-web means disablement to a bat; and probably, too, the quarrels of bats among themselves lead frequently to such injuries, and are the most powerful check on their increase—like so many very successful animals, man included, their worst enemies are their own kind For a bat that cannot fly is doomed, since bats have staked their all on their wings; they not only cannot stand on their hind limbs like birds, but they cannot even stand up on all fours like other beasts, but are limited to crawling. Hence, although they are not unable to rise from the ground, they avoid a flat surface, and are much more at home when they can hang up by toes or thumb-nails, the toes being preferred, as the upside-down position allows them to wrap themselves in their wings, and also affords a better take-off for flight, which otherwise would have to be begun with a back-somersault; such a somersault on settling they do not mind, for in Nature it is being "quick off the mark" that matters most.

The thumb is the only finger of the bat's fore-paw that has no part in the construction of the wing; it is strongly clawed, and is used not only for climbing, but at times for fighting, and even for picking up or holding food. The hind-limb is also very wonderful in its way, for it has the same freedom of movement as an arm, while the foot turns as freely as our hand, and yet the whole limb does the usual hind-leg duty in the straddling crawl which is a bat's walk.

The wing-web of bats is for the most part naked, though some show a certain amount of fur on the sides near the body and on the tail-web, and this naked wing is extraordinarily sensitive to temperature and air currents. Thus the bat's sense of touch is as superior as ours, as are the dog's scent and the hawk's sight, and the creature need not touch an object to be aware of its presence. So it is that bats deprived of sight are able to fly freely about and avoid even such small obstacles as suspended strings.

That they should sometimes collide with glass is conceivable, since glass is a substance unknown in nature, and is, moreover, very permeable by heat, so that to the bat, feeling its way by temperature, it does not represent an understandable obstacle. Just so, the keen-sighted hawk is captured in a net, which it must see but cannot understand. This sense of feeling is most developed in bats that have well developed "nose-leaves," and these often have particularly small eyes. In fact, the bats as a group are remarkably small-eyed, with the exception of the old-world fruit-bats, which are large-eyed, and probably fly mostly by sight, though, as some of them roost in caves, they are no doubt also able to find their way in the dark.

Birds had a long start of bats in evolution, and no doubt the danger from birds of prey is the reason why parachute flyers are nocturnal, because a creature which glides passively through the air is simply inviting trouble from such enemies; and even now, those few birds of prey which take bats seem to have little trouble in securing them. That they are not more partial to bats as food is probably due to the fact that bats, as compared with rats and mice, are not only harder to catch, but are poor value when caught, owing to their large expanse of tasteless, skinny wings. Just so, the broad-winged slim butterflies are seldom troubled by insectivorous birds, while the more meaty moths are ravenously pursued.

The nasty smell of bats is very likely another reason why they are but little preyed upon; and this, no doubt, is also one of the peculiarities which have tended to prejudice man against them, others being their crawling movements and soft, naked, skinny wings, which suggest clamminess, to say nothing of their ugly little faces, which in many cases attain a pitch of goblin hideousness like nothing in nature, suggesting the devil-masks used by Buddhist monks in certain ceremonies.

The flying-foxes, with their keen, intelligent-looking, dog-like heads, inspire nothing but friendly interest when seen close at hand, and might quite probably be popular as pets if they were better known. A flying-fox kept as a pet in London has been known to live twenty years.

Another peculiarity operating against bats in human estimation is the fact that they are generally not easily studied, for people are always ready to distrust what is unfamiliar. But it cannot be said that the bat fairly exemplifies the proverb: "Give a dog a bad name and hang him," for the first bats, found fossil, are perfectly well-developed according to their kind, and many strange beasts have arisen and become extinct since their day; so the bat had hung himself happily by the heels for ages before our own ancestor, starting from a little quadruped which must have been very similar to the bat's, had begun to sit up on his hind legs and take notice.

Even among scientists legends about bats still exist. Many seem to think that their flight is in some way different from and inferior to that of birds; but instantaneous photographs of flying-foxes on the wing show that the movements of the wings are quite similar, and one of these great bats has boarded a ship two hundred miles from land. As has been pointed out, the bats can claim to have more thoroughly mastered the air than their rivals. Every animal, it has been said, has some strong point or it could not live, and some weak point or the others could not live; the bats have an extraordinary number of strong points, but two weak ones—they have no power of resisting cold, and they have rarely developed the instinct of migration.

Thus they are mainly creatures of the tropics; in India there are more than a hundred species, in Europe less than a quarter of that number, none of them of really large size. But at all events, here they are purely the friends of man, and we have nothing to fear from the orchard-raiders and blood-suckers whose misdoings are the only justification for the disfavour meted out to these, the most highly-gifted children of Nature after ourselves.

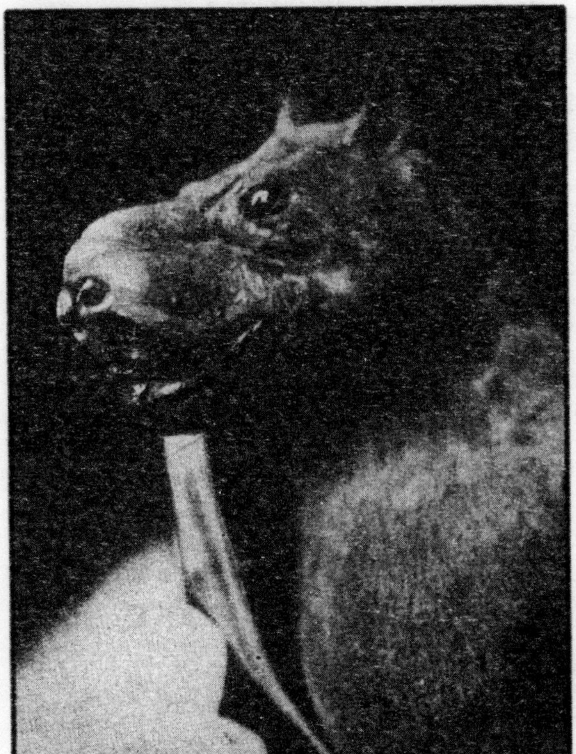

W. S. Berridge

HIDEOUS HAMMER-HEAD

Found in the Gabun district of French Equatorial Africa, the hammer-headed bat is characterised by a relatively enormous muzzle of extremely repulsive aspect. This bat is a fruit-eater with a very great partiality for figs.

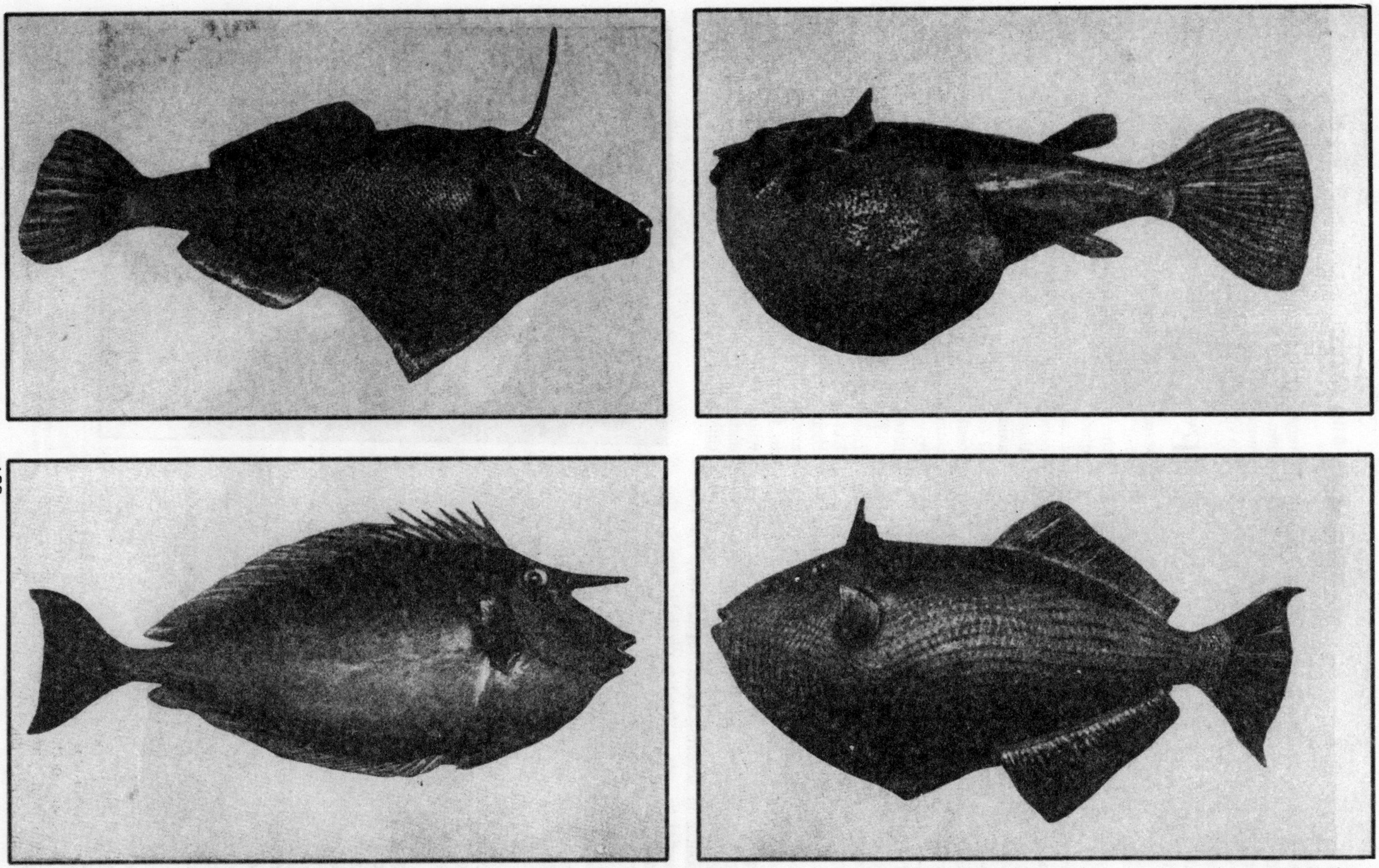

W. S. Berridge

UNCOUTH AND BLOATED FORMS OF THE UNICORN, FILE, TRIGGER, AND GLOBE FISHES

On account of the stout spike protruding from its head, close to the large glaring eye, the unicorn fish (bottom left) gets its name. The trigger-fish (bottom right) and the file-fish (top left) are of the tropics and belong to the same group in which the shape has been distorted from length to breadth, especially in the case of the file-fish. This has the first of the dorsal spines roughened like a file in front and is equipped with strong teeth with which it can bite off lumps of coral whence it sucks the soft organisms within. The trigger-fish cannot lower its first long dorsal spine until the second, which is much smaller, has been lowered, and from this fact it has been named. The globe-fish (top right) is related to the sun-fish and swims in tropic seas.

Chapter XIV

Nightmares of the Sea

By J. Travis Jenkins, D.Sc., Ph.D.

Lecturer in Sea Fisheries, Liverpool University

DURING thirty years' sea-fishing of all kinds, in the pursuit of fish and marine creatures from shrimps to whales, in seas extending from the Arctic Circle to the Tropics, I have come across fish of amazingly grotesque appearance, many of which can only be described as terrifying.

This fact is reflected in the popular names applied to certain species ; for instance we have sea-devils or devil fish, hag fish, scorpion fish, dragonets, toad fish, fishing frogs, crocodile fish and sword fish. Even the scientific names of many species record these peculiarities in such suggestive terms as *monstrosus*, *horridus*, or *infernalis*.

Mere size is not an attribute of ugliness or fierceness since some of the smallest sea fish are of truly terrifying aspect, for instance, the sea-scorpions. The ferocious appearance of these sea robbers is mainly due to their bizarre shape and the presence of formidable spines, but to some extent to the coloration. Many fish can assume a warning attitude or a bullying expression by erecting their spines or deepening or changing their coloration.

The question naturally arises as to the utility of this formidable aspect. Are these fish really ugly and repulsive from the human point of view only, or is this horrifying appearance of some use to its possessor in the struggle for existence, which is constantly going on in the sea as elsewhere ? The question does not admit of a simple answer, since ugliness in fish undoubtedly serves many purposes, which can be more appropriately considered in each separate case, but broadly speaking a sense of terror or warning is conveyed by the fish's appearance, and this sense of terror is a source of usefulness to the fish invoking it. Ugliness is nearly always associated with what is harmful or dangerous.

Some fish are actually poisonous, others are capable of giving an alarming electric shock, and in these cases the coloration and appearance of the fish serve as a warning. In other cases, where the males and females are of markedly different appearance, the males are the more ferocious-looking and this serves more than one useful purpose.

To estimate the effect of terror or fright on fish we must remember that water is much less transparent than air, and frequently sea and fresh water is more or less cloudy. Compared with human beings, fish are short-sighted. The lens of the eye is spherical or globular, and the range of perfect vision cannot be more than a few feet. Consequently, in order to escape from its enemies all a fish has to do is to make a short and swift dash out of its enemies' sight. In the great majority of cases this is sufficient, and the muscular arrangement of the fish's body secures this sudden dart out of sight. Were it not so, it is difficult to see how such defenceless fish as mackerel or herring could survive, in spite of their enormous fecundity. The effect of the monstrous or horrible appearance of a large number of species of fish is therefore unquestionably in use to frighten away or warn off other species.

Take, for instance, the sea-scorpions, which are for the most part small coastal marine fish, common enough in British waters. They are poor swimmers and consequently their unattractive appearance and numerous spines, together with their habit of swelling themselves up, is doubtless a protective measure and prevents their being attacked by larger fish. Moreover, these fish lay a mass of eggs which undergo a period of incubation lasting approximately a month. During this period the eggs are liable to be devoured by other species and would be, but for the fact that the male parent constructs a sort of nest and mounts guard over the eggs until the young are hatched out.

The sea-scorpions are also remarkable for the fact that they are able, under the emotions of greed, anger, or fear, to change their colour. When the male of the short-spined sea-scorpion is sitting on the eggs, it presents a truly formidable appearance for a fish so comparatively small in size.

THE Gobies are also small fish, frequenting for the most part rocky coasts. Their aspect is, considering their small size, formidable, and one species rejoices under the scientific name of *Scorpioides*, that is to say " like a scorpion."

These fish are both shy and pugnacious, and there is a marked difference in appearance between the males and females. They are among the very few fish which have a period of courtship, during which time the male assumes a bullying attitude, fighting with any other male which dares approach him. Here the fish actually pair off together for a time, and it is certain that the terrifying aspect of the male, combined with his pugnacious character, is of importance in driving off rivals and in assisting him to the happy end of a successful wooing.

The term cat-fish is applied to several kinds of fish, which have nothing in common except their repulsive appearance. The common sea-cat or sea-wolf is a marine species inhabiting deep water to the north and west of Britain and is most frequently seen in the Aberdeen market. It is really a giant blenny, attaining a length of over six feet. Of blue-grey colour with black bands down the sides of the body it is the only cat-fish which even remotely resembles a cat.

There is a family of fresh-water fish, the Siluroids, not represented in British waters, to which the term cat-fish is applied. They are abundant in Indian rivers and are really of quite exceptional ugliness. But of all the disagreeable fish of the tribe the chaca

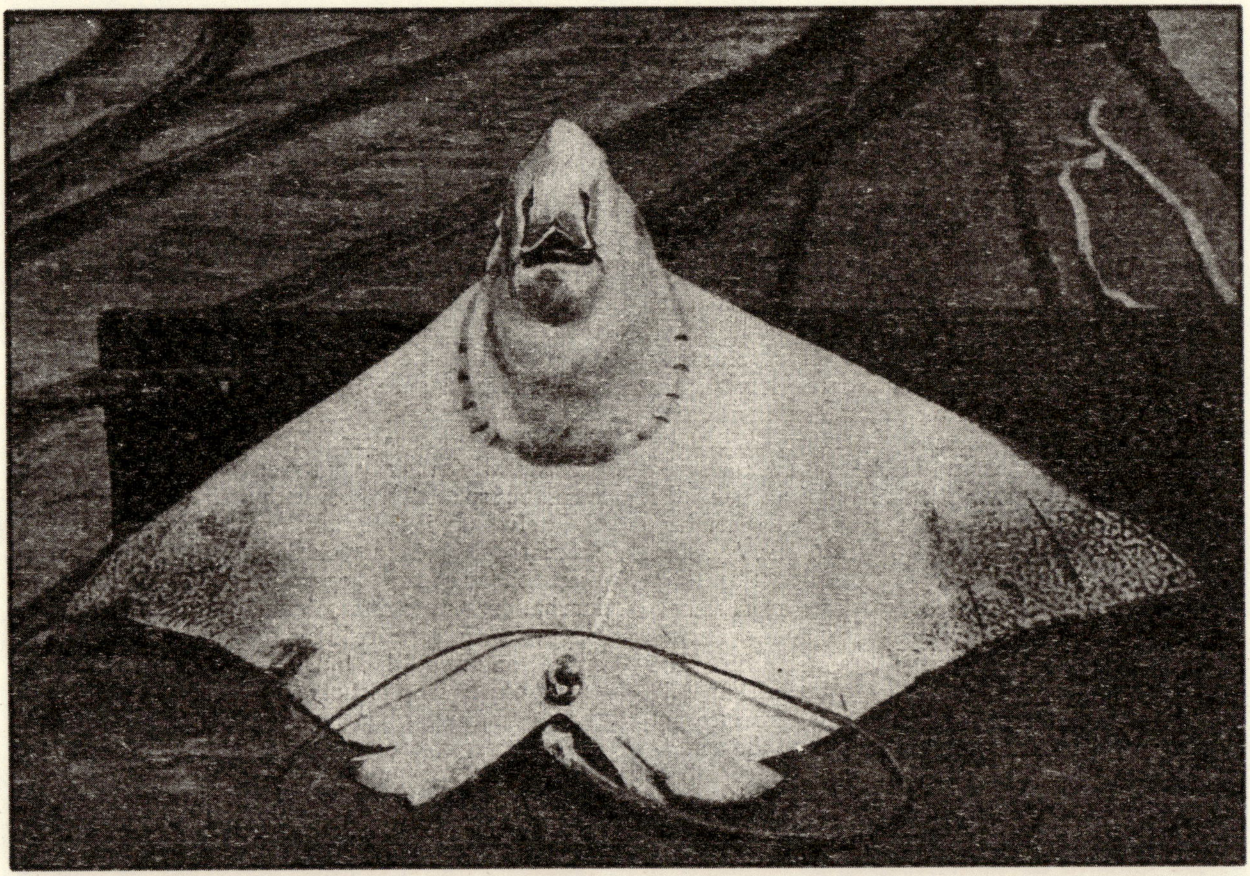

Dr. Haden Guest

WHIP-TAILED EAGLE RAY AND THE JAWS OF A HAMMER-HEADED SHARK

When captured the eagle ray (top) is extremely dangerous on account of its long, whip-like tail which ends in a jagged spine that is capable of producing a very ugly wound. Eagle rays grow to a length of about fifteen feet and feed on clams and oysters, their jaws having a terrific power of pressure. The hammer-headed shark (bottom) is one of the most dreadful looking fish, for it has its head prolonged on either side and at each extremity there is an eye This shark is said to feed on the rays and to be indifferent to wounds from the spines or " stings."

Dr. Baden Guest

THE GHASTLY HORROR WHOSE NAME IS DEVIL FISH

Two tons of devil fish upon a truck make a sight that is better not remembered in one's dreams. Considered as a sight this thing is frightful but when we come to examine it as a fish, there are several points to be noted. Firstly, what looks like a horribly bloated face is really the underside of the head. Notice the mouth with the strange teeth adapted for crushing shell fish. Secondly, the slits above are not eyes but gill-clefts, the eyes, invisible from this point of view being on the upper side of the head as in the case of a shark.

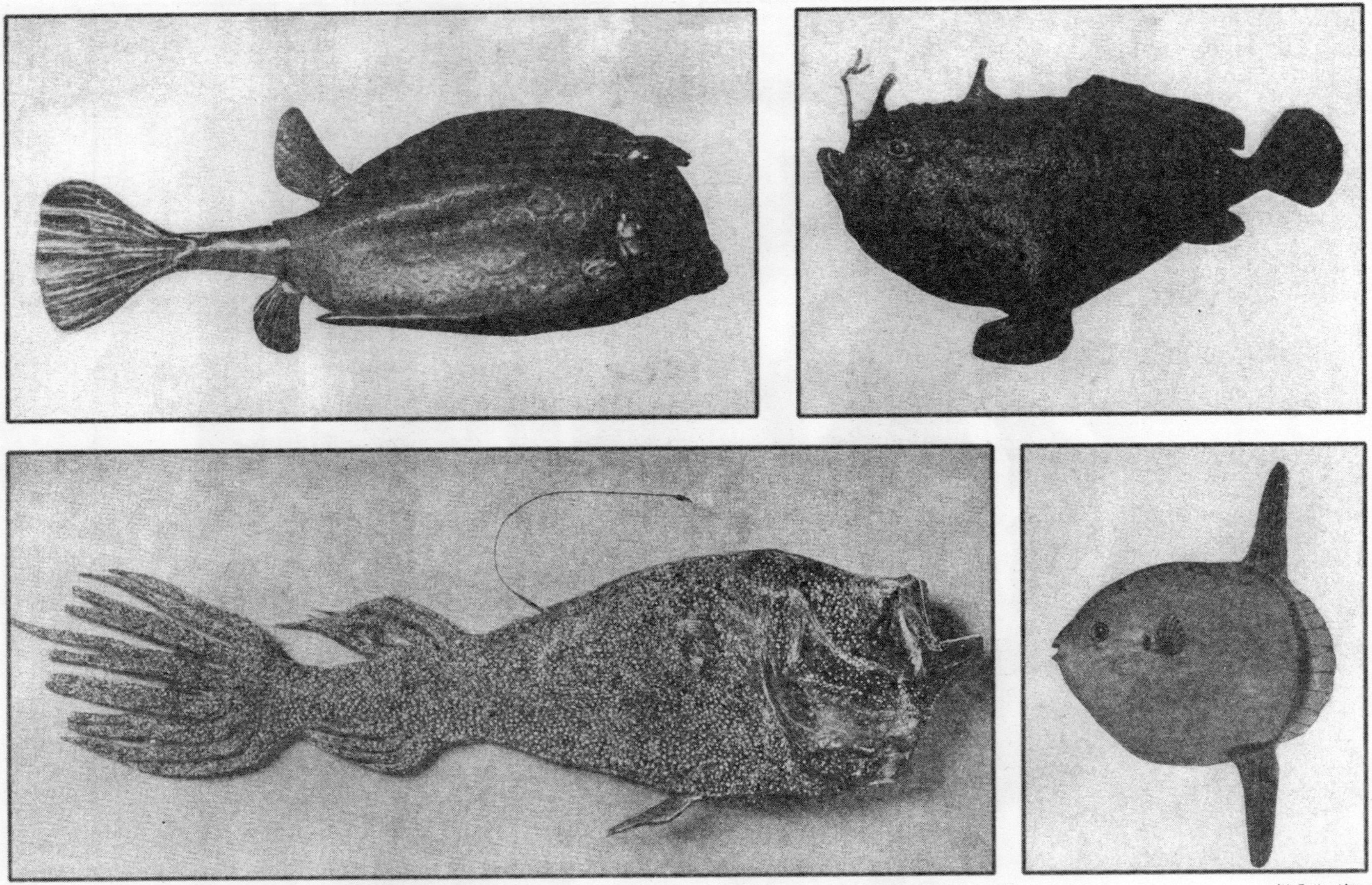

W. S. Berridge

FOUR OF NATURE'S FREAKS FROM THE DEPTHS OF THE SEVEN SEAS

Taken by a British trawler off Iceland in the course of its fishing there was this specimen of the Ceratius (bottom left) which is a very strange fish. This is a female and something over three feet long. The male, four inches long, is seen attached, and looking, at first sight, like a small fin projecting below. This male is carried about by its huge mate as a kind of parasite. On the female, where the dorsal fin in many fish could be, is a kind of rod and line complete with bait with which the weird fish fishes. The sun-fish (bottom right) is a strange travesty of the fishy form, and above we have a specimen of the four-horned trunk-fish (top left) and (top right) the oddly-fashioned frog-fish.

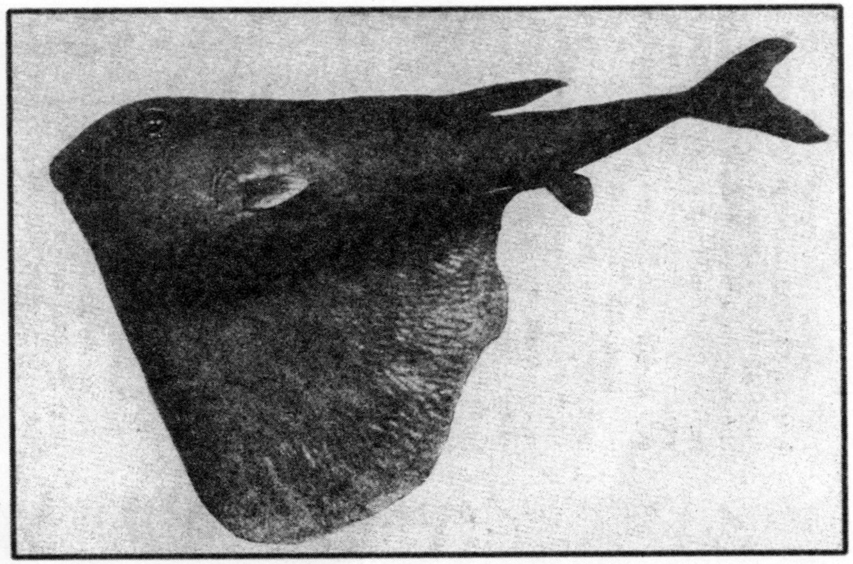

W. S. Berridge

TRAVESTIES OF FISH SHAPES THAT SWIM THE WARM WATERS OF THE TROPICS

While the fish of the frigid and temperate zones are usually sober hued, the vital warmth of the tropic and sub-tropical sun seems to produce bright colours and strange shapes, as well in the sea as on the land. The trunk-fish (bottom right) and the sac-fish (top right) are good examples, the latter haunting the Indian Ocean. The skin of its stomach is elastic to an extraordinary degree and, at full stretch, gives its owner a grotesque appearance. The sac can be blown out with air to alarm attackers. This fish is not more than twenty inches in length. The gurnard (bottom left) is found not only in tropic seas, but in British waters. Despite its appearance it is excellent eating. The remaining photograph (top left) shows a globe fish.

Dr. Haden Guest

NIGHTMARE OF THE SEA IN THE LIGHT OF DAY

All those who are inclined to smile nonchalantly at the angler should remember that the sort of fishing which involves the " playing " and capture of a tiger shark is by no means to be lightly spoken of The name of this fish is, incidentally, in all save ferocity, a manifest libel on one of the most splendid looking of beasts.

The horrid sea-scorpion (*Synanceia horrida*) which belongs to quite a different family from the sea-scorpions above mentioned; and the king of the herrings, or rabbit fish (*Chimaera monstrosa*).. The general appearance of the horrid sea-scorpion, especially of the head, can only be described as monstrous and here again trespassers are warned off, since these fish are provided with poisoned dorsal spines. These spines are in their terminal portions provided with a deep groove on either side at the lower end, in which is a pear-shaped gland containing a milky poisonous fluid. The wounds made by these fish are often deadly. The family to which they belong—the *Scorpaenidae*, or sea scorpions—comprises the ugliest collection of sea-monsters available. As they are all of carnivorous habits and extremely voracious, their mere appearance is a sufficient warning. Of the habits of the king of the herrings very little is known.

A few fish are provided with poison glands, similar in function to those possessed by poisonous snakes, and if these fish are handled incautiously when alive they are capable of inflicting a wound which in extreme cases may be fatal to a human being, and in any case produces partial paralysis or numbness which may last for months.

These poison glands are not associated with the teeth or fangs of the fish, but with spines which are situated either in the back fin, as in the weevers : or in the tail as in the sting rays. These poisonous fish have a very unattractive appearance and are doubtless repellent in respect to other marine fish. The Weever family, which includes two British species, is particularly repulsive, some of the tropical forms having a large, broad, thick head with upturned eyes with a strong resemblance to a bulldog. The abyssal dragon (*Bathydraco*) belongs to this group.

The sting rays or devil fish have a formidable barbed spine behind the fin. These fish are of enormous size and we frequently took them in the trawl in the Bay of Bengal. Specimens up to

is the most horrible to behold. It conceals itself in the river mud from which it is in colour hardly distinguishable. A number of loose filamentous projections on the skin serve to camouflage it. With wide-open mouth it remains hidden in the mud waiting to pounce on any fish that may happen to wander within reach of it. It is of truly loathsome aspect.

There are at least two species of Horrid fish.

twenty feet in breadth, measured across the back, were not uncommon and it was impossible to approach them until they were dead on account of their terrific struggles and lashing blows of the barbed tail.

Nature has provided these poisonous fish with a warning appearance. When the weevers are alarmed they erect their dorsal fin, which is not only poisonous but deep black in colour. They bury themselves in

FINNED DEATH THAT MOVES IN THE TWILIGHT UNDER THE WATERS

Out of the dimness of the sea there comes suddenly an evil shape, built for power and speed. The head ends in a point like the blade of a spear and at its base are two eyes which never change from their one fixed expression which means hunger. Beneath comes the mouth, furnished with ghastly sets of teeth to serve this thing which seems made only for horror. And yet the shark is neither more nor less dreadful in its own sphere than the everyday cannibal trout of a pleasant English stream.

W. S. Berridge

the sand so that this fin only is visible, and is a most effective protection against and warning to predaceous fish. Similarly an Indian cat-fish (*Plotosus*), which is armed with dangerous spines, wounds from which are much feared by the natives of India, since they cause severe inflammation or even tetanus, is provided with a breast fin brilliantly coloured in red and yellow, the erection of which by the fish is undoubtedly a warning device.

Generally speaking, poisonous or other dangerous fish avoid their enemies. This is understandable when we realize that the poisonous fish itself suffers more or less serious injury when its spines penetrate the skin of another fish or animal, since they are often damaged or torn away altogether. So that many of them, but not all of them, exhibit warning coloration. The electric eels and the Scorpenoids, for instance, are not specially provided with any particular warning colours.

ANGLER FISH AND THE MASKED CRAB — E. Step

Provided with a "fishing rod," a kind of tentacle growing out of its head, the angler-fish (bottom) waits concealed until some passing fish is attracted by the flap of skin at the end of the rod. As soon as the victim comes within reach it is snapped up within those evil toothed jaws. Above we see the head of a masked crab.

THE muscular system in some fish is modified in a peculiar fashion so that electric organs have evolved out of the muscular substance. Such fish are capable, when alive, of giving a severe electric shock to other fish or animals. In British waters the only species is the torpedo fish or electric ray, but in foreign waters the electric apparatus is encountered in other forms, and we have an electric eel and an electric sheath-fish of the fresh waters of tropical Africa. In all cases these fish have an unattractive appearance and coloration which undoubtedly have the effect of warning off intruders.

Eels, whether fresh water or marine, can hardly be considered handsome fish. They are found in the very deepest waters of the oceans where one species, *Saccopharynx*, has such an extraordinarily distensible stomach that it can swallow a fish several times larger than itself. All eels are very voracious. They are provided with formidable teeth, and there can be no doubt that their repellent aspect is a warning to others to keep away. In the sea, eels attain a length of at least sixty feet with a maximum thickness of eight feet and there can be little doubt that the occasional appearance of these gigantic eels at the surface is one of the origins of the famous and persistently recurring stories of sea-serpents.

The members of the Globe fish family are provided with spines. They are also able to swallow air and so assume a globular form. This peculiarity has procured them the name of balloon-fish among Europeans and pillow-fish among Malays. At the same time that they swallow air and blow themselves up like the frog in the fable, they also erect their spines and deepen the brilliant coloration with which they are provided. This combination of circumstances, giving them a truly repulsive appearance, is naturally a protective measure.

But the real nightmares of the sea are the sharks, the smaller species of which are dogfish. There are a large number of kinds and they are found in all the seas of the world, some living near the bottom —the ground sharks—and others near the surface. Even when removed from their natural element they are formidable, and not safe to approach.

Elwin R. Sanborn

HUGE JEWFISH, A NIGHTMARE OF THE DEEPS

F Martin Duncan

STRANGE STONE CRAB AND LOATHLY OCTOPUS

Belonging to the same family as the hermit crab, the stone crab (bottom) lives entirely in the sea and is noticeable for the way in which it is covered in spines. The top photograph shows the creature most dreaded of all the sea's inhabitants—the octopus. It likes a lair among rocks where it can prey upon crabs, which form the greater part of its food. Its saliva appears to be poisonous to the crabs and it acts very quickly. Octopi are common round the Channel Islands, where they have been known to attack bathers. The eight " arms " are, in some kinds, joined by a membrane forming an umbrella-like structure. The creature is a true nightmare of the sea.

A large shark can easily bite through a man's body with one snap of the jaw, and this fish is the real bully of the ocean.

One of the most curious is the hammer-headed shark, which is quite common in the Indian Ocean. In rare instances stragglers are found in British waters. In this fish the front part of the head is broad and flattened and produced on either side into a lobe at the extremity of which an eye is situated. The front part of the head is consequently exactly like a hammer. It is difficult to see what use this peculiarity is to the fish.

One of the greatest terrors of the seas, which, at the same time, is of monstrous appearance, is the octopus. This creature is not really a fish, but a mollusc. It has been known from time immemorial, as it is frequently delineated or carved on Greek objects of art such as vases, gems, coins, and ornaments. The octopus was the model on which the story of the Lernean Hydra with its hundred heads was based, the killing of which was one of the labours of Hercules. It is also the origin of many of the marvellous stories of sea-serpents.

The octopus has eight long tentacles or arms provided with suckers. Some of the tribe have ten arms, and are quite capable of attacking the largest sea creatures. Even whales are not exempt from their attacks, as frequently whales, killed by whaling ships, have their bodies scarred all over with saucer-shaped ulcerated depressions marking the grip of the octopus.

These marine molluscs are of gigantic size. In Japanese waters they have been known to upset the boats of the native fishermen, and there are traditions of similar occurrences in the Polynesian Islands.

The Angler family contains a larger number of sea-monsters than any other. The most bizarre fish in English seas is the angler or sea-devil. This particularly repellent fish is devoid of scales and has specially soft flesh. The head is greatly enlarged and is out of all proportion to the rest of the body. The lower jaw protrudes and is provided with several rows of formidable teeth. No other living fish has such a terrible mouth. The most remarkable feature of this fish, however, is the prolongation of the first dorsal fin ray into a long filament, detached from the rest of the fin, and provided at its extremity with a leaf-like appendage.

When the fish is at rest, partly concealed on the bottom of the sea, this tentacle and appendage look for all the world like a fishing-rod and line with bait attached. There can be little doubt that the movements of the appendage attract other fish, which directly they swim in near to investigate are snapped up in the cruel jaws of the angler. The habit of the angler is to lie dormant on the sea bottom. Its whole structure and feeble muscles prove plainly that it is no swimmer, so that in order to obtain its food it has to rely on patience and an ingenious angling device. In the case of the angler the general appearance of the body, which is provided with filaments and in some species with scattered conical tubercles, imitates the sea-bottom with its fronds of seaweed and pebbles, so that the ugliness here is not a warning appearance but an attempt at concealment.

Anglers or frog-fishes are of wide distribution as regards depth and geographical area. Our own angler is most common in the North Sea. Owing to its horrid appearance it was long regarded as unmarketable, and it is only of recent years that it has been sold in a much camouflaged condition. Incidentally the angler has come to be considered a valuable fish of late years, since its pancreas is well stocked with insulin, the most efficacious remedy for diabetes.

A deep-sea representative of this family, which like some of the deep-sea eels can swallow a fish larger than itself, is the Melanocetus, a name which literally means black sea-monster. One of these fish from the depths of the Atlantic, though only four inches long, had a fish measuring seven and a half inches in length and one inch in thickness coiled spirally in its stomach. Another ugly brute of this tribe is the Antennarius. Like the angler a feeble swimmer, it conceals itself on the bottom between corals, stones and seaweeds. It coloration is so similar to its surroundings that it is almost an impossibility to distinguish it from its environment.

To enumerate all the monstrous-looking sea fish would require a separate volume. They are found everywhere, in water fresh and salt, in the greatest depths of the oceans and in shallow coastal waters, in rivers, lakes and lagoons, in the tropics and in the Arctic and Antarctic zones.

Take, for instance, the bull-fish (*Bovichthys*) of New Zealand. Seen from above, the head of this fish has a striking resemblance to that of a bull. Even the horns are imitated by projections at the side of, but not separate from, the head of the fish. Then there is the *Pataecus*, a member of the Blenny family, named after the Phoenician deities of peculiar dwarfish shape whose images formed the figure-heads of Phoenician ships. These fish might serve as a model for a dragon.

Again there is the fish of the Amazon Valley which is named after the devil, *Satanoperca*.

The sea-pikes (*Sphyraena*) may be grouped among the few sea-monsters which are popularly supposed to be partial to human flesh. The best-known member of this family is the Barracoota, which is much feared in the tropical seas which it inhabits. Bathers in West Indian waters must beware of this fish since it is truly formidable and a voracious type. The head is long with a protruding lower jaw armed with most formidable teeth, giving it a very ferocious aspect. It is commonly supposed to be even more dangerous and intimidating than the sharks. Not only so, but its flesh is considered to be dangerous, and people consuming it often show symptoms of poisoning.

Many bathybial or abyssal fish are characterised by their terrific appearance. Since these fish live in regions of tremendous pressure and perpetual darkness they are modified in many ways.

Chapter XV

How the Serpent Got Its Poison

By Claude E. Benson

SURELY of all creatures on the face of the earth none is more detested and dreaded than the snake. Examination of the evidence shows this feeling to be unfair and unreasonable. Of the entire genus of snakes some two-thirds are entirely innocuous, and of the dangerous remainder nine out of ten will fly rather than fight, while the really aggressive venomous snakes can be numbered on one's fingers. It is a case of a mischievous minority making itself unpleasantly notorious and thus discrediting an entire class.

From this minority the great constrictors may reasonably be excluded. One may naturally fear a creature which can hang from the drawing-room balcony by its tail and pick up the dustman out of the area, but a python, although by far the more dangerous, does not arouse in most people the feeling of repulsion associated, say, with a rattlesnake.

The strength of these great serpents is enormous. If any man possessed the mere "punch" of a boa, no pugilist could stay with him in either swiftness or effectiveness. Some years ago an "amateur" in serpents, who kept a kind of snake nursery not very far from London, was toying with his pets. All at once a boa—it was not more than eight feet long—which was lying on a table, without the slightest provocation let go at him with its head. It sent him flying into a corner of the room with all the wind knocked out of him and a bruise as big as a saucer on his breast-bone. Had it struck him on the solar plexus, it would in all probability have killed him.

That was with the closed mouth. Now a constrictor's jaws, like those of almost all non-venomous snakes, are equipped with three sets of teeth—upper, lower, and palatal: one on each side of the upper jaw, one on each side of the lower jaw, one on each side of the palate; six rows in all. Some have front teeth on the upper jaw, which is insignificant ; none have front teeth on the lower jaw—no snakes have. The importance of this fact, as will presently be shown, is very great in coming to a proper understanding of our subject.

The snake's teeth are long, sharp and recurved. If a python opened its mouth like an ordinary creature, a dog for instance, and bit like an ordinary creature, the bite would be sufficiently unpleasant, but a python does not open its mouth like an ordinary creature. It quite literally opens its entire head till the jaws are in the same plane, that is, at right angles to the neck, so that when it strikes every tooth tells—and the stroke is delivered with the force of a powerfully operated battering ram.

Such is the preliminary attack. The character of the decisive action may be gathered from the following incident. A man was performing at a circus in Spain with a seventeen-foot python. He had it twisted round him in the ordinary snake-charmer fashion, when something went wrong. Possibly he had forgotten to dope it by putting it in cold water and reducing it to the familiar comatose condition. Anyhow, without warning and seemingly without provocation, it drew its coils together. The man gave one shriek and dropped. The audience thought it was part of the performance. But it was not. That man's bones were found to be broken in eighty-four places.

Apart from these monsters, the non-venomous snake is one of the most harmless, helpless creatures of its inches imaginable. Deaf as a post all the year round, blind as a bat at intervals covering half a year, so delicate of frame that a tap from a cane will

W. S. Berridge

HOUSE-HAUNTING CHICKEN SNAKE

Those who live in the southern parts of the United States often encounter the chicken snake in their houses in some localities. Its colour is dark olive-green, with brown stripes and it gets its name from a reputation for entering chicken-runs and stealing young birds.

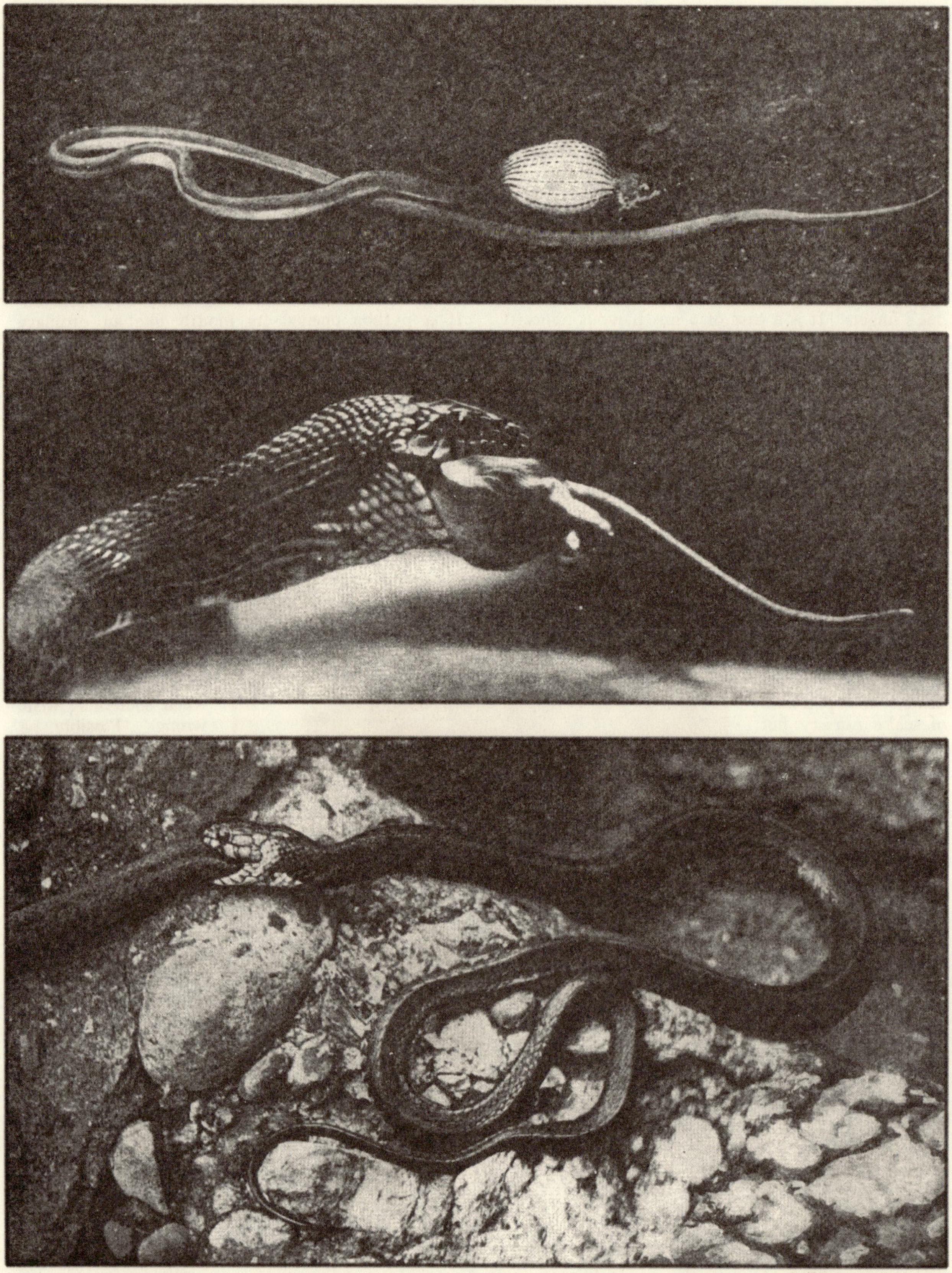

F. W. Bond and Neville Kingston

WONDERFUL SWALLOWING POWERS OF SOME MEMBERS OF THE SNAKE FAMILY

Grass snakes are the most familiar of English reptiles, although in the north they are rare, and in Scotland unknown. This species, of which we have an example here (bottom photograph) may be readily distinguished by the yellow band round its neck, whence it is also called the ringed snake. It is harmless to man but, sometimes attaining a length of five feet and over, can swallow a viper, as we see. Above are a pilot snake swallowing a rat, and (top) the egg-eating snake which has special growths on its spine for crushing eggs it has swallowed.

F. W. Bond

HOODS THAT MEAN DEATH: HAMADRYAD AND INDIAN COBRA

Cobras live in the jungle and, as a rule, avoid human beings, which is lucky since their bites have such venom that death occurs sometimes within two hours. The familiar feature of both cobra (top) and king cobra or hamadryad (bottom) is the so-called "hood" which is a temporary dilation of the skin of the neck used by the snake as a warning. When expanded the hood is supported by the front ribs which, in this part of the snake's body are specially adapted for the purpose. The hamadryad haunts ruined temples and feeds on other snakes

HOW SNAKES CLIMB TREES

Certain snakes have become expert tree climbers, working upwards from branch to branch or taking a turn with their tail round the bole and so pushing themselves upwards. Here are a coluber (bottom) and a royal python (top).

shatter the exquisite construction of its backbone. it still holds its own in the scheme of nature. It even thrives. Sometimes indeed it becomes a kind of household pet, as, for example, the rat snake in rat-infested establishments.

ALL snakes were innocuous once. The mamba, most dreaded and deadliest of all, would have been a first-class ratter and might have been a household pet had it only retained its original virtue. How came this fall from primeval innocence? The reply entails a short excursion into comparative anatomy.

The popular distinctions between the two reptiles, the snake and the lizard, may be dismissed in two words as irrelevant. All snakes are legless. A lizard without legs, such as the so-called Glass Snake, is very uncommon. A snake has neither eyelids nor external ears. Lizards have both. The distinction is in the chin. The chin of the lizard is joined by sutures, like that of the lord of creation, in fact. A snake has no chin at all, and here the significance of absence of front teeth on the lower jaw becomes manifest. Had the snake a teeth-bearing chin-bone the amazing and unique mechanism of its head would be an utter impossibility.

For a snake can take its head practically to pieces for swallowing purposes. It has a pair of lower jaw-bones, like other creatures, but they are connected at the fore end by a ligature which is capable of extension and also of contraction. The aft end is linked up in like manner with the skull, the only solidly built part of a snake, not socketed into the jaw as in mammals. Consequently, it does not matter if the mouthful is two or three sizes too large. The snake does not accommodate the morsel to the mouth but the mouth to the morsel. Of course, it ought to choke during the operation, but it gets over that difficulty by sticking its windpipe out of the corner of its mouth and sucking in air and provender at one and the same time by different channels. Once past the gullet the food goes down comfortably enough, despite its bulk. A snake has no breast-bone and its skin will stretch to requirements.

The process of feeding, that is of getting the food down the gullet, is as follows. The prey is first seized and, once it is entangled in the six rows of recurved teeth, escape by resistance is impossible. Then one of the lower jaws is hooked in hard and drawn back as far as it will go. A similar process takes place on the other side. The prey is thus dragged back into the mouth and down into the gullet by alternate movements of the independent lower jawbones. Vipers sometimes use their great fangs to assist the process, independently and without losing a drop of poison. This last is a marvel of mechanism. The prey glides in easily enough over the recurved points of the teeth, but it cannot wriggle forward, for wriggle it does. Generally speaking it goes down alive and kicking very hard.

Now, in the case of a frog or suchlike defenceless creatures, these struggles do not interfere with the process of deglutition. It is quite a different matter when the intended dinner is in the form of, say, a weasel. In that case the prey, like the frog, struggles to free itself but by different methods, to wit, by biting an avenue of escape out of the snake's skull. As the serpent can no more disgorge its prey than the prey can wriggle out, the upshot of such encounters is invariably a live weasel and a very dead snake.

Nature ofttimes provides safeguards for its weaklings most beautifully, for example, in the protective mimicry of the butterfly, most outrageously in the effluvium of the skunk, most appallingly in the venom of the serpent. If the mechanism of the snake's head is wonderful, the development of the poison mechanism is yet more marvellous. It must be remembered that the original object of this development was protective, to enable the snake to exist, with immunity from destruction. It became in the course of time a deadly peril to beasts and men. The process of development was on these lines.

A portion of the salivary gland, which lies behind the eye, was modified and transformed into a venom gland. From this a tube was laid along either upper jaw, terminating in a papilla in the centre of the gum. A groove was formed in the base of the eye-teeth on either side of the jaw. These are in pairs and are the front teeth. Snakes with this arrangement, unlike the constrictors alluded to, have no teeth across the front of the upper jaw. The groove, rudimentary at first, was extended in successive developments down to the tip of the fang, which also became through successive generations enormously enlarged. Round the venom gland was wound a powerful muscle which was inserted on the lower jaw, and this, when contracted, not only shuts the jaw but propels the venom along the tube and expels it by the papilla.

SUCH is a crude outline of the poison apparatus in the rough. The weak points are obvious. First, the snake could not close its mouth without expelling the poison and so wasting it. Secondly, there was no apparatus to ensure the poison being discharged down the groove of the fang into the wound. The first defect was remedied by a strong sphincter muscle close to the end of the duct which must be relaxed before any venom can escape, snap the snake never so viciously. It is this muscle which enables a viper to use its fangs to assist in getting its prey down without losing venom. The second defect was remedied by the fang sheath.

It must be understood that the fang, even among the less developed snakes, is a delicate instrument: in the great vipers it is very delicate, of unwieldy length and very lightly attached. If, for instance, one flicks a napkin at a viper and it strikes, a smart jerk will switch out all its functional fangs and the snake will be rendered entirely harmless. Only for a time, however. There is a reserve of fangs and the foremost of these are moved forward to take the place of those dislodged, a movement which is cunningly aided by the healing of the gum over the wound left by the accidental displacement.

Neville Kingston

SNAKE HEADS AND POISON FANGS

From the bottom upwards these photographs show: the severed head of a rattlesnake with the skin removed to reveal the poisoning equipment; a rattlesnake's head as seen in life; the head of a reticulated python and the jaws of a puff adder.

W. S. Berridge

WHIPSNAKE THAT STRIKES FROM AN AMBUSH IN A TREE

Matching perfectly the foliage amidst which it lurks the whipsnake kills its prey—bird or lizard—by making one or two coils round a branch with its tail and striking, the great length of its body giving it a formidable range of action. On the ground the whipsnake is awkward in its movements but in a tree its very thin and elongated body moves with alarming rapidity.

That these delicate weapons should be protected by a sheath, in the same way as a sword, is perhaps not so very remarkable. That the sheath should be formed by a prolongation of the gum is perhaps almost to be expected. What, however, is extraordinary is that this sheath when wrinkled up should form a shield which deflects the expelled venom right down into the open base of the fangs. Some of the venom always does escape. Buckland, the naturalist, nearly met his death through a drop of this free venom which he imagined had circulated through the body of a rat.

In Africa there is a horrid cobra, the ringhals, which invariably spits at you, although it has fangs and can use them. Moreover, it also invariably spits in your eye, which is disastrous for the sight.

This, then, is the combination. The snake strikes and the fang pierces. Here we have a slight wound which might be dangerous, even fatal, for there is generally a certain amount of stale venom remaining in the fang-groove, but this is not all. To discharge the venom the snake must snap its lower jaw, thus driving the fang home, and simultaneously contract the venom gland and expel the venom through the papilla whence it is deflected into the open base of the fangs, down the groove therein, out at the point, and into the uttermost part of the wound. When a healthy, deadly snake thus bites home, the chances of recovery are remote indeed. Most of the cures that are effected are for mere scratches or half-bites. The remote ancestors of this dangerous family were content with quite small venom fangs, and retained a number of solid teeth behind them to assist in the process of swallowing. The conception was to strike the prey, let the venom do its paralysing work, and then, as soon as all danger of reprisal was over, to banquet.

To ensure escape from retaliation, it was desirable to get the head out of danger as quickly as possible. Consequently the most specialised snake will switch back its head the moment the blow has been delivered. It looks ridiculous to see a big rattler jerk back its head after having struck a guinea pig, but it is a very interesting example of atavism and an illustration of the why of the swift recovery after the stroke. When angry, a venomous snake will sometimes hold on like a bulldog. There is a historic example recorded in the last chapter of the Acts of the Apostles. That snake was a sand natter, which has a bad reputation for temper.

In the process of time the functional fangs were enlarged, the solid teeth behind discarded, and the tooth-bearing bone shortened. At the same time a short, insignificant bone, between the inner end of the tooth-bearing bone and the skull, was prolonged till in highly specialised snakes, such as the cobra, it now occupies two-thirds of the length of the upper jaw. A convenient name for this is the transverse bone. Naturally in the process most, sometimes all, of the solid teeth on the upper jaw were discarded so that the highly specialised venomous snake now possesses only four rows of solid teeth, those on each side of the palate and of the lower jaw, those on the upper jaw being supplanted by the deadly poison fangs.

THE reason for these structural alterations was that the fang had grown too big for the mouth. It became essential to impart a certain amount of mobility to the fang-bearing bone, so that the fang might lie quietly back normally and be erected when needed for action. This bone was therefore shortened and modified and to the inner end of each transverse bone a muscle was attached. This muscle was then brought forward and fastened off in the centre of the front of the palate. It looks very much like a bowstring at full stretch, and when contracted it pulls the transverse bone forward. The front end of the transverse bone then presses against the fang-bearing bone, causing it to revolve partially, thus erecting the fang all ready for use.

W. S. Berridge

BLACK CRIBO OF SOUTH AMERICA AND THE BURROWING BOA

Belonging to the same family as the moon-snake is the cribo (bottom) one of a genus containing about seventeen species found in South America and as far north as Mexico. Many are venomous, but Cribo never attacks man, and is only active at night. In the upper photograph is a burrowing boa or shielded cryx found in Northern Africa and Southern and Central Asia. When hungry this serpent will crawl down crannies in the rocks in search of prey and will also burrow in the sand, and from this characteristic it gets its name.

Natural History. N.Y.

ANACONDA, GREATEST OF THE SERPENTS, BY THE BANKS OF THE AMAZON

Ten yards is a fearsome length for a snake, but a full-grown anaconda sometimes exceeds even that. It is non-poisonous, nor indeed has it any reason to rely on venom. Its teeth decrease in size from the front of the formidable jaws to the back, and when striking, its jaws are opened so wide as to be at right angles to its body. The power in the blow it can give is enormous, but even more deadly are its powers of strangulation. The anaconda is native to the dense Amazon forests where it spends much of its time more or less immersed in water.

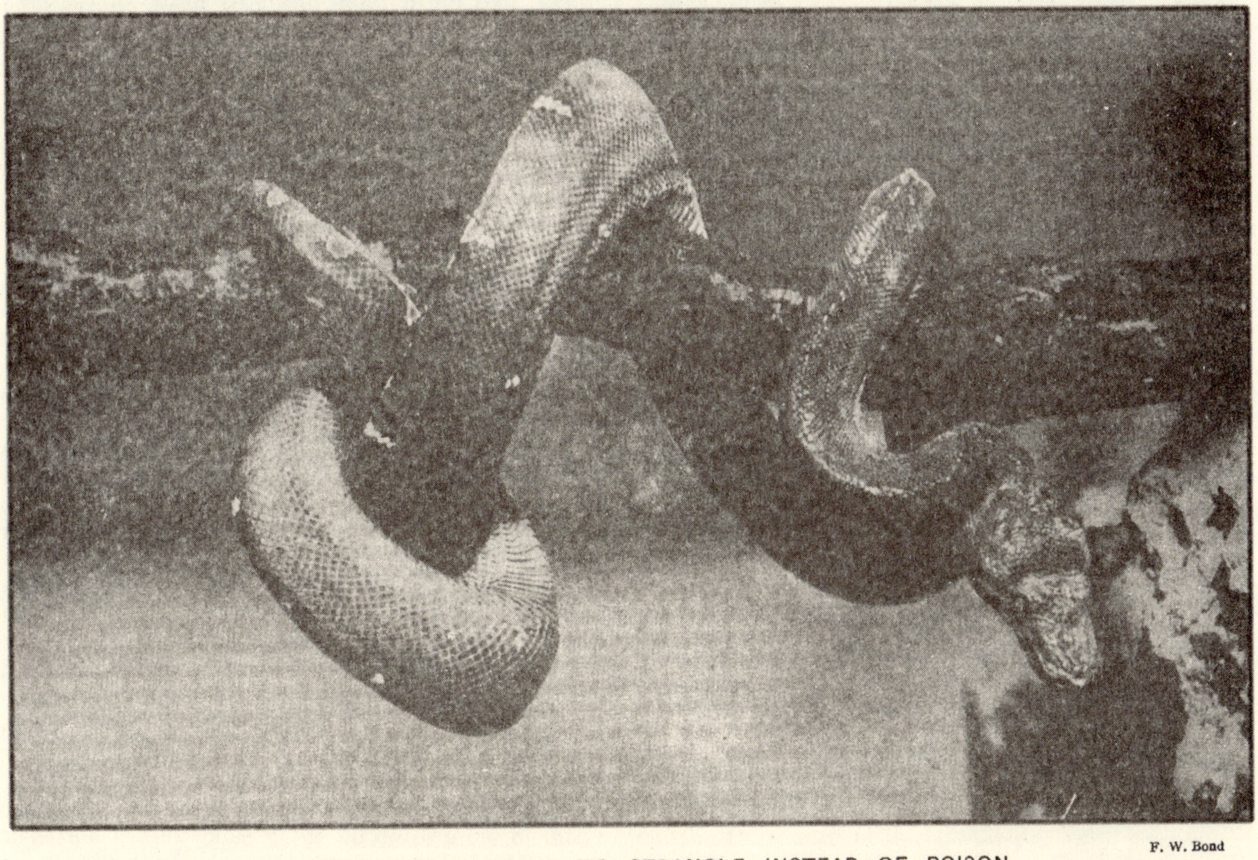

F. W. Bond

BOA WHICH HAS LEARNT TO STRANGLE INSTEAD OF POISON

Confined to South America save for one species, which is found in the great island of Madagascar the boa is, like the anaconda, a snake which kills by crushing its victims within its coils. It feeds on the smaller mammals, from rats to the lesser kinds of deer, and hunts by night. Its range is from Venezuela to well within the Argentine. There are a number of species of which we see here the boa constrictor (top), which may attain a length of twelve feet, and has a skin handsomely marked in yellow and brown, and (below) the tree-boa.

The Serpent's Poison

Natural History, New York

BRIGHTLY-MARKED COPPERHEAD POSSESSED OF DEADLY VENOM

One of the deadliest of snakes in North America is the copperhead, which is widely distributed throughout the United States save in the northern parts. The whole body is a beautiful copper colour with the head lighter than the rest. Its average length is about three feet, and it is found in the tall grass near water and feeds on mice and birds. The jaws have a particularly wide gape. Another name for the copperhead is moccasin snake, and part of its deadliness lies in the fact that it strikes without any warning.

Such, in brief, is the wonderful story of the evolution of the venom fang of the poisonous elapines, of which the best-known representative is the cobra. The cobra possesses a pair of large fangs on either side of the jaw, and two or three faintly grooved teeth behind them. In the most highly specialised of these snakes, the coral and the mamba, only the fangs remain.

THE vipers started from the other end of the jaw—that is, from the back. The earlier specimens are known as the back-fanged snakes. Here, again, the gradual development can be clearly traced from an insignificant little fang close against the gullet, which could not conceivably begin to operate till the prey was half-swallowed, to a formidable array of big fangs behind the eye. Then there comes a hiatus, an unfilled gap between the back-fanged snakes and the vipers.

These last boast only a pair of venom fangs a side on a very short bone. All the rest of the upper jaw is occupied by the toothless transverse bone. An examination of the fang-bearing bone is illuminating. What has happened is clear. As the elapines discarded all their solid teeth behind the fangs, so the vipers have discarded not only all the solid teeth in front of the fangs, but most of the jawbone with them, and, with this section of the jawbone, all the fangs but a pair on each side.

The fang mobility achieved by this arrangement is amazing; the sweep of the point from rest to action passes through a quarter of a circle. The fangs themselves normally lie back along the palate, and the mouth has to be opened wide to permit of their erection. There is no difficulty about this, for the viper, like the python, opens its head till the jaws are in the same plane, the fangs being incidentally erected till they are at right angles to the jaw. But what about closing the mouth with a snap? Must not the fangs drive through the lower jaw? It has been observed that the ligature of the chin can be contracted, and the viper, when it misses a stroke, contracts its chin so that the fangs slide back outside to be tucked away comfortably later on.

It is frequently stated that the snake has hollow or perforated fangs. As a matter of fact, it has not, although the mistake is quite a pardonable one. What has happened is this. A groove was, as has been noted, formed in the base of the solid tooth to act as a channel for the venom. This groove was afterwards extended down the entire length of the fang, but still a great deal of venom escaped between the edges. To remedy this the edges began to fold over towards each other, gradually narrowing the channel of issue—in the cobra they are about a hair's breadth apart—till they finally coalesced as in the case of the mamba, the coral, and all the vipers. At first sight it looks as if the fang had been drilled down the centre, but on examination, the line of juncture can be detected even with the naked eye. A section of a fang is interesting. It shows the process of incurvation quite clearly; and it is seen that the curved outer coating of dentine surrounding the venom channel encloses a semi-circle of pulp.

We read of snakes springing at people. A snake can no more jump off the ground than a horsehair cushion. The most it can do is to raise the fore third of its body. The typical cobra does so, and its stroke is forward and downward after the manner of a cut. Now, inasmuch as to make the bite absolutely effective the cobra must close its jaws as the fangs go home, it is clear that the stroke must be relatively ineffective along a considerable portion of the line. If one places one's elbow on the table with the hand loosely open and the palm down, and then slaps one's palm on the table, the danger-points will be just where the fingers naturally straighten themselves and just before the finish.

The viper strikes, as a rule, from coil, after the manner of a thrust, and is rather more likely to get home. On the other hand, the toxic properties of cobra venom are more active than those of viperine, and so the balance is evened up. It is interesting to note that viper venom is practically identical with, though more powerful than, that of the back-fanged snakes, thus establishing the connexion between the two which has sometimes been questioned owing to the hiatus in the transition process. Were it not that sundry visitors to the Zoo still speak of a snake's tongue as the "sting," it would seem unnecessary to state that the tongue's chief use is that of a feeler. Consider what all this means. It means that the once harmless snake, in order to be able to secure its prey with immunity, has, in a period unknown, developed an apparatus whereby paralysing venom can be sent direct to its mark with the least possible waste, that it has evolved most efficient weapons for this purpose, weapons which can be quickly and automatically replaced in case of loss or injury, weapons which it keeps protected in a sheath when not in action, and that it has constructed a most delicate mechanism for the elevation and retraction of the fangs, both of which actions take place within the time occupied by the snapping of the jaws.

Nothing has been said here about sea snakes, but it may be mentioned in conclusion that whereas the venom of the mamba paralyses warm-blooded mammals, that of the venomous sea snake, a horrid creature with a head not much bigger than a thumb, paralyses cold-blooded fishes.

F. W. Bond

ASP, OR HORNED VIPER, A TERROR OF THE SANDS

Cleopatra, it will be remembered, met her death—as the story goes—by the bite of an asp which she had procured for the purpose. There are two species of this deadly little snake, one in the Sahara and the other in Egypt, and both lie half buried in the sand awaiting their prey. The bite is very deadly and seems to be frequently administered entirely without provocation. The horned viper has the power of rubbing its coils together when excited, so that the friction on the scales causes a rustling noise.

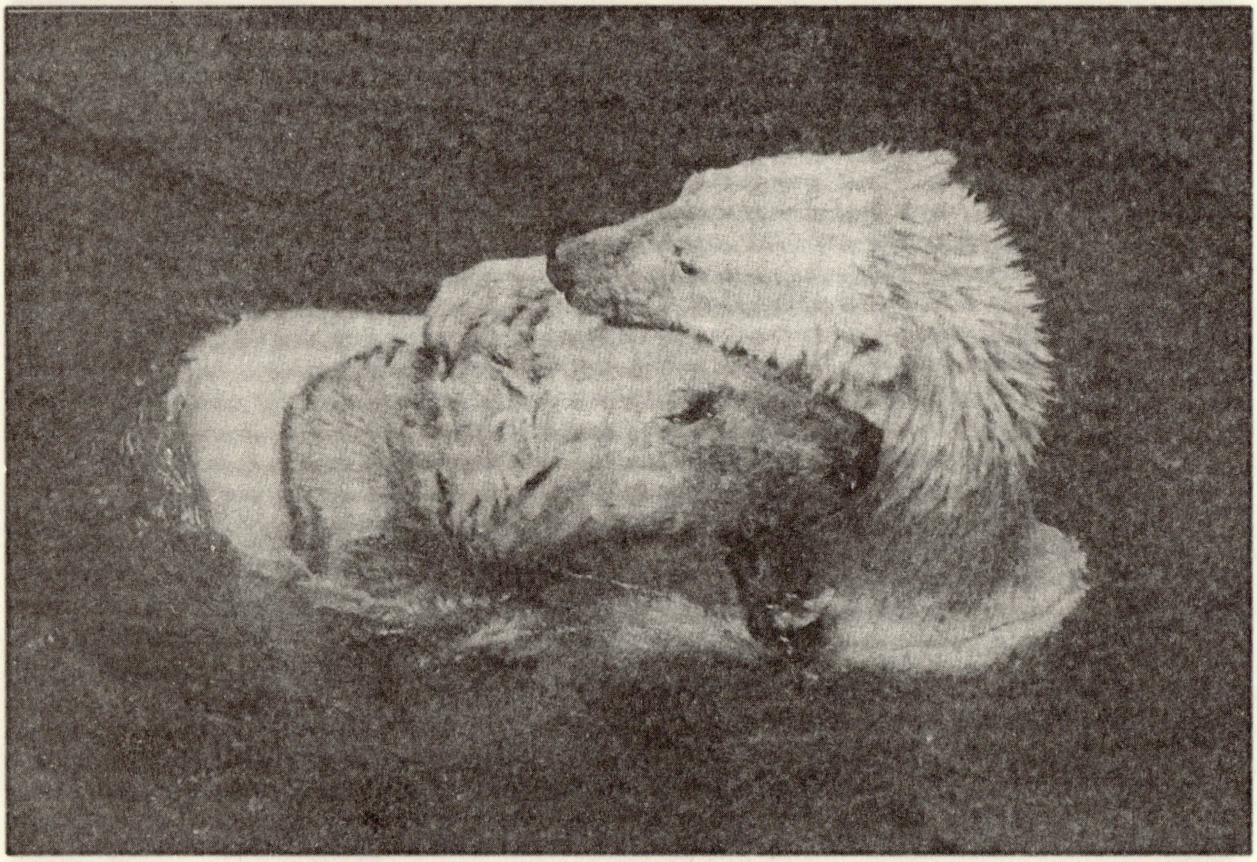

Neville Kingston

PLAYTIME AT THE ZOO: POLAR BEARS IN HIGH SPIRITS

When the polar bears become playful they collect a crowd as quickly as any animals in the Zoo. No doubt the fact that their gambols are amphibian is largely responsible for the size of the audience. There are special windows cut in the concrete wall near the bottom of their swimming pool and one can peer through the green murk and see dim white forms whirl past, or an inquisitive snout come right up to the glass. Wrestling and mutual ducking (bottom) are favourite games, and sometimes a lucky bear gets a ball to play with.

Chapter XVI

Playtime Among the Birds and Beasts

By W. P. Pycraft

Author of "The Infancy of Animals"

On the subject of the play of animals we really know very little. And this is partly because we neglect the many opportunities presented to us of carefully watching animals in their natural state. Since we shoot them, and hunt them on every possible occasion, it is not to be wondered at that they flee from us at sight. That this behaviour has been instilled into them by painful experience is shown by the fact that when explorers have landed on islands uninhabited by man, or among the vast penguin colonies of the Antarctic, neither beast nor bird showed any fear.

Now and again some lover of nature will contrive to lie in concealment in the known haunts of some particular species and patiently wait till, believing the dreaded enemy to be far away, a whole family party will perhaps creep forth from their hiding-place and resume the occupation suddenly broken by the intruder who means no harm. Most people, surely, have read Charles Kingsley's delightful description of young otters at play in his Water Babies. But how many even of those who hunt otters regularly have ever seen the like?

What is the origin, and the meaning of this "play"? And at what stage in the evolution of animal life does it make its first appearance? We may be fairly certain that play has no place among the lowly protozoa, nor among the fixed sea-anemones—for play means movement. But we may be tempted to regard the aerial evolutions of may-flies and midges as a form of play. As I write, myriads of these minute flies, or "midges," are dancing in the sunlight all around me. And a few moments ago, in the room I have just left, a half-dozen of the small species of house-fly known as "fannia," were gyrating madly in wide circles in the centre of the room, every now and then twisting and turning around one another with incredible speed, as though performing some favourite waltz! None of these performers was feeding, nor were they searching for food. May we not suppose, then, that they were animated by the sheer "joy of living"? They were, in short, "playing."

Yet it is curious that only some winged insects, and these are all adults, be it noted, display this most desirable emotion. The bees, for example, have no playtime; ceaseless labour is theirs, save only in the case of the drones among the hive-bees. The dance of the fireflies at night seems to be a form of play. Yet there are few other beetles which give themselves up to such frivolity. Among the Invertebrates, in short, play seems to be an impulse possessed only by some insects. One can hardly imagine a playful slug; nor are crabs or starfish likely to disport themselves in this way!

Among the Vertebrates we find the first apparent evidence of play in the fishes. The mad flights of the flying-fish are generally attributed to frenzied efforts to escape capture by under-water pursuers. But since the performers commonly cross one another's tracks in all directions, it would seem that on such occasions they are merely "playing." And here, we have play with a "meaning." They are "practising" for more serious moments; for their strange "wings" have undoubtedly been evolved to enable them to escape under-water pursuit. If there be fishes that play one would expect to find similar cases among the frogs, toads, and newts, since they are higher in the scale of life; but no such cases have ever been recorded, nor do we find any among the reptiles.

I can imagine some of my readers remarking that newts, at any rate, "play," and so do water-tortoises, crocodiles, and lizards: quite so. But this brings me to a quite important phase of my argument. We must distinguish between different kinds of play; expressing different impulses, or emotions. There is the play of the midges and house-flies to which I have already alluded. The performers here are staid adults; and their gyrations seem to be pointless; at most a mere expression of physical fitness, yielding, doubtless, at least a vague sense of pleasure. And there is the play of young animals, which has a very definite meaning, as I hope to show. Finally, there is a whole series of complex forms of "play" commonly associated with sexual maturity, and described as "courtship" displays.

Reference has just been made to "staid adults" among the insects whose play is apparently meaningless. But among the higher animals we find innumerable cases of adult play which has no reference to "love-displays."

Those who have taken long sea-voyages must often have watched the play of porpoises and dolphins round the ship. This, at any rate, seems to be the most reasonable interpretation of their gambollings, and the huge humpback and other whales have been seen leaping out of the water and falling with a resounding splash with an abandon which suggests nothing else than an expression of pent-up vigour that must find an outlet.

Animals in captivity, if they be not too closely confined, display no less animation. Monkeys at the Zoo, for example, are particularly playful. And I remember watching, some years ago, two polar bears at play. The game was, apparently, to push one another into the swimming pool. The successful one then leaped in after his playmate when there began a tussle, each apparently trying to push the other under water. As soon as one or the other succeeded in making his escape there began a wild race round the edge of the pool and the jostling began again!

The play of a cat with a mouse is of another kind. The rough and tumble scrimmages of monkeys and

F. W. Bond

"MONKEY TRICKS!" A MERRY TRIO OF ORANG UTAN AND TWO CHIMPANZEES

While the orang-utan (bottom) swings from the steel supports of the roof of his cage with solemn enjoyment, a neighbour chimpanzee finds enough puzzles in a mandoline to keep him amused almost indefinitely. The other chimpanzee (top left) is sitting in what is really the remains of a trapeze. The wooden bar has been wrenched out of place by mischief-making hands, and the ropes thoroughly well entangled. Almost any time is playtime among the monkeys and all but the largest apes.

Ne ihe kin ston

"KING OF THE CASTLE" AND BEGGING GAMES PLAYED IN CAPTIVITY

Certain games are common to the young of animals and man. and a kind of "king of the castle" with a basket for the castle was often played at the London Zoological Gardens by a certain tiger cub and his lion cub friend. The defence and attack are obviously being carried out with spirit. In the lower or bear section of the Mappin Terraces the begging antics displayed are always a "good draw." In the upper photograph there is a polar bear with a brown bear making belief to beg on the concrete edge of the trench which takes the place of bars.

Neville Kingston

TWO DIFFERENT WAYS IN WHICH ANIMALS PLAY DEMONSTRATED BY A YOUNG TIGER AND A BEAR

There seem to be two distinct kinds of play among the animals. The more usual is the game involving the practice and perfection of some feat which is useful in their ordinary life or, in the case of caged animals, of what would be useful in their wild state. But some animals do really play, sometimes, for the fun of the thing. The young tiger playing with his keeper is really performing, in a very mild way, the same evolutions as it would if the man had attacked it in real earnest. To have even a young tiger's paw drawn across the face must take some getting used to. The Indian bear, on the other hand, which is trifling with a piece of ice, is obviously not practising anything but just amusing himself and, incidentally, ourselves as well.

Neville Kingston

THE EARLIEST PLAYTIME OF ALL: ZEBRA COLT WITH ITS MOTHER

If an animal is going to play, its first games and practical jokes will be with its mother. Watch a kitten being washed as an illustration. But an example of this fact very seldom seen is shown splendidly here where we have a young zebra upon its hind legs to bite and jostle its parent with the invincible high spirits of the young animal which as yet has no care even in captivity. Wild animals seem fierce enough to human beings and so the patience often shown by the adult under much juvenile troubling appears the more interesting.

bears and the racing exploits of porpoises may probably be regarded as physical exercises, taken, albeit unconsciously, to "keep fit"; and one may, perhaps, regard the play of the cat with a mouse as an instinctive effort to keep in practice. All the cat tribe behave after this fashion, for they have to effect their captures by a stealthy approach and a sudden spring demanding quickness of eye and stroke. The dog tribe chase their prey and kill it as soon as it has been run down. They have, therefore, no incentive to defer the killing.

But we all know how much a dog likes to chase a ball which he will bring back time after time to be thrown again. Dogs love to simulate anger at any attempt to rob them of what, for the moment, is their "prey." I have in mind a small terrier belonging to my daughter. Bonzo loved to seize on a piece of stick, lay it at her feet, and invite her to throw it away. Any attempt to take it from him after its "capture" was met by fierce snarls and growls, as he held the precious capture between his teeth. But these "angry" sounds were but make-believe, fo presently he would release his hold and stand ex pectantly to have it once more thrown into the air Here, be it noted, is behaviour reminiscent of th wild dog. Generations of domestication have no quelled these primal instincts.

Many forms of play have their roots, so to speak in behaviour which domestication has almost deprivec of meaning, and certainly of usefulness. Thus horse when feeling particularly "skittish," will rear up o their hind legs and strike out with their fore-feet and will then presently turn and kick with their hinc feet. Since these are now shod broken legs may result, but in the original wild horse this probably very rarely happened.

And now let us turn to the play of young animals. This is not merely the sign of boisterous good health, nor is it purposeless. It is also worth noting that only some kinds of young animals play, and among these that play is in the nature of coming events which cast their shadows before. It is a preparation for

Neville Kingston

CONTORTIONS OF THE BABY LEOPARD WHEN REALLY EXCITED

Cats of all kinds are the champions at twisting and squirming, and the kitten, when worked up, goes through the most extraordinary contortions. Just so the baby leopard will roll on its back, tearing madly with all its claws, then leap up and wildly paw the air. This photograph caught it in mid-career, captured a split second's worth of the lithe savagery of its movement and gives it to us here in all its natural extravagance of gesture and unrestrainable fierceness of expression.

crises in after life; for activities which, unless they be efficiently performed, will lead to an early death.

Caterpillars, which we sometimes forget are young butterflies, or moths, do not play. The whole of this stage of their existence has to be spent in long bouts of feeding, broken by fasts as the successive moults are due. Indeed, there is no evidence of play taking place among any of the invertebrates while immature.

But watch a kitten at play. Its "games" have reference to mouse-catching. Sometimes it will be noticed that kittens throw themselves down on their sides and tear imaginary victims with their hind feet, whereby we may see how larger victims than mice are rent to pieces. Puppies and fox-cubs play at fighting, and thereby, though unconsciously, gain skill for real combats which will be inevitable later.

YOUNG sheep and goats play at butting one another, as well as leaping. This is true not merely of wild species, but even of our own farm animals. They will never need the skill this early training gives, but it is interesting to note that they retain the instincts of their wild ancestors in undiminished force.

One might go on multiplying instances of this kind, but enough has been said to bring home the fact that "play" in young animals is no meaningless activity but a most interesting and instructive foreshadowing of events wherein only the efficient survive.

And now we must turn to another very remarkable series of activities commonly regarded as so many forms of "play," but which have no counterpart, no preliminary forecasts, in the immature stages.

These refer to what are called "courtship" displays. If such be "play," then it is play of a very different kind from that so far described. For "play," so far as we have discussed it, is a form of "make-believe," but the instances now to be considered have a direct and immensely important object—the continuation of the race.

Maturity, in so far as the animal world is concerned, in only gradually attained, and most animals become sexually mature before they are fully developed.

When sexual maturity is arrived at, certain glands, and especially the reproductive glands, discharge substances known as "hormones," which effect profound changes in behaviour, in addition to their functions in regard to reproduction, and the development of what are known as the "secondary sexual characters." But it will be easier to interpret this behaviour after a few typical examples have been given. Let it suffice to say, for the moment, that "courtship displays" are found only where the two sexes are represented by two individuals leading a free, separate existence, though even here conjugation may be effected without a "display." The butterflies and moths, for example, make no "courtship displays," but are drawn together by scent, which is generally diffused by the female, and can be detected by the male over great distances. But this by the way. Displays of the kind now to be discussed are to be found in creatures as low in the scale of life as spiders, and scorpions, and end only with Man.

LET me cite first the most astounding story of the spider's courtship. To begin with, he first spins a silken web and thereon discharges the all-important spermatozoa. He then draws up this fertilizing fluid into his hollow palps, and then approaches the female with fear and trepidation, as well he may; for unless he keep all his wits about him he will be promptly seized, and eaten! No two species behave in the same manner at this critical time, but one which I have in mind, *Saitis pulex*—it has, unfortunately, no name in common speech—approaches the female of his choice, walking as delicately as Agag, till within a few inches of her; then, lowering the legs of one side, till his body is tilted over towards her, he moves in a semicircle before her, then reverses the movement in the opposite direction, gradually getting nearer. She now makes a dash towards him, but he, fearful, raises his two front legs as if to ward her off, and retreats backwards. Again and again these movements are repeated, till at last he whirls madly round and round her, and she too starts whirling in a giddy maze. There is a halt, and all begins over again. Then she slowly moves under him and the mating is accomplished! Unless he can instantly escape he will be eaten!

Under the fever of love even the dull and apathetic crocodile will execute most undignified caperings in the presence of his mate. He will twist and turn, or rather twirl, on the surface of his chosen pool, with head and tail raised high in air, and his capacious barrel of a body swollen out to bursting-point. These antics are performed to the accompaniment of bellowings and roars heard at no other season of the year. But more than this, an appeal is also made to the nose, as well as to the eyes of his apathetic mate, for during all this parade of his amorous feelings he exudes from glands in the lower jaw and tail an overpowering odour of musk. At last his protestations have their reward, but the point to be noticed is that the emotions of the female are only to be aroused by an immense expenditure of energy on the part of the male.

These "love-displays" attain to a wonderful variety among the birds. That strange species the frigate-bird, for instance, has a very striking form of love-play. Under the beak is an inflatable scarlet bag. During his moments of amorous excitement this is distended till it looks like a great scarlet balloon. A dozen males may sit together on the branch of a tree overhanging the sea, with their air-sacs thus inflated. As soon as a female approaches they utter a strange cry, like wow-wow-wow-wow, and then clatter their beaks like so many castanets. Some will then fly out over the sea and prepare for another display!

Neville Kingston

A TOY TO BEGUILE THE SCORPION'S SPARE TIME

It would not occur to everyone that the scorpion might like something to play with during its leisure. But an indiarubber mouse seems to have provided some diversion to this particular one, even if its actions were not very "playful" to look at. We see it in the act of pretending to kill the mouse. It will, presumably, never be known whether this was a game so far as the scorpion was concerned or whether it merely disliked the indiarubber mouse. At any rate, the spectators had plenty of harmless fun.

Nevi.le Kin ston

THE HORNBILL FINDS A NEW PLAYMATE AND DANCES IN TRIUMPH

Africa and India are the dwelling-places of the hornbill, but although so far from home, the bird is light-hearted enough in its cage. In the wild state it spends most of its time on the ground, and is but a slow, unwieldy flier, so that it does not miss the freedom of the sky as so many of the larger birds seem to do who must sit ever with eager wings folded. Below one of these birds is examining an indiarubber frog, and above we see it, filled with the joy of life, executing a kind of hornbill hornpipe.

Neville Kingston

PENGUIN AND PELICANS IN PLAYFUL MOOD

The same indiarubber frog that was lent to the hornbill seen in another page was tried on the penguin as a toy (bottom) and placed in front of a piece of fish. The first thing the penguin did was to remove the food out of his new playmate's reach. The pelicans (top) always provide amusement whether in a frisky mood or not as they waddle about in their pen. Here we see two of them performing some strange antics with their long bills and evidently enjoying a game that two can play at.

Nymph at pond bottom

After about eleven months

It climbs a plant

Splits its skin

Begins to emerge

It rests for a little

Releases its tail

Five minutes later

The wings are stretched

They are dried

The perfect insect

MARVELLOUS METAMORPHOSIS OF THE DRAGON-FLY FROM THE SWIMMING GRUB TO THE BEAUTY OF THE AIR

During the long process of change which the dragon-fly grub undergoes there is no resting as in the case of the caterpillar. The grub or nymph, as we see it in the extreme top left photograph, lives a life of continuous activity at the bottom of its pond, preying on other water insects. This it does by seizing its victim in a massive and powerful pair of jaws which convey the food to the mandibles. The nymph is also provided with a special means of locomotion, consisting of an apparatus for sucking water into the body and then expelling it, so that the reaction drives the creature forward. About twelve months are spent in the water, and then the nymph climbs up a plant, its skin splits and the flying insect emerges to its life in the sunshine. Photographs by J. J. Ward

Chapter XVII

The Amazing Round of Insect Life

By Edward Step, F.L.S.

Author of "Marvels of Insect Life"

When we consider that the insects are at once the most numerous in kinds and the most extravagantly fertile of all land animals (some fishes are more prolific), it is astonishing that through the ages man has learned so little about them.

Of a few we have discovered a trifle, knowledge forced on us often owing to their power of causing us personal annoyance, or by their utilising our food supplies for their own sustenance; and from this very imperfect information we judge and condemn the entire race. We make an exception in the case of the honey-bee, because we are able to rob it of the fruits of its industry. We also welcome the ladybird to our gardens, not only because it is brightly coloured, but we have read that it helps to keep down the greenfly pest. Certain flies and bugs assist in that work, but seldom receive recognition or thanks from the gardener. The female glow-worm, too, is sacrosanct because of her mystic light more than as an acknowledgment of her destruction of snails. Few of us know it as a beetle; and if we met with it in the daytime, when the luminosity is switched off, its fate would be that of other "creepy-crawly things."

How these creatures in summer become suddenly so abundant as to force themselves upon the attention of the least observant is still to most of us a mystery. Their prevalence is accomplished in a variety of ways and at diverse stages in the life of the insects in question, which know in some subtle fashion when it is the time for activity. In some form or other they have been with us through the leafless, flowerless months, and know more of probable weather changes than does the Air Ministry. The parent insect may lay a batch of eggs in autumn, and these will remain until the appropriate food plant is active, when the eggs hatch and the young larvae begin feeding; or the gravid female may pass the winter in secure retirement, coming out in spring to deposit her eggs on the new leaves. In other cases it is the larvae, hatched in autumn, that hibernate, resuming their active feeding in spring; more frequently the winter is passed in the chrysalis stage, a method that enables the perfect insect to emerge with freshness in spring, mate, and produce a new generation.

But for some of the insects that we see here in summer the winter climate of Britain is, usually, too severe for their survival in any stage; and for the following year's representatives of these species we are indebted to the enterprise of female immigrants from the Continent that have flown the Channel or the North Sea; these lay their eggs here in early summer. Without these reinforcements we should have to remove the Large Garden White, the Painted Lady and the Clouded Yellow butterflies from the list of British butterflies.

The Painted Lady is a notorious migrant in many parts of the world; and in most years enormous swarms of it leave its headquarters in North Africa for other countries. Our own share of these reaches us in successive waves in May and June, sometimes again in September. These lay their eggs on our thistles, and from the eggs are developed the home-grown butterflies we see when autumn comes.

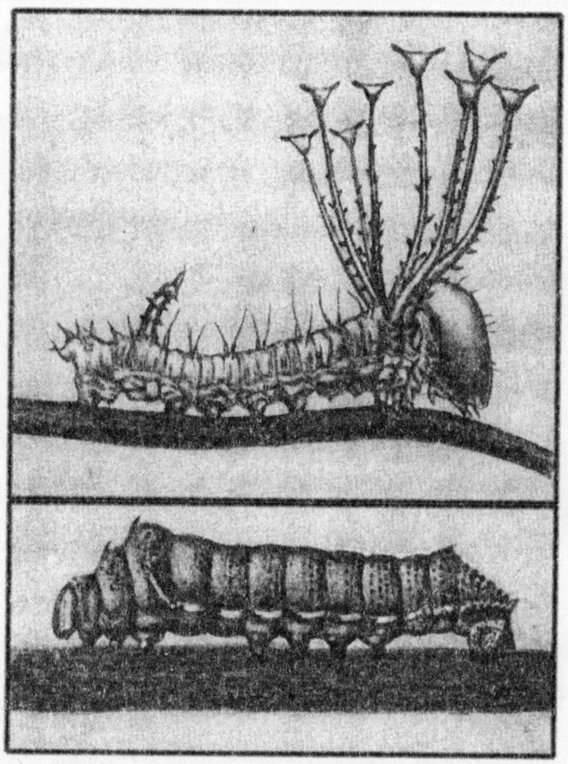

L. H. Jouvet

WEIRDEST OF CATERPILLARS

Caterpillars are extremely vulnerable as they lie on or crawl about plants. Some species, such as S ssphinx molina, shown here in two stages (the top one magnified), have developed growths like tentacles presumably to terrify attackers.

The common course of butterfly development, under the name of the "metamorphosis of insects," is one of the elementary lessons in natural history, but the details are often forgotten and need restating. The egg—variable in shape, and often beautifully decorated with symmetrical patterns in relief—hatches, and a minute caterpillar emerges and begins to attack the green food proper for its kind, which it finds ready to hand. Some, by way of appetiser, begin by consuming the egg-shell.

Throughout the caterpillar stage the insect feeds almost continuously, growing rapidly and, in consequence, needing to cast its distended skin about five times, each day consuming food equal to many times its own weight. The caterpillars of most butterflies complete their growth in

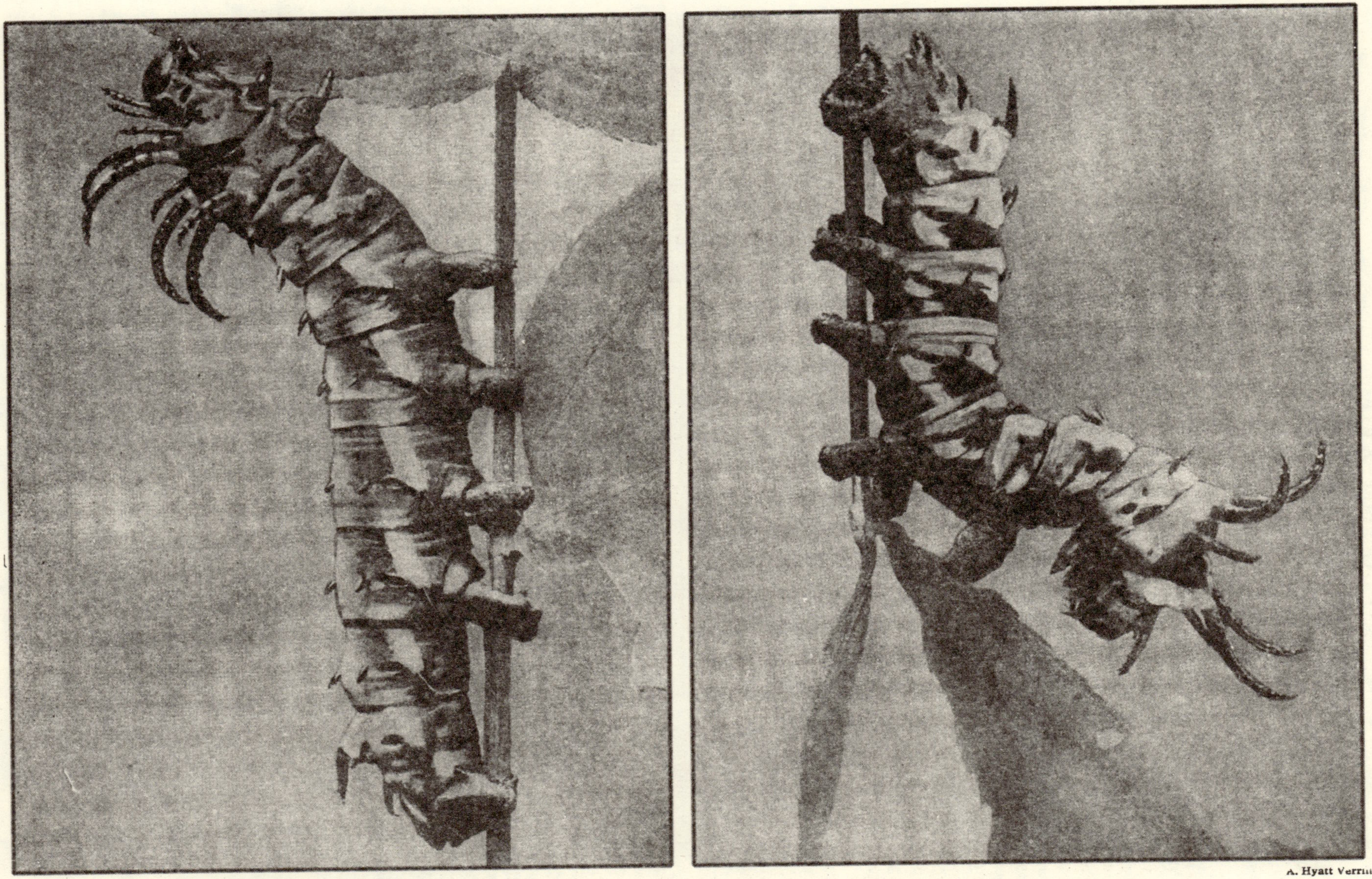

A. Hyatt Verrill

FEEDING AND RESTING POSITIONS OF THE EVER-HUNGRY CATERPILLAR OF CITHERONIA REGALIS

There is no hint in the appearance of this strange-looking creature that it will eventually turn into the moth which we see on the opposite page. The caterpillar of Citheronia Regalis, seen here in its actual size, is rather alarming when viewed at such close quarters. In the left photograph it is in its feeding position with hungry jaws fastened to a leaf. On the right is the same caterpillar in the position it adopts just before beginning its change into a chrysalis. Notice the strange plume-like appendages on the head apparently calculated to repel even a hungry enemy.

This giant caterpillar is found along the eastern sea-board of America. Notice that in feeding it hangs upright but that just before becoming a chrysalis, it hangs head downwards.

Pupa and cast larval skin

Freshly hatched caterpillar, magnified

Pupa, natural size

Full-grown caterpillar, natural size

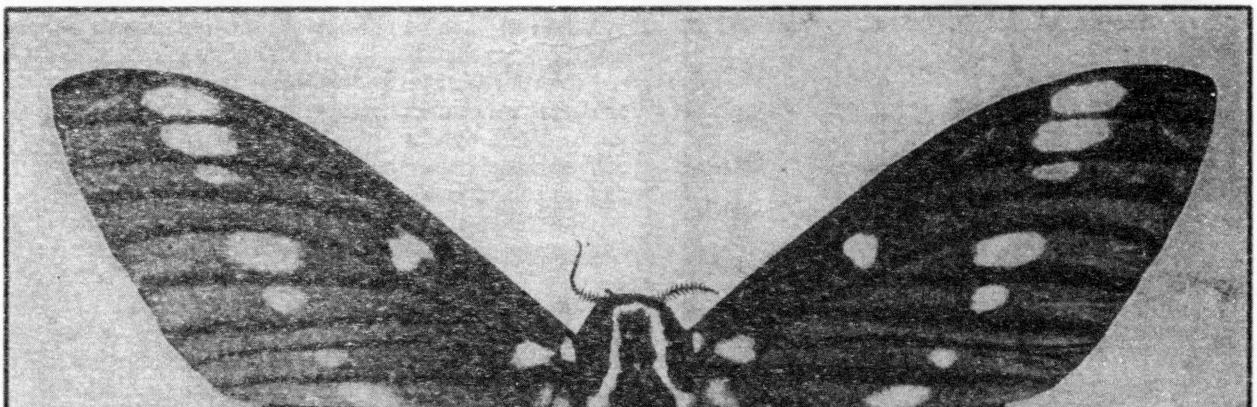

A. Hyatt Verrill

The male moth, natural size

STAGES IN THE STRANGE TRANSFORMING OF CATERPILLAR INTO MOTH

Many caterpillars make their first meal upon the remains of the egg from which they have hatched. They find themselves already deposited on the plant or tree which is suited for their food, and so can settle down at once to eating. Quickly the growth goes on, necessitating a series of new skins, each skin splitting and revealing the caterpillar in a new one. Finally, a kind of varnish is exuded which hardens into the outer shell of the chrysalis whence the perfect moth will emerge so utterly different. The photographs show the moth Citheronia regalis.

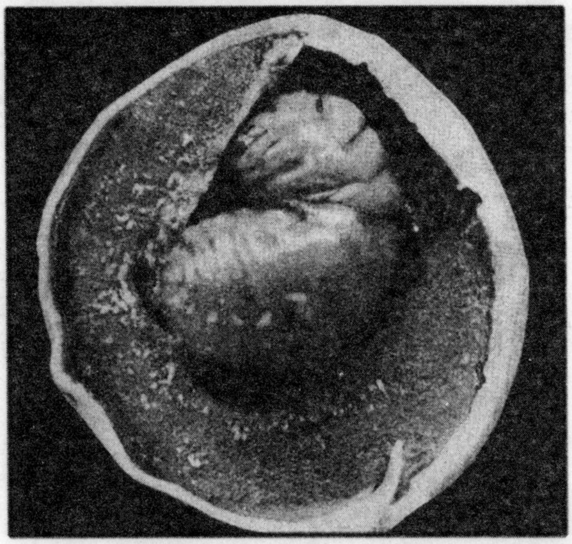

H Bastin

DESTRUCTIVE GRUB OF THE PEA-WEEVIL

While many of the beetle family do much good work, there are certain nefarious members, among them the pea-weevil. The lower photograph shows the grub as it lives and feeds on its host. Above is the creature into which it eventually turns.

a couple of months; those of the goat and leopard moths, feeding in the wood of living trees, spread the process over several years. When the requisite amount of reserve material has been accumulated the caterpillar throws off its skin once more, but this time a different form is disclosed.

What we see now is the undeveloped butterfly or moth, showing the form of its wings, legs and antennae covered by a protective coating of varnish. The internal organs of the caterpillar have been broken down into a semi-fluid condition, from which the organs of the adult insect must be built up on a different plan. The caterpillar jaws that had been fitted for cutting up vegetable solids would be of no use to the butterfly, which feeds by sucking nectar from flowers, so a tubular mouth has to be constructed with a suitable digestive apparatus. In addition to the rebuilding of the legs from the small five-jointed feet of the caterpillar, the four large wings with their covering of innumerable microscopic scales have to be evolved, with suitable muscles to work them, and the compound eyes have also to be developed. More important than these, the sexual organs must be elaborated. When all these transformations have been completed the skin of the chrysalis splits and the teneral butterfly walks out and clings to the plant, remaining still until its flabby, crumpled wings have smoothed themselves and expanded, and the long legs have hardened and become usable.

From this point there is no further increase in size; growth is complete. This is a fact ever in need of remembrance, for it is a common error to regard the Small Garden White as though it were a juvenile example of the Large Garden White, and to speak of small flies as young flies. We may meet with dwarf aberrations of any insect, but if they have wings we may conclude that they are fully adult insects and will grow no more.

THOUGH many of the butterflies and moths take nearly a year to complete their course of development, reckoning from the time the egg was laid until the emergence of the perfect insect, of others there may be two or more generations in the same period; on the other hand, many moths whose caterpillars are internal feeders in shrubs or trees, require two or three years for the completion of their cycle. The duration of life differs greatly in the very varied forms of insect life: the greenfly or aphis may begin and end its course in a few weeks; at the other extreme we have the seventeen-year cicada of the United States whose normal span of life is from thirteen to seventeen years, the whole period spent underground feeding upon roots and developing its wings before it makes its first appearance above ground. The eggs are not laid in the ground, but in slits of tree branches, the young nymphs on hatching at once seeking the earth, burrowing to the depth of a foot or more. The generations overlap and some are in evidence most summers, but at the end of the maximum period they appear in great numbers.

In most of the insects exhibiting a very marked difference of form in the several stages (which has given origin to the term "insect metamorphosis") the principal feeding for the building up of the adult is effected in the caterpillar or larval stage. Arrived at full growth and the final change of skin, insects of this class take little if any food; it is not the clothes-moth that destroys our silk and woollen fabrics, but its caterpillar. A striking departure from this rule is seen in the gnats, to be referred to later. Bees and wasps that are so industrious in the gathering of food, do this work mainly in order to lay up stores for the sustenance of their helpless young. Many beetles, however, are fairly voracious in their winged, or perfect, state.

On the other hand, there are families of insects, such as the dragonflies, earwigs, cockroaches, grasshoppers, and bugs, in which the course of development goes on smoothly from the hatching of the egg to the perfect state without any abrupt changes of form such as we have described. Changes take place, but they are so gradual that there is no cessation of feeding or activity. The food is the same at maturity as it was in infancy: so no change in the character of the mouth-parts or the digestive organs is needed, whilst the development of wings and sexual organs is spread over a comparatively long period.

From this statement it appears that the abrupt transition from one stage to another—from larva to pupa, and from pupa to winged adult—is due to the need for a revolution in the alimentary system; but some doubt is thrown upon this by the fact that many beetles consume the same kind of food during the adult stage as they ate when grubs, yet they pass through a quiescent pupa stage as abrupt as that of the butterfly. There are, for example, the ground-beetles, active and carnivorous both as larvae and beetles; the cockchafer in its winged state continues a vegetable diet in the shape of green leaves, though its portly grub is so well stuffed with reserves after from three to five years of feeding on the roots of grass, corn or beet, that it has to lie doubled upon itself. The somewhat similar grub of the stag-beetle, that spends four years in eating decayed wood in tree-stumps, is content at maturity with the juices from crushed oak shoots. The jaws of the male of this fine beetle, enlarged to a semblance of huge antlers, are of little use beyond ornament, though it has been said that rival males fight with them; but the muscles controlling them do not appear to be powerful enough for the infliction of any considerable physical harm.

ANOTHER well-known group of beetles whose food is of the same nature in both larval and perfect stages, is that of the ladybirds; but here the diet is fellow insects and restricted to the gardener's black beast, the aphis or greenfly. From the moment of leaving the egg the grub begins to consume the greenfly, and continues the good work for about a month, killing at the rate of thirty to forty an hour. There are several overlapping generations during the summer, so that the destruction is continuous. If on a given patch of infested vegetation the clean-up has been finished before the current batch of ladybird larvae is full-fed, they resort to cannibalism: the strongest eating the weak in order that a sufficient number may become beetles and hibernate to ensure the continuance of the race next year. The survivors pass the winter in some snug retreat, where at times they associate in vast numbers. We have disturbed such sleepy assemblies, numbering many hundreds, under the loose bark of a dead tree. It is said that in the Rocky Mountains such retreats are hunted for, and the beetles collected and housed through the winter, so that in spring they become active a fortnight or so earlier than they would do out of doors. They are then distributed to the fruit-growers, who can set them out in batches on their trees before the "blight" has had time to increase greatly. One species has been introduced from Australia to California in numbers because of its destruction of the scale insects that attack oranges and their kind.

Among those insects that are predaceous throughout life and that do not undergo any abrupt changes or pass through a period of quiescence, are the splendid dragonflies, of which the larger species afford the finest examples of wing-power. Before they reach the winged stage they spend a year or more crawling over the bottom of ponds or streams, or climbing the stems of aquatic plants in pursuit of prey. This consists of other water-insects, worms, the tadpoles of frog or newt, small fishes, etc. To fit it for this predaceous life, it is endowed with a set of powerful

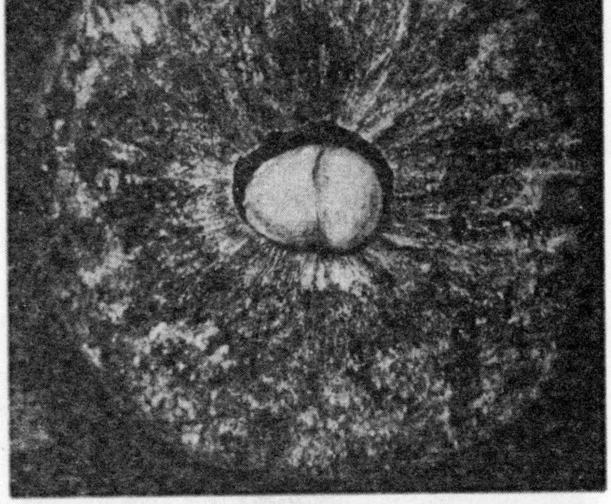

H. Bastin

AN OAK APPLE AND GALL WASPS

Those brown globular growths on oak twigs called oak apples are produced by the gall wasps. They puncture a young shoot and lay their egg (top), and when the gall or "apple" forms round it (bottom) a grub hatches out, which later becomes a tiny wasp.

Eggs on leaf

Larva

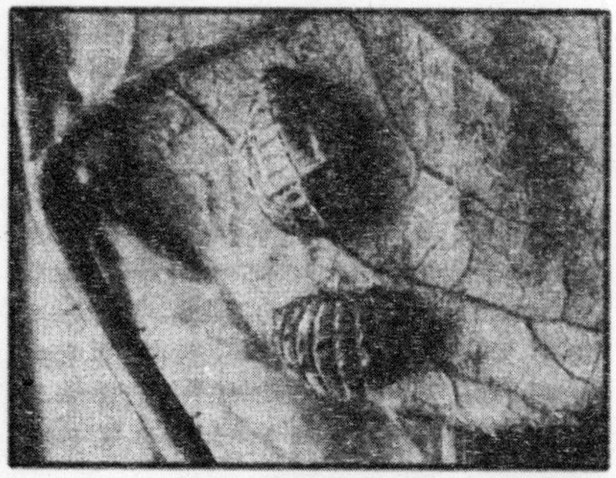

Two pupae

Beetle just emerged

Fully developed

Wing cases opened

PICTURED LIFE-STORY OF THE SMALL BEETLE CALLED THE LADYBIRD

A ladybird is about the only kind of beetle which the ordinary person will allow to walk about on the hand. But it is not always realized what a useful function this brightly coloured little insect performs. Its food is the greenfly, that pest of rose-trees, and but for the ladybird the greenfly would become a very serious menace indeed. Our photographs by J. J. Ward show the development of the British species, the two-spot ladybird, from the cluster of eggs laid upon a black currant leaf through the dull-coloured larva to the perfect, coloured beetle.

cutting jaws, and the lower lip is extended into a long, hinged arm with a pair of sharp hooks at the broad extremity. This instrument, kept ready for immediate use folded under the creature's legs, can be shot out suddenly to capture any desirable prey, bringing it back to the dragon's jaws and holding it there until consumed. In his hind body he has an expanding chamber lined with a delicate tissue in which the blood circulates and takes up oxygen from fresh supplies of water. When he desires to cross the floor rapidly in pursuit of prey, the chamber is contracted strongly, and the water, ejected backwards with force, drives his body forwards.

THE parent dragonfly dropped her eggs into the water or laid them upon some aquatic plant, so that on hatching the larval dragon found itself under suitable conditions to begin its life of rapine. The pond, like the sea, teems with varied living forms; and it is not long before the dragon larva has grown powerful and able to secure any victim he may desire.

Midway in the dragon's career there appear two pairs of buds from his forebody above the hindmost legs, and later these reveal themselves as the tightly packed developing wings of his aerial stage. Then, one summer's day, he feels impelled to take the air, and climbs up a flag or reed and fixes the hooks of his feet securely in his support. His skin splits for the last moult, and he walks out feebly and hangs limply to the stem. In a little his four netted wings spread long and broad, his body lengthens and becomes coloured brightly, the whole integument acquires firmness, and without teaching he discovers the use of the wonderful planes that will carry him through the air at the speed of an express train. Dr. Tillyard has timed the flight of an Australian species, and found that it was at the rate of nearly sixty miles an hour. From now on, selecting a woodland ride or a stretch of hedgerow as his hunting territory, he flies swiftly back and forth, turning shortly at the end of his beat or to cope with the doubling manoeuvres of a smaller quarry, capturing and eating all other insects that may cross his path. Country folk call him "horse-stinger" and "devil's darning-needle," but he has no sting.

Daddy longlegs, the crane-fly, that becomes so conspicuous and annoying in autumn, when the wet outside or the light inside prompts it to come indoors, and indulge in absurd antics, is from its size a convenient example of the vast fly family—the insects that have only one pair of developed wings. The second pair has been reduced to tiny knobs at the end of slender stalks, difficult to see in most flies unless searched for, but in daddy quite obvious.

The female daddy-longlegs may be seen walking over grassland, where her very long legs are a help rather than the encumbrance they appear to be. Now and again she sinks between the grass-blades and bending her hind body at right angles she digs the pointed end into the soil. In every shaft sunk she deposits one of her numerous black eggs ; and as they are all deposited singly and apart she has to traverse a considerable area in order to dispose of them all. From these, in spring, hatch out the dirty-looking, cylindrical, footless grubs, which are known to the agriculturist and the gardener as the destructive and hated " leather-jackets."

The mission of this grub is to keep down the too rapid increase of grasses and other plants by eating their roots, often cutting them across the collar, so that the green parts wither and die. The rooks and starlings know the sign and descend upon these yellow patches, probing the lawns and meadows with their sharp beaks to get at the succulent grubs. Those that escape this fate, in due time become elongated chrysalids, with the future wings showing plainly in their wrappings and the body ringed at every joint with stiff bristles. These permit them to wriggle forward when they have exhausted one grass-tuft, and are used in autumn in order to push the fore-parts of the chrysalis above the surface. In badly infested grassland, about October, large numbers of these strange objects may be seen sticking vertically out of the ground, their oddity increased by a pair of curved, horn-like processes standing out behind the head-parts. These are hollow, and admit air to the developing daddy. Soon, the chrysalis skin splits at the top, and the adult fly emerges gradually, and hangs out its long legs and wings to straighten and become firm for use in the new aerial life.

DADDY'S progress through life is not typical of all the two-winged flies. Their number in distinct species is enormous : so we find that they are very varied in their life-histories. The gnats and mosquitoes spend their early life in water, the big-headed, long-bodied grub floating inverted, breathing through a siphon that is thrust up into the air, what time the other end of the larva is capturing microscopic food.

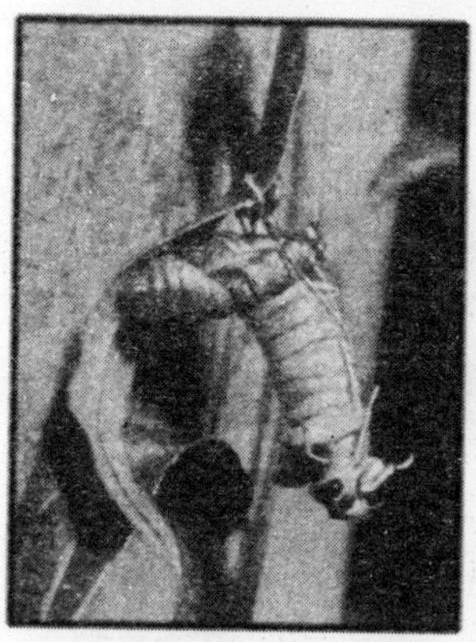

Perfect insect emerging

The cicada with wings partly expanded

Wings fully expanded

Wings spread to show their structure

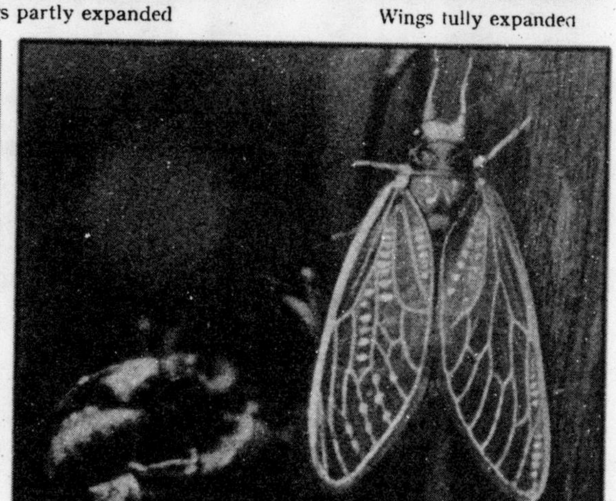

Two hours after emergence

THE CICADA FULFILS ITSELF IN THE SUNSHINE AFTER SEVENTEEN YEARS UNDER THE GROUND

Cicada eggs are laid in the stems of plants, and. six weeks later these eggs hatch and the emerging larvae fall to the ground and quickly bury themselves. It is seventeen years before they see the light of day again. This time is spent in feeding on plant juice extracted from roots and in gradual growth. All this preparation reaches its climax exactly seventeen summers after, and the larvae emerge from the ground and crawl up the tree or plant stems. There the wonderful transformation illustrated by these photographs takes place Photos by Ned J. Burns.

When the chrysalis stage is reached, the future gnat resembles a miniature tadpole, with breathing-tubes (now from the head) pushed through the surface film of the water. The new-born perfect gnat issuing from the chrysalis skin as it floats on the water, has to balance itself very carefully or it would be drowned on the threshold of its winged career. As a rule the female is the only bloodsucker, and she seems to require to be distended with mammalian blood before she can lay her eggs. Among the gnats or mosquitoes are species that are the agents in the spreading of many terrible diseases. Some of the aquatic grubs take in among their food microscopic forms of life that require to be swallowed in order that they may be transferred later to the blood of higher animals when the perfect insect taps their veins. This blood-sucking of the females is the means by which dengue, malaria, elephantiasis, yellow fever and other troubles are spread.

Some of the insects that are more intimate attendants on the bodies of uncleanly people, such as bugs, fleas and lice, are also the carriers of germs which set up disease in the human subject, and sometimes animals of a higher order play a part. Thus a specialised flea that infests rats and other small mammals carries the bacillus of bubonic plague, and when that flea indulges in human blood it passes the germs into the system of its victim. Trench-fever during the War was caused by the excreta of the body-louse; which also carries typhus. Typhoid germs are carried freely by the feet and tongue of the house-fly, which can leave them on our food and so ensure their admission to our bodies. Sleeping-sickness is spread by the tsetse flies of Africa.

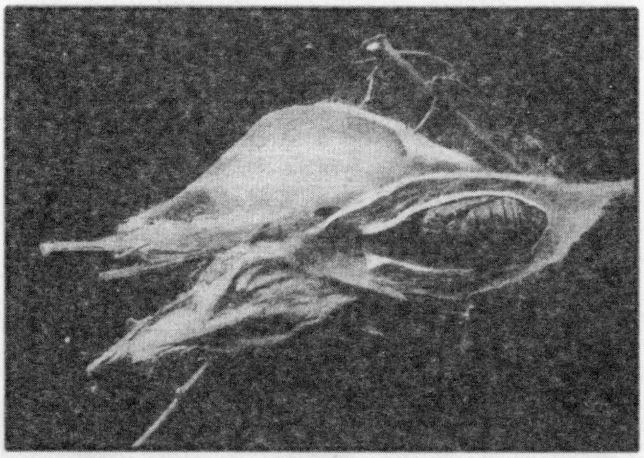

E. Step

INSECTS WHICH MADE THE GIFT OF SILK TO MANKIND

There are a number of moths whose caterpillars spin silk casings or cocoons to cover themselves when in the chrysalis stage, but only the silkworm proper produces just the right quality for making the thread. Above we have the three stages of caterpillar, chrysalis surrounded by the silk cocoon containing about 1,500 feet of silk, and the emerged moth. Nature invented the cocoon for the moth, but man has subordinated the moth to the cocoon with the result that the moth has degenerated and lost the power of flight.

Chapter XVIII

The Beauty Parade Among the Birds

By H. J. Massingham

Author of "Dogs, Birds and Others"

THERE is no subject more delightful in itself, more significant for increasing our knowledge of life and its true values, and more involved in obscurity, prejudice, and rule-of-thumb ideas than the theme of bird-lovers. When the average country-lover thinks of the courtship and mating of birds, he has no alternative but to recall the theory of sexual selection as it was set like cold lard in the third quarter of the last century. Like others of our theories of what goes on in wild Nature, the Darwinians out-Darwined Darwin, and it is only of recent years that the light of experience has corrected the formulae of hypothesis. The credo of the Darwinian disciple is that birds are to be thought of as automata, each sex of which performs certain quite different functions when the biological routine of the breeding season pulls the trigger. The male is excited to a violent erotic frenzy which he expresses by "antics" and by displaying his plumage to the most decorative advantage so that he may obtain possession not of the hen-bird that he "loves" but of any female who will yield to his frantic spell-binding.

The hen-bird on her side remains completely passive to the male's advances, but at the same time (a contradiction in terms) exercises choice as to which of her competing suitors she will award the prize of herself. The theory of sexual selection then goes on to declare that she selects the gaudiest or most virile or generally attractive male with whom to mate, with the result that the second and third-raters fail to rear families. This is the story of the evolution of elaborate song and bright plumage through the elimination of the more backward and unattractive candidates.

Common sense disposes of some of these postulates, strict observation of others. If they represent a natural law, why is monogamy the prevailing custom in bird-life? For it is only among the polygamous species that a majority of brilliant males court a minority of plain and unresponsive females. Everybody knows how the birds-of-paradise vibrate and expand their dazzling plumes as they jig along the boughs before the drab, indifferent hens; how the blackcock assemble in "leks," a sort of bare arena where the males tread a measure in a tranced ecstasy and the prosaic grey hens turn their backs upon them, pecking about within the charmed circle of ruffling and capering rivals without taking any apparent notice of the cavaliers wooing them and challenging one another in Pistolian bravado.

The capercaillies fan their tails, tense their throat-feathers and dart out their necks on the Scottish pine-branches; ruffs meet in tournament for the ruffless reeves on the tilting ground; great bustards turn up their whiskers, inflate their pouches, stiffen and vibrate their flecked plumage, leap like marionettes and paw the ground. Other species like them, pea-fowl for instance, and particularly game-birds, do seem to follow out the rule of the spinsterish quiescent female and the blindly promiscuous and mechanically desirous male. But there are many exceptions to it even in this class of bird, and Darwin himself has described how the pea-hen sometimes courts the cock and how a homespun mallard-duck wooed, won and successfully mated with a male pintail. If, again, the female is endowed with the privilege of choice and uses it, how can she be described as phlegmatic? No cock-bird on this earth can mate with a hen unless Miss Barkis is willin', so that direct force and all the more subtle expedients of pressure so evilly prominent in human life are utterly unknown in bird life. How, once more, do the theorists of the correct rôles assumed by male and female in the avian Courts of Love account for the courtship habits of certain species where the female is as passionate and determined a wooer as Anne in The Devil's Disciple? She is the literal ruler of the roost. Among the ostriches, rheas, tinamous, phalaropes and hemipodes (bustard-quails), incubation and the education of the young is the charge of the male; among the painted snipe it is the female who is the most resplendent in plumage, while with the phalaropes—Nature's darlings, since she adorns them so comely-wise and hides them away in her wildest retreats—it is the female who is the charmer. He flies and she pursues; she gently and sometimes brusquely presses her suit, passing and re-passing before her reluctant love with arching neck, curvetting above him on ceremoniously waved wing and appealingly bowing before a fellow too bashful to be won without all the evasions, subterfuges and make-believe frigidities deemed to be the perquisites of the other sex.

ANOTHER supremely important series of love-making truths, very damaging to this cut-and-dried theory, concern the intricacies of mutual courtship and have been brought to light by those great pioneers of discovery in our age—Edmund Selous and Julian Huxley. Birds are undoubtedly more emotional, more temperamental, but less ready to profit by experience, than the higher mammals. To mammals the fairy godmother bequeathed the gift of plastic intelligence, to birds that of feeling and from it to create that radiance of dress, beauty of form, and grace of flight of which the art of loving has been the parent. For into the mating ardour, birds male *and* female, have packed most of the utilitarian functions of daily life. Huxley has described the honeymoon of the Louisiana egret. The hen will sit on a branch resting

Neville Kingston

GOLDEN AND PEACOCK PHEASANTS IN THE POSTURES OF COURTSHIP

Perhaps the most beautiful of all its kind is the golden pheasant (bottom), from the wilds of Tibet and China. The gold and crimson of the plumage provide the male bird with a most resplendent livery in which to do his courting. The peacock pheasant (top) takes full advantage of the green and purple "eyes" on his tail feathers, and bows low before his apparently unconcerned mate. Such indifference must be most disheartening even to such a persistent wooing as the peacock pheasant's.

Neville Kingston

WHEN THE ARGUS PHEASANT'S FANCY TURNS TO THOUGHTS OF LOVE

An extraordinary manoeuvre has been devised by the argus pheasant for his mating season. He throws up his wings in front of his head so that his face is quite hidden, at the same time squinting archly through a chink in the feathers as though to observe the effect of all this impressiveness upon the hen bird. She, however, is so uncomplimentary and so little appreciative as to go calmly on in her search for something to eat. In the lower photograph we can see the eye of the cock bird peering anxiously through.

were wasting their time! Hours of every day unprofitably thrown away in languishment, bushels of nervous energy dissipated in endearments! How uneconomic is the art of love!

HUXLEY has noted how the red-throated divers have elevated and converted their useful powers of diving and swimming under water into "ceremonials of passion." The kestrel and peregrine falcon, in their wooing flights, employ their powers of swooping down on their prey for exhibition before their mates, and the Adélie penguins offer the stones they use in nest building to their lady-wives with a stately bow, spreading their flippers sideways the while, then raising their heads as though in stilted worship, and humming. The warblers display with twigs or leaves in their beaks, just as keepsakes and valentines are sacred to human lovers. Great crested grebes will spend hours of the day in bouts of shaking pond-weed before each other, their breasts almost touching and reared up to show the flashing under-surface. Then the weed is nibbled or exchanged and serves as a love-symbol every bit as important and binding to them as a necklace or

her head for hours on end against the cock's flanks, still, as old Chaucer said, "as any stone." Suddenly the pair raise their wings and with solemn loud cries intertwine their necks in a true-lover's knot. Then each bird amorously runs the beak through the raised aigrettes of the other, "nibbling and chaffering them from base to tip." Back they sink to their former motionless trance of proximity. When one of them goes food-gathering, the other greets his or her return by crying aloud, rising to full length on the branch, arching and spreading the wings, fanning out the aigrettes and head plumes and bristling the neck feathers. And this mutual love-making continues for month after month, long after the young are hatched and flown. Consider how, according to the law of biological utility (invented by man), those birds

D. Seth-Smith

HOW THE KAGU PAYS HIS ADDRESSES

With the kagus the love-making is mutual and not confined to the male, as with the pheasants. The birds lay beak to beak, holding high the plumes of their crests. The male also performs a strange kind of dance with much solemnity, and (bottom photo) bows himself with wings outspread. The kagu is a native of New Caledonia, a French colony in the South Seas.

Neville Kingston

D. Seth-Smith

LIGHTNING DISPLAY OF ITS EXPANDING COLLAR BY AMHERST'S PHEASANT

China is the home of Amherst's Pheasant, and this bird has a unique way of expressing his feelings in the mating season. The "collar" which adorns his neck is in a moment shot forward with a flick and then shot back again. Both photographs were taken just at the instant when the collar was at full stretch. The bird looks through the frill at the female to mark the effect on her of this very abrupt and startling display. The whole movement is carried out almost as quickly as the movement of a camera shutter.

D. Seth-Smith

SUN BITTERN PARADES THE SECRET BEAUTIES OF HIS FEATHERS FOR HIS MATE'S DELIGHT

In the ordinary way the sun bittern of Central and South America is not in any way striking for the tints of its plumage. But when the bird meets its mate there is a sudden change which is a revelation. The wings are spread wide and turned up and a wonderful colour scheme of grey, white and red appears. One is reminded of the markings of some beautiful butterfly when looking at these lovely feathers. Between the wings the bright plumage of the tail appears, and it seems as though the bird had presented to our view three fans, overlapping as in a pattern. It is rather striking that the sun bittern should keep his beauty so secret and that it is only his chosen mate who should know it.

D. Seth-Smith

RUFF RESPLENDENT IN HIS WEDDING GARMENT

In the mating season, from the end of May till the last days of June, the male ruff, which has at other times the same plumage as the female, undergoes a remarkable change. A frill, like the ruff of the Elizabethan days, appears round the neck, and above this two large tufts of feathers are formed. In this guise the ruff encounters his rivals in not very serious combat in the presence of the female, though the sham fight may sometimes exceed the limits of chivalrous behaviour. So soon as the breeding month is over these gay garments disappear.

broken sixpence is to us. The sexual life of birds has in fact reached the degree of epigamic development when an extraneous object is invested with emotional associations and so given a kind of life independent of its own value.

If the normal activities of bird life are thus pressed into the service of making love, not for a day and a night but for months at a time, it is obvious that courtship and mating cannot be the perfunctory affair of male epilepsy and female acquiescence the Victorian dislike of our kinship with the animal kingdom (combined with their ideas of feminine sexual repression) assumed it to be. From this point of view, the courtship of the great crested grebe is wonderfully instructive. In the first place, the female is, if anything, often more "forward" in wooing than the male, while the rôles of typically masculine and typically feminine are constantly interchanged, just as the most perfect manifestations of human love flower when a man has a feminine tincture in his make-up and a woman something of the masculine salt. Thus, each sex is in a sense the creation and creator of the other, for each in turn enacts the other's part, the female bold and dashing as the male, the male as softly blandishing as the female.

It is plain, too, that the rhythms of endearment, tenderness and almost ritualist caressing by which the complex hymen of these birds is conducted and prolonged carries us far beyond the exclusively physical greeds and surrenders of the Victorian theory. The physical element is part and parcel of the biological. Nobody can watch grebe courtship without being struck by its harmonies, as though each bird were acting in a pre-ordained drama, and I defy any unprejudiced observer not to exclaim, "Why, these birds are in love with each other." They approach each other with the necks lying along the water and when breast to breast leap upright and seem to stamp the surface of the water with their shields gleaming an iridescent white in heraldic opposition.

The hen-bird catches the dangling weed in her mate's beak and each bird sways from side to side to, as it seems, an unheard melody, or treading water a few steps forward and then back. Or they will throw up their heads, opening and closing their beaks with formal grace, the Elizabethan ruffs outfanned below them. I have seen ravens performing similar motions and then, joining their beaks, swing to and fro, with depressed wings in a kind of blissful enchantment as

Neville Kingston

EGRET WHOSE WONDERFUL WEDDING GARMENT NEARLY LED TO ITS EXTINCTION

All over the world the egret, which is a white species of the heron family, was slain in thousands during the mating season for the sake of the feathers called aigrettes or ospreys which were highly valued for feminine adornment. The feathers in question consisted of beautiful silky filaments hanging down the back in the case of the Great American Egret seen here. These lovely plumes are only worn—both sexes have them—in the mating season. The civilized nations have now banded together to discourage the ugly trade in ospreys.

Neville Kingston.

SNOWY AND GREAT AMERICAN EGRETS IN BRIDAL PLUMAGE

As a penalty for being beautifully robed in snow-white feathers during the season of mating, the egrets were nearly exterminated. But, just as wild flowers are the more delightful when growing in their natural place, so we can see from these photographs of the egret that its feathers are only seen at their best on the bird as it lives. Stuck in a hat or a fan they lose the marvel of the purpose for which they were made. Below is one of the snowy egrets found in Florida, and above a couple of Great American egrets keeping their wedding finery in order.

C. Reid

Neville Kingston

PEACOCKS DISPLAYING THE WONDER OF THEIR TRAINS TO INDIFFERENT MATES

Tail coverts are prolonged in all the peacocks far beyond the length of the tail feathers themselves, and it is this covering which, when expanded, makes the glittering splendour which is usually referred to as the peacock's "tail." India, Ceylon and Assam are the native homes of the peacock, where it is found in the jungles near water and usually near cultivated land. Since, in India, the birds have been regarded as more or less sacrosanct they have bred with little molestation. No bird has such an imposing gesture to make before his mate.

it is possible to formulate a general law which radically differs from the Victorian theory. Where the sexes are alike in plumage or one sex is as beautiful as the other, active courtship is mutual. The fact that it is the cock-bird who usually sings offers no real difficulty, because, as Selous has pointed out, all nuptial notes are a kind of song and these are uttered equally by both sexes of a vast number of species. I may even go further and suggest that those species in which the female or the male is the monopolist in courtship are sidetracked off the trunk lines of evolution. These are usually polygamous. In the interchanges of love-making, frequently prolonged long after the young are hatched and certainly

though their bodies rolled to the monotonous plaint of an Hawaian folk-tune. Sung under a South Seas moon to the passionate throbbing of ukuleles and steel-stringed guitars.

Selous has maintained that the courtship of birds absorbs their functional behaviour to such an extent that it is responsible for nest-building. Thus the nest of the great crested grebe is a bower, a love-couch, what the ancients called a "thalamum." The grebes make a love-play out of the materials of the nest, and this is likewise true of lapwings (whose hardly credible powers of madcap wing display are the product of nuptial exaltations), of thrushes, blackbirds, rooks, swans, divers and pre-eminently of the bower-birds, whose ornamental nests are primarily a love-offering.

D. Seth-Smith

GREAT BUSTARD AND A TURKEY "DISPLAYING"

When displaying for the benefit of the female the bustard (bottom) inflates an air pouch in its throat and extends its quill feathers, thus appearing to increase in bulk. The turkey (top) makes the most of its markings and its wattles, as we see here.

THE lapwing advances towards his or her mate in a set, mesmeric attitude, halts, raises the tail and falls into a peculiar rolling motion which scoops out the nesting hollow. Both sexes fall into the same curious hypnosis. So the wheatear spins round like a slow-motion top, crouching in a hollow and plucking and dropping wisps of grass. Nest-building and elaborate and truly aesthetic forms of sexual display have thus developed concurrently out of a formless and primal urge. In 173 out of 212 species of British birds, the male aids the female in constructing the nest, and, if mating and nesting are parts of one whole, it is clear that both sexes are equal participants in all the solemn and significant fervours and ceremonies of courtship in this joyous and almost ritual beginning to the renewal of life by virtue of the ardours of parenthood.

Of this truth there are so many examples that

resumed in the following season, the male exercises as much choice as the female and the female as much initiative as the male. Thus the process of sexual selection is a double one and each sex has "acquired

Neville Kingston

AN AMOROUS TURKEY AND THE EXTRAORDINARY EFFECTS OF COURTSHIP EMOTION ON THE MAQUARI STORK

Despite its name the turkey (right) which we see making a great fuss in the hopes of impressing some hen-bird—turkeys are polygamous—has nothing to do with the land of Turkey. It is a native of North and Central America, and was unknown in the Old World before the end of the fifteenth century, when the explorers of new-found America brought back some specimens. Turkeys were probably introduced into England by ships trading with Turkey, which had called at Spain on the homeward voyage and picked up the birds as a novelty. This, or some similar course accounts for their name. The Maquari stork (left) from South America goes through the most amazing contortions, bearing its beak right back and making its throat feathers stand up like a sugar loaf.

D. Seth-Smith

SIMPLE BUT PROUD DISPLAY OF GIANT WINGS BY THE CONDOR

Largest of the birds of prey, the condor lives among the vast peaks of the Andes and belongs to the vulture family. But it feeds on living things such as lambs and kids as well as on carrion. Its great wings may measure as much as eight feet from wing-tip to wing-tip, and in the breeding season, the male spreads these pinions, the symbol of his great power, before his mate. Condors nest on the rock ledges among the mountains, but in the ordinary way go to roost by companies in the trees. The condor is not found outside South America.

such beauty as it possesses in accordance with the taste and choice of the opposite one." The theory that the male is wound up to a kind of indiscriminate and mechanical fury, while the female is the apathetic recipient of his attentions, fails to explain why the sexes remain constant, as they surely are more likely to do when they mate by what has been called an "elective affinity" formed out of mutual ardour and founded upon mutual preference.

LET me give a few more examples of mutuality in the lyrics of sound, gesture and colour each sex contributes for the delight of the other. Darwin, with his usual fair-mindedness, has described how the hen capercailzies flit round the males as they parade, and this instance is the more remarkable in that the species is polygamous, and the hens are drabs whose responses are held to be inactive. When the South American jacanas, a species allied to our water-rails, display, male and female vary a rapid fluttering with a slow butterfly-like heave of the wings. The dingy-hued hen-blackbird expresses her appreciation of her mate's prancings and posturings by a beatific drooping of the wings. A pair of red-throated divers will both utter a wild epithalamic cry with the neck held arched and rigid and then with heads and necks lying flat along the water and bodies almost submerged, they will advance very joyfully to meet each other in a series of little plungings.

The manikins have a wooing song and dance in which the cock and hen keep hopping up and down alternately, singing tolédo, tolédo ("to" at the crouch, "lé" at the spring and "do" when they alight). Albatrosses will waddle round each other for a quarter of an hour at a stretch, though walking is very arduous for them. Then they will interlace their necks and rub them against each other's downy feathers. The bills are tucked into the wing and then tossed in air with a mixed groan and scream. Like so many long-billed birds, they snap their beaks and join them, blowing out their breasts the while. Mated cranes pursue their amorous exchanges by hopping and skipping about each other, by little pirouettes and more stately minuets. Fulmars indulge in mutual languishing motions, while the males and females of the shag tribe display the brilliant gamboge of the mouth for each other's delectation. Why, asks the clear-minded Selous pertinently, should the habit have survived if his revelation of his treasure had not been for her and her similar response for him?

Many instances, again, have been collected of jealousy operating so forcibly among the hens of oyster-catchers, Kentish plovers, redshanks and other species that they will drive an intrusive male right out of the lists of love. This very definite contradiction of passivity or indifference in the female has even been observed among the dowds of polygamous species like blackcock, ruffs and reeves, peafowl and others. It certainly gives birth to a suspicion as to whether the females of any species are ever such lack-lustre, passionless creatures as imperfect observation has described them. There may be other reasons for this seeming lack of interest in the male's desperate devices, and if that is the case, one wonders whether the so-called polygamous species are not rather promiscuous than Oriental in their nuptial customs. And it is unquestionably true that it is the females rather than the males of some species where love is shared and active in both sexes who open the ceremonies by making emotional advances to their partners.

The whole problem is one of unique interest because in love between the sexes mankind is nearer to the birds than to the mammals. It is only among birds and men that courtship reaches an emotional and psychical complexity lacking to mammals and the more lowly organized members of the animal kingdom. When we study the mating habits of birds whose courtship is mutual and who pair for life, one is forced to the conclusion that men and women only differ from males and females of the wild birds (domesticated animals are nearly always degenerate) in three respects. Mankind has been released from the biological tyranny of the mating season in the first place. Secondly men and women bring, or rather are capable of bringing, a higher mental evolution and a more subtle play of emotion to their love-making than is possible to birds. And, thirdly, our natural feelings have been modified, sometimes out of all recognition and not infrequently to the heavy detriment of human values, by our social institutions. But these are differences not of kind but of degree.

Neville Kingston

BRILLIANT TRAGOPAN OR HORNED PHEASANT

Among the bamboo woods of China and India lives the tragopan or horned pheasant which is celebrated for its remarkable brilliance and beauty of plumage. In the mating time the male birds perform the most elaborate displays, giving the full effect of their intricate markings and resplendent colourings as all the pheasants do.

The Victorians made their great mistake when they attempted to separate the loves of men and birds as different in kind. As Selous has written with such passionate irony:

> There must be no preferences, no love-matches here (namely, in the kingdom of birds). All must be in obedience to a blind sexual instinct, something very animal, about which we, of course, know nothing. Unlike ourselves, the female brute must be ready to mate with any male brute chance may throw in her way, and, if it throw several, she must be absolutely impartial between them, there being neither looks, soul, nor money for her to found a choice on. Therefore she will go to the strongest and know no better, for love she knows not, nor can parental authority and filial obedience combine here to give the preference to riches or title, coupled with age or disease.

When the Victorians elaborated the theory of the sexually excited cock-bird (as though he were a kind of rotary machine stimulated by a biological accelerator) and the passive hen-bird (as though she were a kind of inanimate lightning-conductor), were they more influenced by the society of the time than they would have cared to admit? Is the "coyness" of women an institutional rather than a natural endowment, and is the axiom that man is the wooer and woman the wooed a passing phase of social convention? At any rate, a study of the mating habits of birds lends no support to it, for what we call "equality of the sexes" is the predominant law in that kingdom, and it is highly probable that the permanence of union which is so striking a character among so many species is the consequence of that equality, which takes the form not of competition between the sexes in the feministic fashion, but of mutual cooperation and an equal ardour in the joys of matehood. When our grandmothers submitted to the cruel laws of Victorian marriage, either they were acting a part in obedience to male domination and the repressive standards of conduct then prevailing or the "marriage of convenience" left them permanently unlit. Such passivity was at that time deemed a virtue.

The courtship of birds shows us a better way. The biological urge of the sexual instinct has undergone such a development that the brilliant colours; the exquisite graces of flight and movement in the air, where migration or food-catching is not the motive; melody; ornamental structural characters; prolonged rites of courtship and mating; equal ardours, affections and constancy, have all been built up from this primary force. When we on our plane ally the instinct with which we are born to the spiritual on the one hand and the natural on the other, the experience of great men and of great lovers has often proved that there is no real disharmony between them. Let us praise the birds who have shown us on their plane what possibilities in the co-operation of heaven and earth are open to us on ours.

Special Press

GLORY OF GLINTING PLUMES AS THE PEACOCK SPREADS ITS TRAIN

To the wonder of the spectacle of the peacock's train, spread like the riches of an emperor to dazzle the eye, is added the wonder of its construction. Amid the exquisite lace-work of the plumage appear, as it were, many watching eyes which gleam now green now blue. This is due to the formation of the surface and the consequent breaking up of the light to form different tints. The train is an extension of the tail covert, not the tail itself.

Chapter XIX

The Attitude of the Animal to Man

By Dr. R. C. Macfie

IT requires two to make a quarrel or a pact, and the attitude of animals to man depends largely on the attitude of man to animals.

Man himself is merely an animal ; through animals he evolved, and in bone, nerve, and muscle he carries indelible record of his animal ancestry. From the worm he got his red blood, from the tunicate his backbone, from the fish his camera eye, from the triton his five fingers, from the duck-billed platypus and the ant-eater his mammary glands ; from the kangaroo his nipples ; from the hedgehog and anaptomorphis his placenta and his neo-pallium. Yet ever since he swung himself down from the trees and became *homo erectus*, he has been at war with most of his animal kindred. He began his human career, not as shepherd nor as farmer, but as hunter. As cave-man, he fought the sabre-toothed tiger, the woolly bear, the mammoth, and the hyena ; and fishes, birds, and beasts were regarded almost exclusively from a gastronomic standpoint.

That was natural enough. A man sharing a jungle with beasts of prey has to choose between being feeder or fodder. A man who has no milch cows and no cornfields, must kill to get meat for his larder and must not be too particular what he eats—mammoth perhaps for breakfast, an undercut of tiger for luncheon, and loin of bear for supper. Man was a hunter and the animals were his food.

But in time he learned more wisdom ; he discovered that co-operation was sometimes more profitable than competition, that tamed animals had their uses, that a living dog was worth more than a dead lion—that it was more convenient to keep meat alive in a paddock than dead in a larder. He found he could dominate an animal more effectively by taming it than by maiming it, by harnessing it than by trapping it, by milking it than by hamstringing it, and his whole attitude towards the animal world and towards life underwent a change. Civilization, indeed, may be said to have begun with the taming of wild grass and of wild animals ; and the domestication of the wild ox or aurochs may be said to have been the foundation of the home. On a horse civilized man rode to war ; with a sheep's wool he covered his nakedness, in a cow's udder he stored his daily food.

Some of the first treaties with animals required courage and enterprise : it required the courage of a lion-tamer to bit, bridle and saddle a wild stallion, and the enterprise of a Lindbergh to milk a wild mare ; for in those days of struggle to survive there must have been incorrigible distrust between man and other animals.

Strangely enough, the very first addition to man's household as a boarder was one of the ravenous wolf tribe—a boarder now known as the dog. It is difficult to believe that primitive man ever tamed or tried to tame a wolf, for wolves are extremely intractable and treacherous animals. It is more likely that the primitive dog adopted into the human household was a hybrid, which had lost in the crossing most of its wolfish vices, and much of wolfish appearance. To-day there are several genera of the family-Canidae, to which wolves belong—wolves, jackals, dingoes, foxes, and so on—and a cross of some of them or of genera now extinct may have produced a tameable animal.

IMPATIENT OF CONTROL

Generations of service on behalf of man have not tamed the natural longing for freedom and impatience of restraint in the horse. Here is a fine stallion on a stud farm in Sussex, wildly pawing the air at the end of his long rein although he sees his master every day.

A dog's likes and dislikes are mainly of olfactory origin, and it is quite possible that 'freaks' born with an innate liking of the human odour went up to man with a wagging tail. Or it

J.G. Wells

BIRD AND BEAST GAIN CONFIDENCE UNDER THE RIGHT TREATMENT

A spider monkey at the London Zoological Gardens found a friend he could trust in a schoolgirl (bottom left) who spent much of her holiday time there. Less intelligent creatures than monkeys get to know their friends. One of the sea-gulls which frequent the Serpentine in Hyde Park (bottom right) perches on the hat of a man who regularly feeds it. A trumpeter bird, naturally very shy, does the same for its keeper (top left) and the squirrels of Regent's Park are notoriously tame when they can scent food to their liking (top right).

Underwood

HORSE AND RIDER—COMPANIONS AND FRIENDS

Arduous service is the lot of horse and man in the Canadian Mounted Police—formerly known as the Royal North-West Mounted Police—and it is hardly to be wondered at that the rider gets fond of the animal on which the successful performance of duty and even life itself must often depend. This is a sharp contrast in the horse's attitude shown with the photograph in page 183 and a reminder that to win the confidence of even the domestic animals needs competence care and experience.

may be that the first domestic dogs were adopted as puppies, and were tamed by a domestic environment. There seems to be an instinctive desire in most men and children to make pets of young animals, and petting can modify an animal's innate character. In Australia there is to-day a wild dog-like animal, the dingo, which hunts and destroys sheep, and yet if it be domesticated as a puppy it can be trained as a sheep-dog.

However the association between man and dog came about, it is certainly an association of great antiquity and of great mutual value. Man has no alliance equally intimate with any other animal outside his own family, and the friendship of the dog for man is quite unique in its loyalty and many-sidedness. All breeds of dogs—and there are now about two hundred—instinctively trust mankind, and even dogs naturally fierce, are gentle with children, and obedient to their masters. There is indeed a reciprocal affection between dog and master, and a dog will defend its master and its master's property even to the death, and, if it lose its master, will sometimes refuse to eat and will die of sorrow and grief. Ulysses' dog Argos died of joy when his master returned, and as we write it is reported in the papers that a boarhound is so inconsolable over the suicide of his master that he will probably have to be destroyed.

MAETERLINCK says that the dog is " our intimate and impassioned slave whom nothing discourages, whom nothing repels, whose ardent trust and love nothing can impair," and in "The Blue Bird" he makes the Dog say, " There is Man, and that's all. We have to obey him and do what he tells us! That is the one and only fact! I recognise no one but him! Hurrah for Man! Man for ever! In life and death all for Man. Man is God." In every case the dog seems to accept man as leader of the pack, as comrade and as playmate, and in most cases seems able to differentiate between master, friend, stranger and enemy.

So faithful is the dog that in medieval monuments the dog is placed at the feet of women to symbolise affection and fidelity, and many of the Crusaders are represented with their feet on a dog to show that they followed the standard of the Lord as faithfully as a dog follows its master.

During bygone centuries man has been selecting the most intelligent and affectionate dogs, and so canine intelligence and affection have probably increased; but dogs have also been bred for other purposes and to this purposive breeding we owe the remarkable breeds of dogs that tend sheep instead of worrying them, the Eskimo sled dogs, that drag the sleds wearylessly across the ice the setters and the pointers, equipped with "all-testing, all-inquisitive nose."

In some cases dogs are taught to be docile only to their masters and to attack strangers; and there are, of course, breeds of dogs naturally fierce and treacherous; but dogs as a family regard man as a god to be followed and obeyed. According to Thaler most dogs are exceedingly sensitive to ridicule, and never forgive a man who ridicules them. The bark of domesticated dogs would seem to be a step towards language, for it is not found in savage dogs, and is most particularly and strongly developed, and most flexible of the needs of varying emotional expression, in highly-bred dogs.

The cat was probably domesticated a little later than the dog, and, as in the case of the dog, it is difficult to explain its first domestication, for a wild cat is even more untameable than a wolf. Domestic cats of all kinds have intelligence and grace, but though they may have affectionate manners they seem to lack true affection, and never show implicit faith in any man. Except as "mouser" and as ornament the cat has little social or economic value.

UNUSUAL "ATTITUDES" OF MAN TO ANIMAL

The charms of music have always been held to be a link between man and animal from the time of Orpheus to the Pied Pipe of Hamelin and onwards. A nightingale can be stimulated to sing by a 'cello and some similar sort of attempt is being made by the Zoo keeper and a cockatoo. A six-foot diamond python (top) can be affectionate enough to lick its keeper's face.

It sits in "monumental calm"
immobile, imperturbable,
Like one whose vision seeks the Imminent
Behind these symbols and appearances,
The face within this transitory mask.

Much more valuable as a domestic animal is the horse. Civilization without horses could not have made much progress, for it was mainly their horse power that enabled the Aryan races to conquer the barbarians, and the Spaniards to conquer Mexico and Peru. Horses had their original home in the steppes of Central Asia, and the first horsemen were Mongols.

Strength, endurance and size made the horse valuable in agriculture and transport; and, though now it is being ousted by petrol and steam, the part it has played in the past must never be forgotten. Yet the horse is not a particularly intelligent animal, and, though it has a certain amount of affection for the hand that feeds it, the feeling cannot be compared with the intimate affection of a dog. A horse is little more to man than a machine: its response to whip and rein is mainly reflex and automatic, and man is little more to a horse than whip, rein and nose-bag, and manger. Even the mule has more intelligence than a horse. Still less intelligent—though it, too, has played a part in civilization—is the camel, which clothes, carries and sometimes feeds its masters. It is considered by Thaler to be "the dullest and least improvable of all our servitors." Its attitude towards man seems to be that of a stupid and unwilling yet patient drudge.

Possibly the most intelligent of all living domesticated animals is the elephant. What courageous man or nation first subjugated and harnessed an elephant is not known; but a mighty and fearless man he must have been.

The readiness and rapidity with which an elephant adapts itself to captivity and to association with man is most remarkable. Within a few months it is quite friendly, and in a short time is willing to co-operate in the capture of its kindred. It is easily taught to do certain kinds of mechanical work—even work requiring some skill and some use of the reason—and it is as faithful as a dog in its attachment to man. It quickly distinguishes between individuals, is capable of remembering kindnesses with gratitude and cruelties with hate, and is almost human in its attitude towards man.

WHEN MAN AND BEAST CAN TRUST EACH OTHER

Even in the wilds of Canada the bear is sometimes agreeable to an armistice in the eternal quarrel with man. In this case we have one of the privileged bears which live, for ever protected, in the Kootenay National Park in British Columbia. No one ever harms the animals and consequently some of them have learnt to treat man as a friend.

Coming to the mammals of the farmyard, we find little to encourage us to believe that they have much, if any, personal feeling towards man.

The subjugation and domestication of aurochs, boar, wild sheep, and wild goat marked a great step in the progress of civilization, rendering possible villages and communal life. Wild bull and boar have been changed into the comparatively dull and sluggish ox and pig, and marvels of breeding have been accomplished so that a milch-cow may give twelve times its own weight of milk in the year; but the tame animals regard man with indifference, neither loving nor fearing him. The shepherd may love the sheep and call each by name; the collie may watch over them with a solicitude almost maternal; but the sheep take little interest in either shepherd or sheep-dog, and even the Irish pig in the Irish shanty has little interest in its human fellow-boarders.

In the barnyard the same attitude of indifference prevails. Cocks, hens, ducks, geese, turkeys, regard their owners merely as purveyors of food, while the ostrich is notorious for its stupidity. This is probably

FOX AND FARMER, LIFE-LONG ENEMIES, ENJOY EACH OTHER'S COMPANY

An excuse for fox-hunting is that it keeps in check one of the pests of farming. The cunning of Red Reynard in the raiding of hen-runs is proverbial, and the farmer is the last person liable to keep a fox as a pet. Yet one farmer in Sussex has kept a fox which has become used to following him about just as a dog might do. Even on a fishing expedition the two friends share a boat together, and thoroughly enjoy themselves too as we see. Never was a greater paradox in man's customary relation to the animal.

simply because no particular physiological reaction to man is necessary for their welfare or safety. A wagging tail may have survival value for a dog; it has none for a turkey, which is bred mainly for its pectoral muscles. On the whole, domesticity makes for stupidity leading to the loss even of instinctive wisdom and initiative.

Of domestic birds, the parrot, kept chiefly for amusement, is certainly the most intelligent. Its grip and its powers of articulation and mimicry seem associated with a certain capacity for affection. At least, it seems to recognise individuals and to regard each with varying degrees of friendliness and trust.

To quote Maeterlinck again: "A few creatures fear us, most are unaware of us, and not one loves us. Among the animals we number a few servants who have submitted only through indifference, cowardice or stupidity: the uncertain and craven horse, who responds only to pain, and is attached to nothing; the passive and dejected ass, who stays with us only because he knows not what to do nor where to go; the cow and the ox, happy so long as they are eating, and docile because for centuries they have not had a thought of their own; the affrighted sheep who knows no other master than terror; the hen, who is faithful to the poultry-yard because she finds more maize and wheat there than in the neighbouring forest. I do not speak of the cat, to whom we are nothing more than a too large or uneatable prey. They do not love us, do not know us, scarcely notice us. They are unaware of our life, our death, or departure, or return, our sadness, our joy, our smile. For thousands of years they have been living at our side as foreign to our thoughts, our affections, our habits, as though the least fraternal of the stars had dropped them but yesterday on our globe."

Maeterlinck is perhaps too pessimistic, but nevertheless it is probably true to say that dogs, horses and elephants apart, domestic animals are indifferent to their owners and do not appear, so far as we can see, to return any affection bestowed on them. Monkeys and great apes can hardly be considered

FOOD AND FRIENDSHIP IN THE PARK: RAINIER, U.S.A., AND RICHMOND, LONDON

Feeding the animals in the park suggests to most people a less startling animal than a bear. Yet parties of tourists through the great Rainier National Park, Washington, U.S.A., where the wild life of America is preserved from the ever-encroaching influence of man, can feed bears from the seats of their charabancs. The more homely picture (top) of a deer in Richmond Park, London, shows caution and tentativeness in every line of the animal's body as desire for food overcomes the shyness of one of the most timid of animals

AFTERNOON TEA WITH A LION AT THE TABLE

Even lions, suitably fed and treated, are trusted by some people who know and understand them. But in the case of the great carnivora—whose very name means flesh-devouring—the attitude of the animal to the man seems as though it would always remain a dangerously uncertain thing. The tamest lion may be accidentally hurt—perhaps stung by some insect—and will snap at the nearest living creature in a moment. And after this first taste of blood no one knows what may happen in the mind of a hitherto quiet and inoffensive lion.

domesticated animals, yet individuals have been domesticated and have proved intelligent and docile, and sociable and affectionate, in their relations with man. Chimpanzees are particularly easy to domesticate and are almost human in their behaviour and moods. Agassiz confessed he "could not say in what the mental faculties of a young child differ from those of a young chimpanzee," and Mr. R. L. Garner, who for many years made a special study of monkeys and apes, had a very high opinion of the character of chimpanzees. Writing of his favourite chimpanzee, "Moses," Mr. Garner says: "Not only was he tame and tractable, but he was never tired of caressing me, and being caressed by me . . . From the second day after we became associated he appeared to regard me as one in authority. He would not resent anything I did to him. I could take his food out of his hands, which he would permit no one else to do. He would follow me, and cry after me like a child, and as time went by his attachment grew stronger and stronger. He gave every evidence of pleasure at my attentions, and evinced a certain degree of appreciation and gratitude in return. He would divide any morsel of food with me, which is, perhaps, the highest test of the affection of any animal. I cannot say that such an act was genuine benevolence, or an earnest of affection in a true sense of the term, but nothing except deep affection or abject fear impels such actions and certainly fear was not his motive.

"There were others whom he liked and made himself familiar with; there were some he feared and others he hated, but his manner towards me was that of deep affection. It was not alone in return for the food he received, because my boy gave him food more frequently than I did, and many others from time to time fed him. His attachment was like an infatuation that had no apparent motive, was unselfish and supreme."

ANOTHER chimpanzee, "Aaron," proved "gentle and humane" and apparently "prompted by the same motives of kindness and sympathy that move the human heart to deeds of tenderness and mercy."

But, of course, all chimpanzees are not paragons, and Aaron's wife Elisheba was "treacherous, ungrateful and cruel in every thought and act, she was utterly devoid of affection; she was selfish, sullen, and morose at all times; she was often vicious and always obstinate; she was indifferent to caresses and quite as well content when alone as in the best of company." The other great apes—the orangs and the gorillas—seem much less tameable, and the various families of monkeys vary much in their capacity for domestication; but none of the apes and monkeys seem naturally hostile to man; and their attitude is more often an attitude of trepidant suspicion than of actual hatred or antipathy.

Another animal which has been domesticated in rare instances is the seal; but it is certainly one of the most intelligent, affectionate and teachable of animals, and in these respects must be placed with dogs, elephants, monkeys and apes.

ALMOST the whole Order of Birds, as might have been expected, is wild. With the exception of the various barnyard birds, of the ostriches, and of birds like canaries and parrots, kept in cages, they live a wild free life and their attitude towards man is hostile, as in the case of eagles, or timid as in the case of sparrows. A few wild species can be tamed so far that they will eat from the hand like caged birds. Most of them are attracted to human abodes simply by food, and when food is scarce they become specially tame. In some cases man has encouraged the semi-domestication of wild birds for particular reasons. Various species of hawks have been bred for hawking, and many wild birds are tolerated because they destroy slugs and worms or because of their song, and in Egypt, for instance, pigeons are protected as sources of manure. Among half-tame birds may be mentioned the robin, the swallow, the martin, the sparrow, the wood-pigeon, the barn-owl, the crow, the mallard, the magpie, the jay, the bluebird, the oriole, the vulture, the hoopoe, the mynah, the swan, the peacock. But such birds are only *half* tame and never learn to trust man, and despite the rich emotional potentialities shown in song and plumage, birds never seem to have any emotional attachment to man.

WHEN we regard really wild animals we find that man usually does produce a distinct reaction either of fear or of anger; but often the reaction seems to be acquired and not innate. In many cases it is man's own hunting habits that make him feared, and until they have had practical experience of man's dangerousness many animals do not show any fear of him at all.

As a rule few animals except bulls, and sharks, man-eating tigers, and lions attack a man without some provocation, and when a wild animal does attack a man without provocation, the impulse is usually fear or hunger rather than mere ferocity. Many animals indeed, popularly regarded as vicious and dangerous, do not attack without provocation. A snake inadvertently trodden upon will turn in wrath, and a lioness whose cubs have been stolen will attack the robber; but as a rule snakes and lions do not attack man. It may have required no divine intervention to save Daniel in the lions' den, and the stories of wild animals that have been cowed by the magnetic force of the human eye may be taken with some degree of scepticism; for it is quite likely that the wild beast turned away simply because it never had any desire to attack. Even the fierce bulls of the Spanish bull-fights usually require to be goaded and starved into fighting fury. But on the other hand, it is to be noted that many wild animals are uncertain of temper, very nervous, easily frightened, and easily provoked, and that every beast of prey lives by killing and when hungry enough will attack man or any other animal within its reach.

There are some hundreds of thousands of species of animals, and it is an extraordinary thing how few of them have been domesticated, and that the most important of those domesticated are descendants of animals like the aurochs, that might seem untameable.

There can be no doubt that a little enterprise and patience could domesticate many more wild creatures. Many birds, such as the heron and stork, could be added to the barnyard, and many new animals could be added to the paddock. The elephant, with all its fine qualities, is hardly used, mainly on account of its huge size, but it should not be impossible to breed a much smaller race. The great apes, though they have intelligence and enormous muscular power, are deficient in docility; but the psychical differences between ape and ape even of the same species are very great and such qualities as docility could be easily selected in breeding.

THE monkeys are usually mischievous and frivolous, but they have energy and activity, and they show constant variations, so it should be possible to breed a race of monkeys useful for agricultural or industrial purposes.

Whether apes or monkeys will ever be bred on a large scale in order to be used for rejuvenating purposes remains to be seen.

There should be little difficulty in domesticating seals, otters, and beavers; and it should not be impossible to train otters, seals, and pelicans for fishing, and to breed crocodiles for leather. In countries where termites are a plague, they might be cultivated as we cultivate oyster-beds. They multiply so rapidly that they can be gathered with a spade. Fried or grilled, they are said to be delicious and delicate eating, and have been compared to sugared marrow, to sugared cream and to paste of sweet almonds. Already we hear that they are sold as food in Java markets.

Again, the esculent swiftlet whose gelatinous nests are so much esteemed by the Chinese, might be protected and bred. They are birds that evidently multiply rapidly, for in Canton alone 25 million nests are annually sold.

Man can make his selection from almost the whole of the animal world, for almost every animal fears him and respects him and is willing to do his bidding, and not only has he choice of almost all animals at present in existence, he has power by scientific breeding to modify them to suit his purposes. There must be many possibilities of domestication still unexploited.

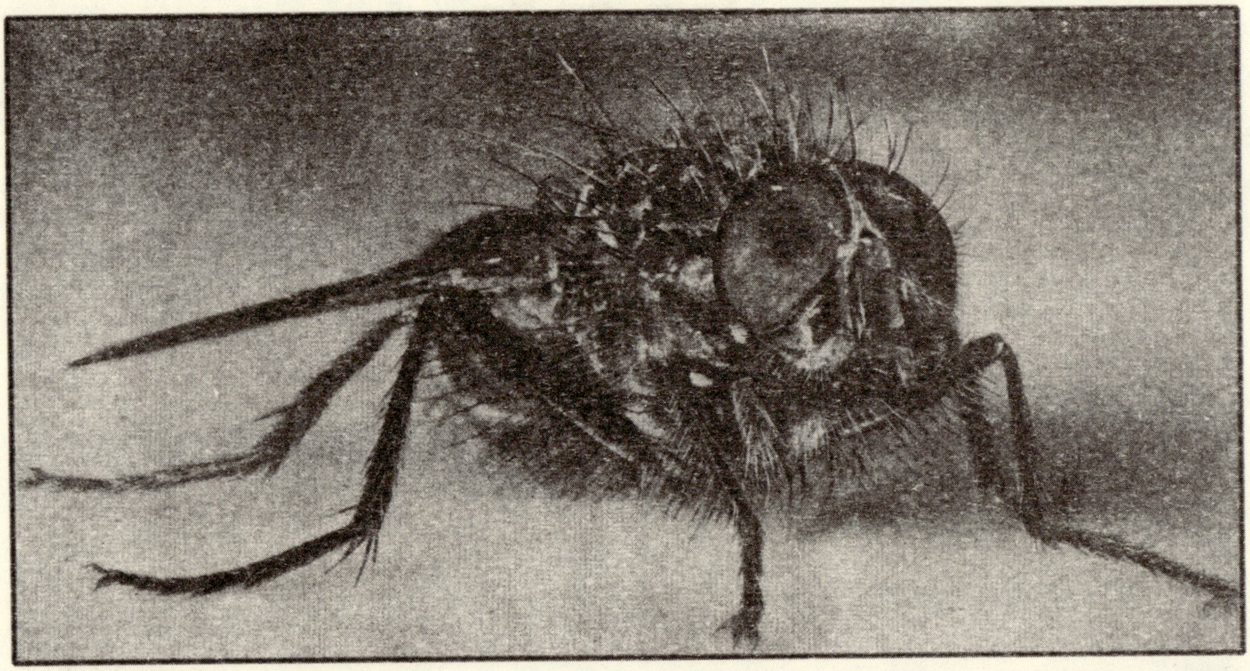

A.E.Smith

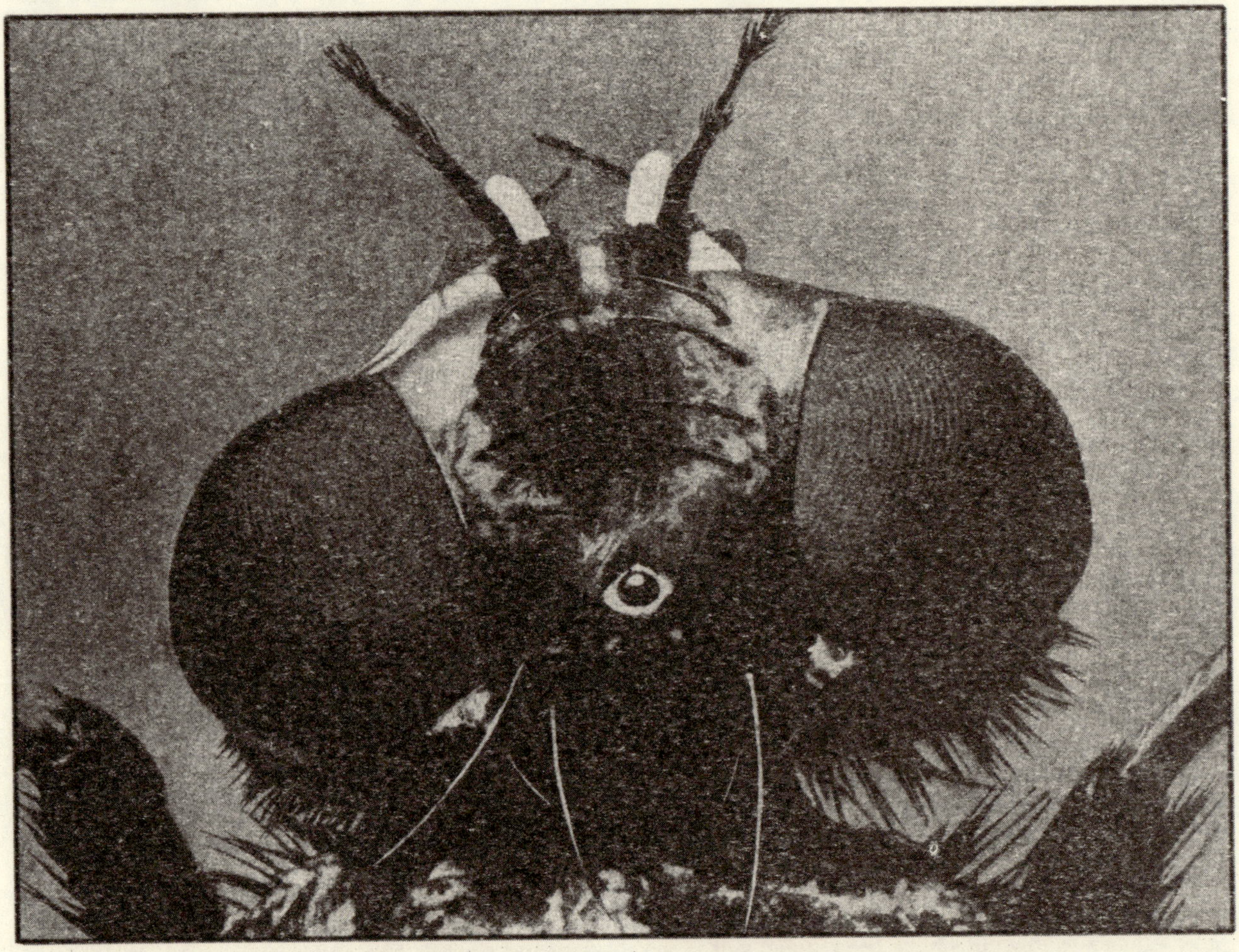

WHY THE HOUSE FLY IS HARD TO HIT: EYES WITH 4,000 LENSES

On the heads of flies a close inspection will show two hemispherical lumps, one on either side, and these are the flies' eyes. The microscope will reveal the fact that each of these masses rather resembles a jewel with an apparently uncountable number of facets. Actually, there are about four thousand of these little divisions and each is a separate lens. By means of the micro-cinematograph it has been possible to demonstrate a portion of the cye of a flv so magnified that an obiect waved in front could be seen reflected, as it passed to and fro, in each lens.

Chapter XX

Eyes of Wonder and Eyes that are Useless

By S. T. Burfield

Senior Lecturer in Zoology, Liverpool University

We all pity the blind man, and in so doing pay tribute to the greatness of the gift of sight. Sight to the normal human being means the ability not only to distinguish between light and darkness, but also to detect variation in the intensity of light and to recognize the form and colour of surrounding objects. The human eye, endowed with these wonderful powers, is the most perfect organ of sight in the animal kingdom; but just as some human beings have imperfect sight—for example, in colour-blindness—so we find various grades in the power of sight amongst other animals, and in the organs responsible for this sense.

Beginning with the Protozoa, those microscopic specks of living matter, we find that the majority have nothing in the nature of localised organs which we could call eyes, yet they react to light to some extent, and tend to move to a position where they find the light of an intensity which suits their particular needs. In these cases we have a simple "seeing without eyes," and it would seem that the general living material of their bodies, their protoplasm, was able to distinguish light from darkness and to detect sudden variations in the amount of illumination.

In some protozoa, however, we find that the light-detecting power has become more definitely localised in the body of the animal, and the simplest type of "eye" is produced. These are known as eye-spots. These spots are distinguished by the presence of some coloured pigment which serves to absorb light falling upon it. One of the best known examples of such an eye-spot among the protozoa is found in the minute green creature (*Euglena viridis*) which often swarms in stagnant water. This animal is markedly sensitive to light, and the eye-spot consists of a tiny patch of red pigment situated near the front end of the tiny body.

Apart from the protozoa all animals have a body composed of large numbers of minute units of living matter. These units are called cells, and with this advance in general structure there comes the possibility of a cell or a group of cells in any part of the body becoming specialised for the better performance of a particular function.

The first of these "multicellular" animals to be considered are those which comprise the group *Coelenterata*, the jellyfishes and anemones being perhaps the best known of these. A well-known little freshwater member of this group, the Hydra, is sensitive to light, and will move to the window side of a glass jar in which it is placed, but no specialised cells for light-perception can be distinguished.

Many of the related jellyfish have collections of cells containing pigment, known as ocelli. At certain places on the margin of the jellyfish there are little groups of sense cells, from each of which a process runs inwards to a nerve network. Between these cells are others containing pigment. In some cases a minute transparent body is developed as a secretion from the cells. This probably merely serves to concentrate the light on the sense cells and may be considered as a kind of lens, though there is no formation of an image. Structures of this kind may be regarded as the first stage in the development of an eye.

Another group of animals, the Spiny-skins (*Echinodermata*), also have eyes of this simple type. An examination of a common starfish will show the presence of a bright red or orange spot at the tip of each arm. Microscopic study shows that this is made up of a number of minute cups, each of which is lined with elongated cells. These cells contain pigment, and their free ends, forming the lining of the cup, are modified as clear, rod-shaped projections. It has been experimentally shown that a starfish deprived of these organs is insensible to light.

The *Coelenterata* and *Echinodermata* are radially symmetrical animals and their ocelli are correspondingly disposed. The next group to be considered, the Worms, have a more or less well-developed head, and the eyes are usually situated upon this as being the most useful position. A considerable number of animals differing a good deal from one another in structure and habit, are included within this group, and the condition of the visual organs shows corresponding variations. Nothing could be simpler than the eye-spots on the head of the common freshwater worm Naïs. Each of these consists of a single enlarged skin cell, alongside which are several smaller cells containing pigment. Other free-living worms have more complex eyes, for example, the common Nereis, found under stones at low tide.

Natural History, N Y.

LIGHTED EYES

Off Banda Island swim the fish called photoblepheron (see also p. 212). They glide in and out among the coral lighting their way with their strange luminescent spots near their eyes.

In the most advanced type found in these animals a lens-like

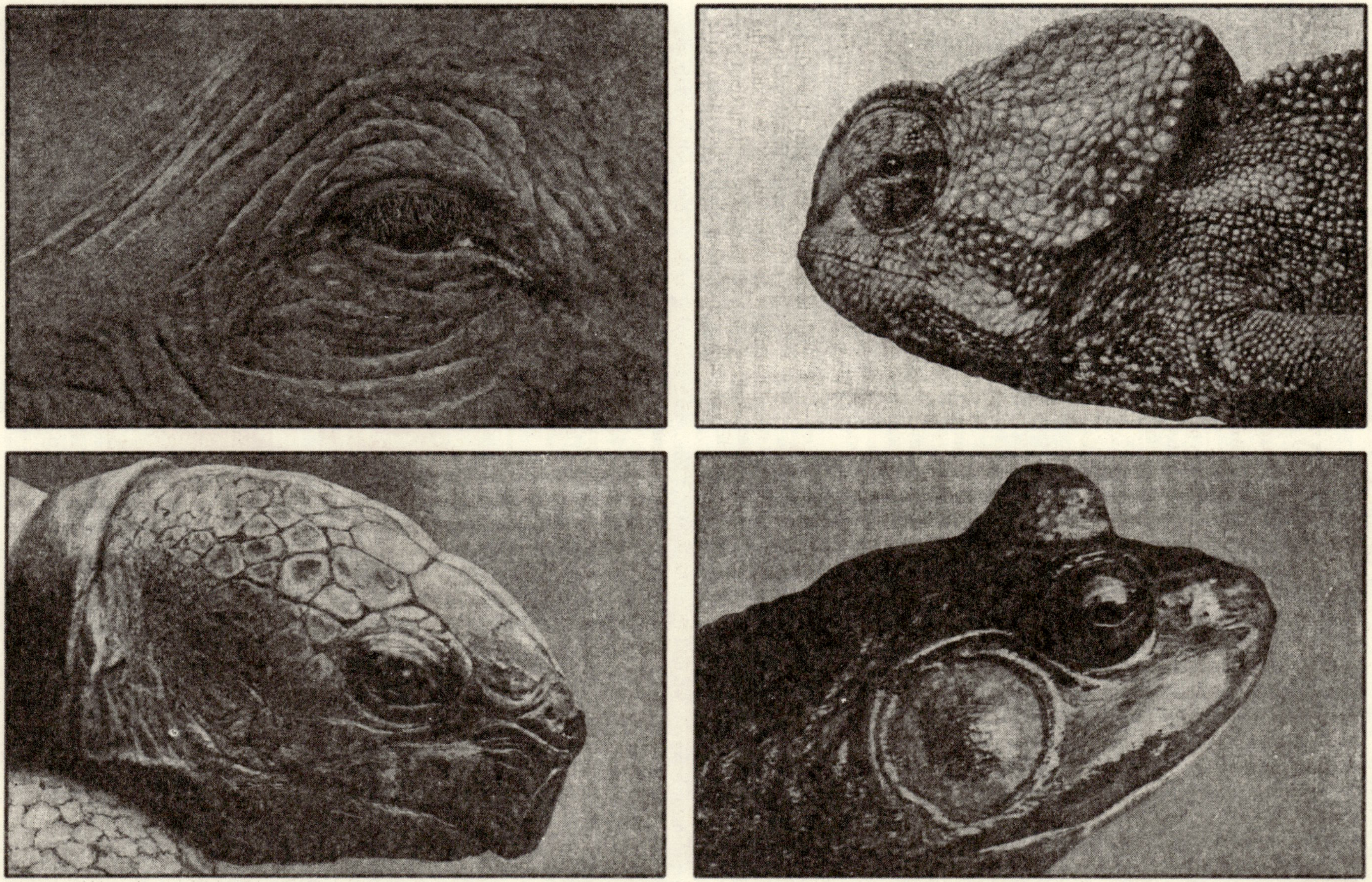

Monger and Marchant — A. E. Smith

ORGANS OF SIGHT AS THEY ARE IN THE TORTOISE, FROG, ELEPHANT, AND CHAMELEON

Man's eye is the most perfect seeing organ in all the animal world, being susceptible to an infinite number of the most delicate impressions. But when we come to four-footed beings it should be remembered that what is considered a defect in human sight may be a special adaptation for the use of an animal in the individual circumstances in which it lives. The variety in eyes is enormous. The tortoise (bottom left) and frog (bottom right) have their eyes differently situated. While the elephant (top left) has, for its size, a minute eye, the chameleon (top right) has a comparatively large one. In the latter case each eye works independently and is covered with a lid having a hole in the centre.

body is formed in the cup opening. It is improbable, however, that more than variations in light intensity are perceived by any of these. The best known of all the worms is the ubiquitous earthworm. This has no definite eyes, but careful work with a flash lamp at night will show that it is very sensitive to light, and it moves away from an illuminated area to the shadow. Moreover, it can easily be shown that the whole skin is sensitive to light to some extent, though this sensitivity is very much more strongly developed at the anterior end.

Among the animals dealt with so far we could find a series of eyes beginning with a simple patch of pigmented cells, passing through a stage in which the patch becomes cup-shaped, up to a condition in which the cup is nearly closed, and finally an eye in which a lens-like body is developed, closing the cup and serving better to concentrate the light on the sensitive cells.

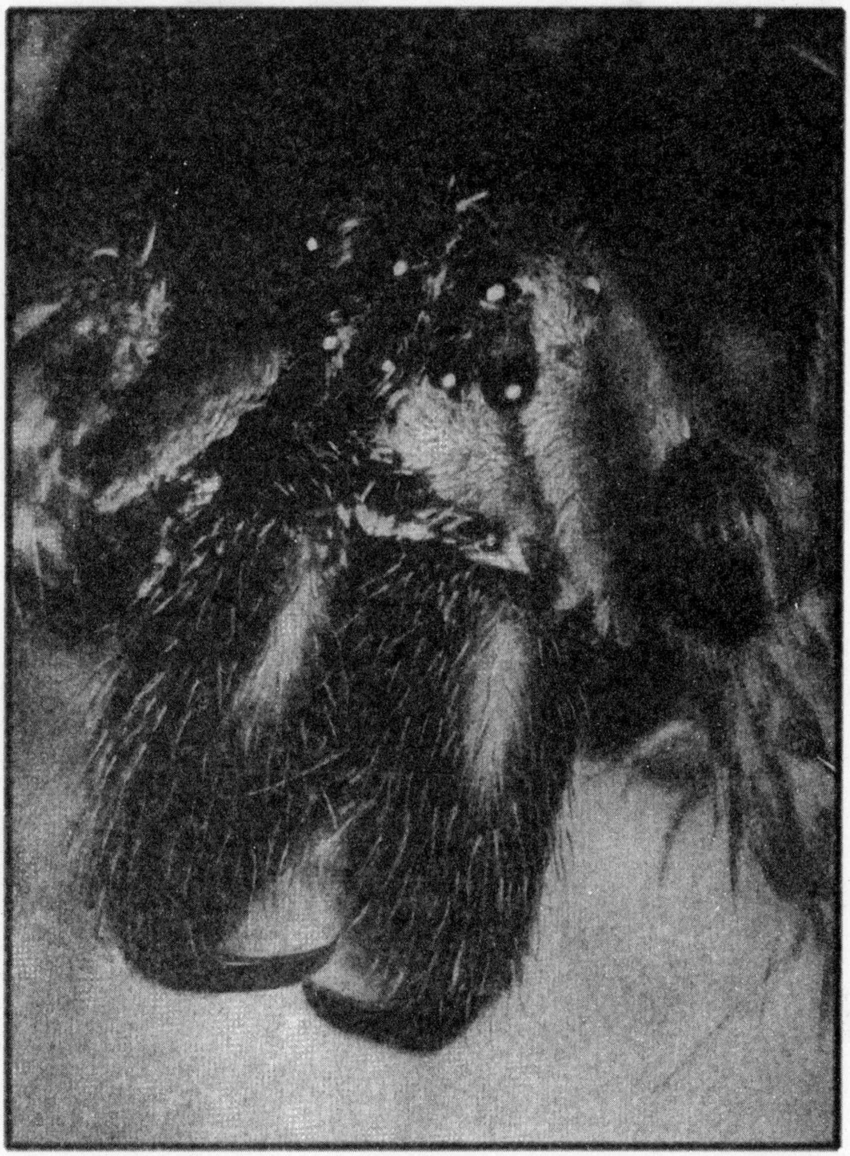

J. J. Ward

EIGHT EYES OF THE SPIDER'S FANGED HEAD

Usually the spiders are equipped with a group of six or eight ocelli, which are eye-like organs but of simpler and less developed construction than true eyes. To what extent the spider sees with its ocelli is hard to determine, for it relies very much on a highly-specialised sense of touch. The lens-like skin which covers the ocelli is moulted periodically, causing a temporary blindness.

The Mollusca, or Shellfish, a group of animals containing the snails, slugs, oysters, mussels, cuttlefish, and their allies, are of great interest in the matter of their eyes. Various stages are found among the different members, from a condition in which there are no localised eyes up to the complicated eye of the cuttlefish. Let us consider a few of the better known forms. The common English garden snail has two pairs of feelers or "horns" on its head. The second and longer pair have at their tip a small pair of black eyes. These are minute sacs, the walls of which are made of light-sensitive, pigmented cells, connected at their base with a nerve leading to the brain. The cavity of the vesicle is nearly filled with a horny lens.

In the freshwater mussel there are merely a number of pigmented papillae at the hind end of the body which are sensitive to light and shade. In the scallop, on the other hand, there is found one of the most complicated types of eye known in the Mollusca, with a well-developed lens and complicated double sensitive layer. There is no head in the mussel-like shellfish, and the eyes are situated on the margins of the fleshy mantle which lines the valves of the shell. This is the more usual position for light-sensitive organs in Mollusca with a two-valved shell. In the scallop there may be from about forty to four hundred of these beautiful organs, gleaming like little red jewels in the living animal as it rapidly moves through the water by opening and closing the valves of its shell.

There is one other type of mollusc that calls for notice. Anyone who has seen a living squid or cuttlefish would be struck by the almost human aspect of the pair of very large eyes situated one on each side of the head. Closer examination reveals the fact that these eyes are not only large but have a very complicated structure and are probably the most perfect form of eye found in the lower types of

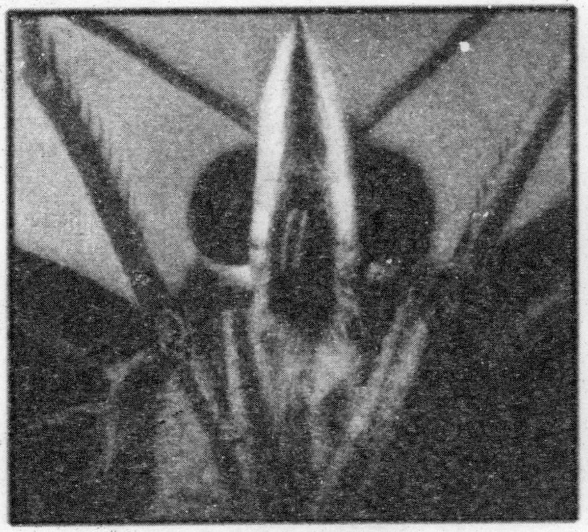

Purple Emperor Butterfly

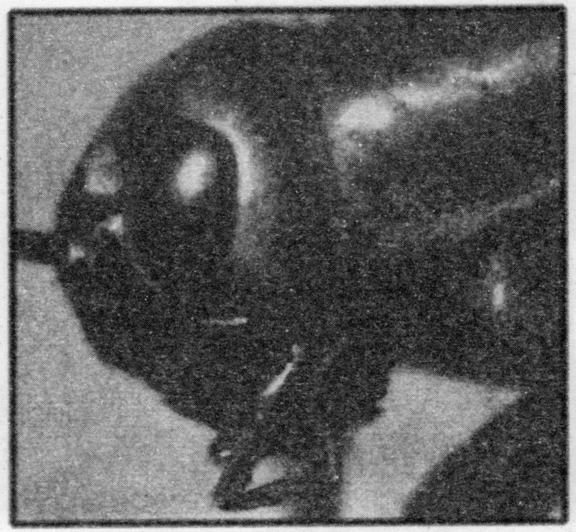

House Cricket

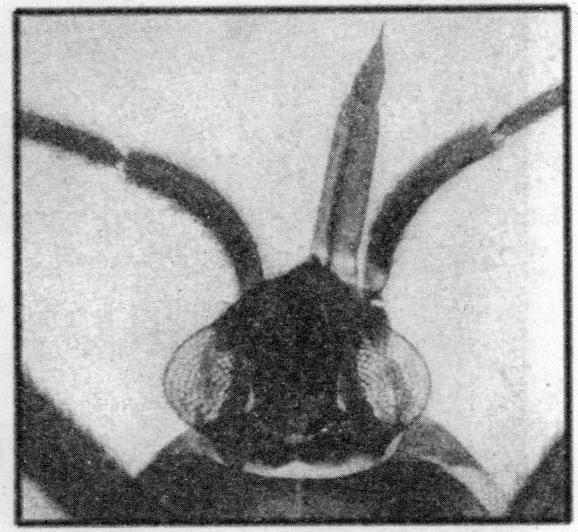

Water Skater

Large White Butterfly

Gad-fly

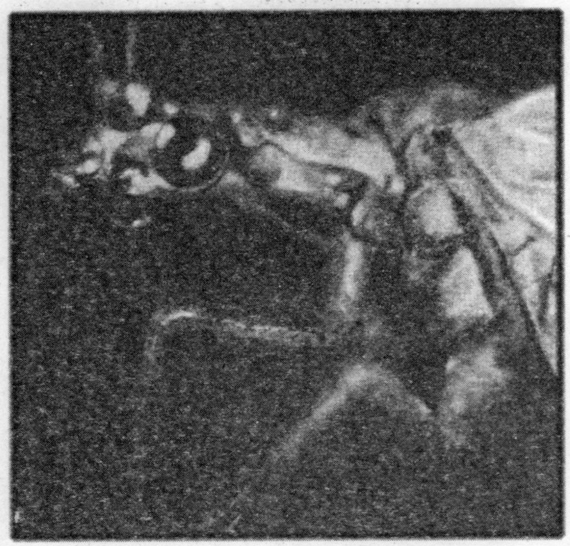

Lacewing Fly

WONDERFUL EYES OF MANY LENSES WITH WHICH SOME OF THE INSECTS SEE

The compound eyes of insects are built up in a wonderful way. The transparent external matter which covers the eye consists of a number of facets, in some insects numbering many thousands. Each of these facets gives a separate image of the object regarded. Below this external layer is a mass of corresponding facets, the surface of the true eye, which are really the upper ends of an equal number of columns which transfer the light messages to the nerves. It is thought that each facet registers an impression of a fragment of the object seen until the complete image is made up, as in a piece of mosaic, and conveyed as a whole to the brain. Further, such an arrangement gives a wide angle of vision for the avoiding of danger. Photographs by J. J. Ward animal life. Their development is interesting because in the individual animal the eyes pass from a simple type, such as we have seen in the snail, to the highly specialised form as found in the adult.

Before we deal with the type of eye found in man, there is a very large and important group of the lower animals possessing a peculiar type of visual organ which must be considered. This is the Arthropod Group (Crustacea, Insects, Spiders, and so on), which possesses a very distinctive type of eye which can certainly perceive the form of objects, and possibly also a certain amount of colour.

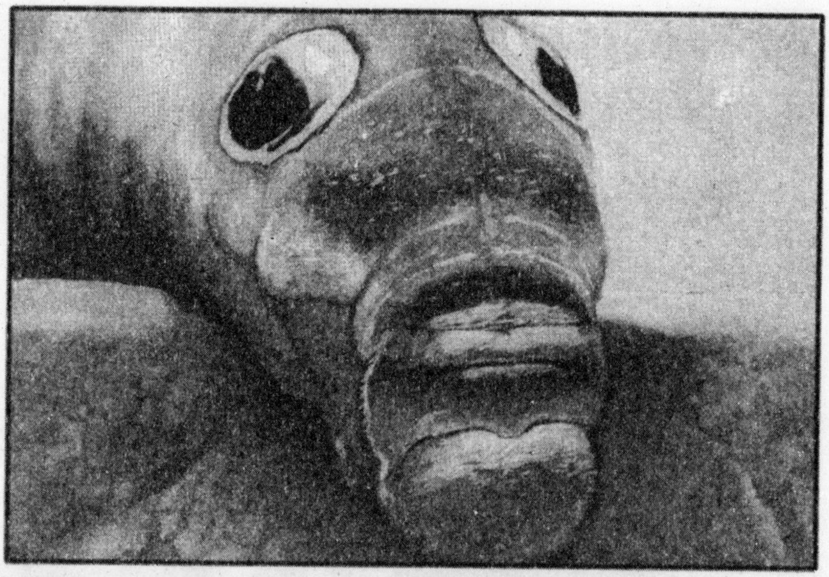

A. E. Smith

EYES AND NO EYES

Dragon-flies have their eyes almost as large as their head (bottom) and some species have 20,000 lenses per eye. The larva of the common swallow-tail butterfly (top) has markings on its body counterfeiting huge eyes, while the true eyes are in the head.

Two types of eye occur in this group, and in some cases these are both present in the same animal. These two types are called ocelli and compound eyes respectively. Perhaps the simplest type of ocellus is to be found in some of the smaller crustacea, and in the young stage of these, called the nauplius. Here it is unpaired and is placed in the middle of the head. One of the commonest of these small crustacea is found in fresh water and is called Cyclops.

The ocelli in these examples are of a simple type, a group of cells with a pigment mass, a nerve connexion, and usually a lens-like thickening of the skin which serves to concentrate the light to some degree. In the large and important group of Insects ocelli are often found associated with compound eyes. The common housefly and the bee, for instance, have three ocelli arranged in a triangle on the top of the head. These ocelli have the general form of the type of eye we have found in many of the Worms and Mollusca. There is a cup lined with sensory cells and pigment cells and a thickening of the skin to form a lens. This is the only kind of eye found in the caterpillar stage of a butterfly or moth. There may be as many as twenty of these eyes in some insects grouped on each side of the head.

The Spiders form a group of animals usually detested by the average man, woman and child. Closer acquaintance with these creatures, however, reveals much of remarkable interest. They are certainly not sharp-sighted nor long-sighted, relying more on a highly-developed sense of touch in their dealings with the outer world, but they have eyes and these are very beautiful objects. Situated on the top or front of the head region there is to be seen a group of usually six or eight of these organs shining like little gems. The exact disposition of these varies greatly in different kinds of spiders, but in all cases they have a structure essentially like that of the ocelli of insects.

An interesting point in connexion with this type of eye is that the lens, being a part of the outside covering of the animal, is cast at the time of moulting and the animal is temporarily blind. In the spiders it is said that the eyes do not all moult simultaneously. Sometimes the eyes are not all of the same appearance, some being black and the rest pearly white.

Now we come to the compound eye, which is so characteristic of the Arthropod. If we examine the head of any insect, such as a fly, a dragonfly, a butterfly or a beetle, we find that it consists largely of two great hemispherical masses, often having a brilliant metallic lustre, perhaps green or purple. These are the compound eyes. If one of these be examined more closely with a hand lens, it will be

Neville Kingston

SPECIALISED PERISCOPE EYES OF A LAND CRAB

Among the several sorts of land crabs is the calling crab, so called because one claw is very much larger than the other, and with this disproportionate limb it makes brandishing gestures as though beckoning or calling to someone. These crabs live in the sand on beaches, where they dig burrows for themselves. At the mouth of these burrows they sit with their eyes projecting above ground like periscopes. When this unusual-looking crab is not on the look-out these long eye-stalks lie at rest along the front of the shell.

seen that the surface is divided up into a number of square or hexagonal areas called facets. These divisions are in the transparent external layer which covers the eye, but they correspond to a similar division of the lower layers, for the whole eye is really built up of a series of columnar units called ommatidia. These units have a complicated structure, but each may be compared to an ocellus. The compound eye in fact is believed to be derived from a group of ocelli.

The number of facets (or ommatidia) in a compound eye may be very large, especially in some of the insects. To give a few figures, the cockroach has eighteen hundred, the housefly has about four thousand, the humble bee four thousand, whilst some dragonflies have as many as twenty thousand.

The mode of working of a compound eye is very interesting. It is believed that in each ommatidium an image is produced by the light from an object or part of an object which is exactly opposite that particular ommatidium. Thus with an object such as a stick only a portion is projected on the sense cells of each ommatidium, and the sum of the resulting images is built up into a single image which is transmitted to the brain. Such an image may be compared to a mosaic built up of many pieces of one size.

There is more in the story of the compound eye than this, however. In many crustacea inhabiting shallow water and in day-flying insects the pigment occupies different positions in the eye according to the intensity of the light. In bright light the pigment surrounds the ommatidia, and a mosaic or "apposition" image is formed as already described. On the other hand, in darkness or feeble light it has been found that the pigment blinds separating the ommatidia are withdrawn and the ommatidia do not now act separately, but a combined image is thrown on the sensory layer. This is the "superposition" image. The eyes of many night-flying insects, as moths and fireflies, are permanently in this condition and are "day-blind." Butterflies, on the other hand, have the pigment permanently expanded and are in consequence "night-blind."

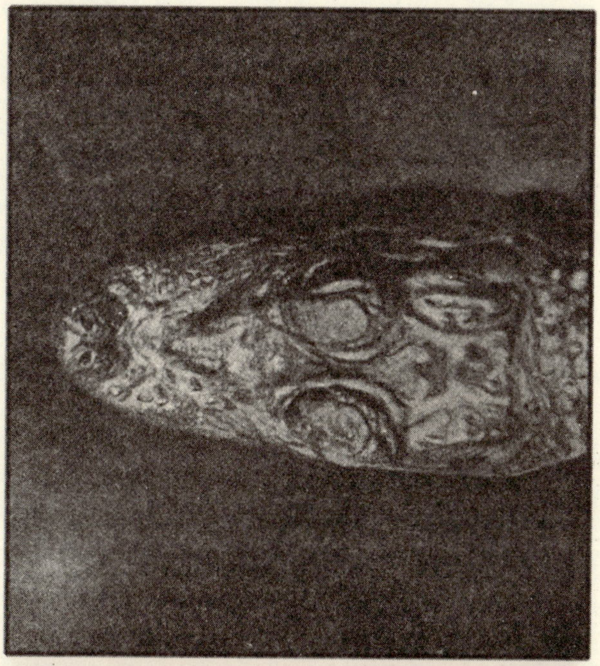

F. W. Bond

Autotype

EYES OF THE CROCODILE WHICH NEVER SHED TEARS

To describe the tears of the hypocrite the phrase " crocodile tears " was coined, apparently from an ancient belief that the huge reptile was in the habit of weeping at the thought of the hardness of fate which decreed that it should have to kill animals for food. Really, the lachrymal, or tear glands, are lacking altogether in the crocodile. Above are the eyes closed (left) and (right) a view from above of a crocodile's head, showing the eye coverings. In the bottom photograph we see the eyes of an alligator.

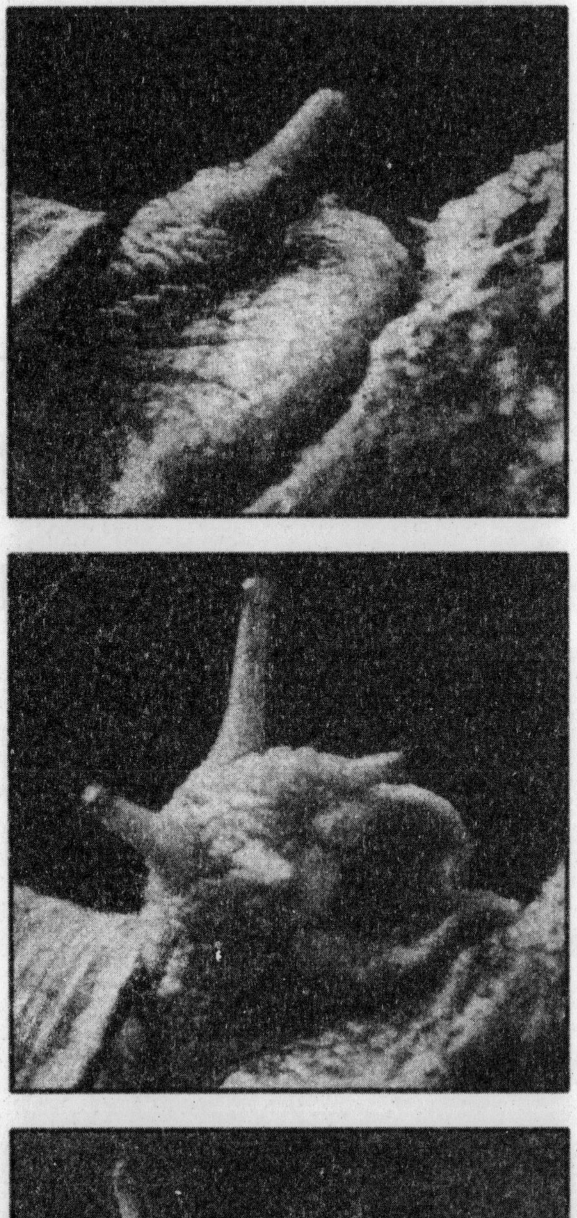

J. J. Ward

THE SNAIL WAKES

In this series of photographs we can observe how the snail's eyes function. The familiar "horns" are, when the snail is in its shell, like the fingers of a glove inside out. When the eyes are to be used the horns elongate as the glove-finger would when put on.

Among the insects the common whirligig beetle (*Gyrinus*) lives most of its life skating about on the surface of ponds and has its compound eyes each divided into an upper and a lower portion, the former being adapted for sight in air and the latter for sight under water. Thus this animal can keep a sharp look out for prey or enemies above and below at the same time. The males of some may-flies also have the eyes divided, one portion being raised on a pillar.

Contrary to what might be expected a great range of variation is found in the eyes of deep sea forms, which apparently are all living under similar conditions. Many stages are found from almost normal eyes to their complete absence. It is not easy to explain this, but a factor which must be taken into account is that a very large number of deep sea animals produce light themselves (phosphorescence), and a considerable illumination is doubtless present from this source even in very deep waters.

The Vertebrata include five types of backboned animals, the Fishes, Amphibia (frogs, newts), Reptiles (snakes, tortoises, lizards, and so on), Birds, and Mammals, or four-footed beasts. Man is placed in the last group. The structure of the eyes is very similar in all of these, so we may take the human eye as an example.

THE eye is a globular structure which lies in a protective socket in the skull. Within this socket the eyeball can be moved about within certain limits by means of some special muscles. The exposed portion of the eye is protected by two movable folds of skin, the eyelids. These folds are continuous with a very delicate transparent layer which passes over the exposed part of the surface of the eyeball and is closely adherent to this. This layer is the Conjunctiva, and inflammation of this membrane produces the condition known as a "blood-shot" eye.

The wall of the eyeball consists of three layers. Only the outer of these is continuous over the whole surface, but all three are perforated at the back to allow of the exit of the optic nerve. The outermost coat is protective, and over the front of the eye this layer becomes transparent and is here called the Cornea. The rest of this protective layer which can be seen from the front forms the "white" of the eye. The next coat, the Choroid, is thin and dark-coloured and contains a network of blood vessels. This layer is missing immediately under the cornea, but a curtain-like circular fold of it extends inwards all round a short distance behind the cornea. This fold, the Iris, has pigment on it which gives the colour to the eye. An aperture in the centre of the fold affords a passage for the light into the interior of the eyeball. This aperture is the Pupil. The iris contains muscles by which the size of the pupil can be altered. Thus the iris acts as a very perfect diaphragm, the size of the pupil opening being regulated according to the brightness of the light; the brighter the light the smaller the opening. In man the alteration in the size of the pupil is not under the control of the will as it appears to be in the reptiles and birds, and the amount of alteration is also much smaller than in the cat and many birds, for instance.

Just within the iris is the Lens. This is a perfectly clear bi-convex mass, like glass in appearance. It is, however, not hard but may be slightly altered in shape. It lies in a very thin transparent membranous sac, which is closely applied to its surface. Around the edges this sac is continued as a sheet of tissue extending from the lens margin to the choroid coat. At the point of attachment to the latter the choroid is thickened, and from here to the sclerotic coat runs a series of muscle fibres, the Ciliary Muscle. The innermost coat of the eyeball is the actual sensory layer, the Retina. This is missing from the front portions of the eye, so that it has the form of a cup. The optic nerve running to the brain arises from the inner surface of the retina facing the lens, so that it perforates all three layers of the eye to get out. The cavity of the retinal cup and the space between the lens and the cornea are not empty, but are both filled with a clear substance. The latter space contains a liquid, the Aqueous Humour, whilst the retinal cup is filled with a gelatinous substance, known as the Vitreous Humour.

Some Vertebrates have an additional development in the eyeball layers. On the outer surface of the choroid in most fishes and some amphibia and turtles there is a silvery layer containing calcic crystals which extends on to the outer surface of the iris, giving this a silvery appearance. On the other hand, in some fishes and carnivorous mammals, such as the cat, and so on, the side of the choroid towards the retina develops a layer with a metallic lustre. This layer reflects light and is the cause of the eyes of these animals shining at night. This glow is due to some light entering the eye and being reflected to the observer. It may be pointed out that no animal can really " see in the dark." Some light is always necessary, as the eye is an organ for the reception of light from some outside source, though some animals have very sensitive eyes and are able to see in very weak light.

With this short description of the vertebrate eye we may now pass to some consideration of how it works as an optical instrument.

The eye may be compared to a camera, both consisting of two essential parts, a layer which reacts or is sensitive to light waves, the photographic plate or the retina, and an apparatus consisting of lens and diaphragm, or iris, which directs the light on the first part and focusses a sharp picture or image of external objects there. Anyone who has worked with a camera will know two fundamental things in the operation of this instrument: the image thrown by the lens on the back of the camera is upside down or inverted and, secondly, to make this image sharp and distinct, the lens is moved nearer to or further away from the plate according as the object is more distant or nearer.

In the vertebrate eye it is equally true that an inverted image is thrown on the retina by the lens.

Neville Kingston

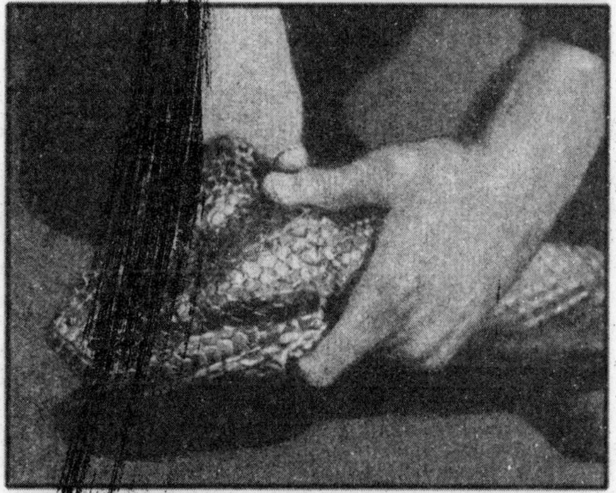

Natural History, N.Y.

F Martin Duncan.

EYES ADAPTED FOR WATER

The common sepia (bottom) has large, almost human-looking eyes, while the turtle's (top) are adapted to its habit of lying all but submerged in the water. The Anaconda (middle) also lives much in water, and so has its eyes in the top part of its head.

Do we then see things upside down? The answer is in the negative, because an object may be considered as a collection of radiants or points from which light is passing into the eye and forming a series of images on the retina, and these images are referred, as it were projected, outward each along its ray line. Thus each radiant point is seen in its correct position in space, and we really do see things erect just for the same reason that we see objects in their right places. But in another way, we reinvert the image of an object in the very act of external reference.

The second point mentioned above with reference to the camera was the focussing of a sharp image on the sensitive plate. In the eye we must also have a sharp image of the object focussed on the sensory cells of the retina if we want to see distinctly. The power of focussing a distinct image of objects at differing distances from the eye is called Accommodation, and it is brought about in different ways in the various Vertebrate groups. Apparently the lower types of fish life, such as the sharks, skates and their allies, cannot focus objects at all. The eye might do the focussing in the same way as the camera by moving the lens further from the retina for near objects and nearer to the retina for distant ones. This is the way in which accommodation is effected in the bony fishes and probably also in the Amphibia.

We could obtain a clear image on the plate of a camera in another way. Instead of moving the same lens nearer to or further from the plate we might change the lens without altering its position with regard to the plate, using a more convex lens for a near object and a less convex one for a more distant object. Accommodation in the mammalian, bird and reptile eye is brought about by a somewhat similar process. By the contraction of the ciliary muscle the lens is more loosely held by the supporting membrane. The lens is not hard, but elastic, and when the membrane which supports it is slightly loosened it becomes more convex. Now it is able to focus nearer objects on the retina. The nerve control of the ciliary muscle is very delicate and in the normal eye the convexity of the lens can be adjusted for objects at all distances. This wonderful arrangement is equivalent to the

Neville Kingston

A THIRD EYELID IN OPERATION

Among the birds the eyes are equipped with a third eyelid called the nictitating—that is, "winking"—membrane. This is drawn rapidly upward over the eye at need. The upper photograph shows a golden eagle's head with the eye open. Below is a crane with the eyelids still open but the membrane drawn over the pupil.

possession of a whole series of lenses of different thicknesses. The normal human eye at rest is adjusted so that parallel rays of light entering the eye are focussed sharply on the retina. This means that the eye is arranged to focus distant objects, in practice those beyond thirty feet. To see nearer objects clearly requires an effort, the muscular effort of accommodation, which can be quite easily felt if one looks at a distant object and then quickly at something quite near.

Let us conclude this article by noting the principal variations in eye structure which are found among the various types of Vertebrates.

In the Fishes the eyelids are poorly developed, or altogether absent, and the eyes are kept moist with water. The lens is peculiar and is specially adapted for vision under water. It is denser than in land animals and is nearly spherical. Both these qualities give it greater refractive power, which is necessary on account of the medium in which these animals live. The cornea is also very flattened. There is no ciliary muscle, so that fishes cannot accommodate by altering the shape of the lens. The eye is passively adjusted for near objects and they probably accommodate for distant vision by drawing the lens back nearer the retina, as mentioned above.

MANY of the fishes from the deep sea are blind, but some have relatively enormous eyes, often elongated so as to appear cylindrical like telescopes. These probably can make use of "phosphorescent" light as is also the case with some forms of the deep-sea Crustacea. Blind fishes are also to be found in underground streams in caves, such as the River Styx of the Mammoth Cave in North America. All these blind forms make up for the loss of the sense of sight by having an extraordinarily acute sense of touch.

Whilst buying any of the common flat fish, such as plaice or sole, many must have noticed the curious, twisted appearance of the head and the odd way in which the eyes are placed. The story of this twist is very fascinating. The very young fish has the more ordinary fish shape like, say, a herring, with one eye on each side of the head in the usual position. As it grows up the fish becomes deeper bodied and then tends to lie on one side on the bottom. Thus, one eye would become practically useless lying on the mud or sand. This eye now moves round the head from beneath to what is now the acting upper surface of the fish, and during this movement some of the head bones and also the mouth become twisted.

There is nothing special to say about the Amphibian eye except to note that the accommodation is brought about as in the fish, and that the lens is nearly spherical as in that group.

There are several points of interest in the Reptilian eye. In many reptiles not only is there an upper and a lower eyelid, but a third lid (the nictitating membrane) is present as a transparent sheet which can be drawn across the eye from the anterior angle. In snakes this membrane is permanently drawn across the eye and the upper and lower lids are absent. In the lizards and turtles there is a ring of small plate-like bones embedded in the outer protective coat of the eyeball. In the reptiles, as in birds and mammals, we also find various glands developed under the eyelids which produce watery fluid for the lubrication and cleaning of the exposed portion of the eyeball. One group of these are called the lachrymal or tear glands. These are lacking from a few reptiles—including the crocodiles! Crocodile tears are, then, non-existent.

Thomas Fall

REFLECTING EYES

Cats cannot see in the dark. There is some light in what is usually called "the dark," and the cat's eyes reflect that light from a layer of matter, round the eye-ball, which has a metallic lustre. Hence the shining eye-balls that we so often see.

Birds, as is well known, have very keen sight and their eyes have several peculiarities. The iris varies in colour from the more common brown of the mammals, and may be yellow or red or even white. The rings of little bones in the protective coat of the eyeball, which were noted already as being found in some reptiles, are present in all birds. These radiate from the margin of the iris and fit together so as to slide over one another slightly. They may be made to squeeze the ball so as to help accommodation for clear vision of very near objects.

The nictitating membrane is well developed and on watching a bird's eye closely it may be seen from time to time drawn upwards over the eye as a semi-transparent membrane. The shape of the eyeball is peculiar. The posterior part is hemispherical. Then follows the central portion shaped like a truncated cone and, finally, a hemispherical corneal region. The eyeball is thus somewhat telescopic in its shape.

Finally, a few words about the Mammals. The general description of the structure of the human eye already given would apply substantially to the eye of any mammal. There are, however, a few points worth noting. The upper and lower eyelids are present, but the nictitating membrane is reduced to a rudimentary fold at the inner angle of the eye. The iris is most usually of a dark chocolate brown colour, due to a similar pigment to that present in the choroid coat of which the iris is a continuation. This, then, is probably the original and normal colour of the eye. The blue and grey eye are the result of peculiar structure and deficiency of pigment. A well-known exception to the brown colour among the mammals is the yellow iris which is characteristic of the cat tribe.

The pupil in man and many other mammals is a round opening, but in two large groups, the cat tribe and the grazing animals, the oxen, sheep, and so on, the pupil is greatly elongated. In the smaller cats it is lengthened vertically and in the grazers horizontally. The larger cats, such as the lion and tiger, have round pupils. The whales also have a horizontally elongated pupil and an extremely thickened outer protective coat to the eyeball. It is also interesting to note that in these animals the cornea is flattened and the lens nearly spherical, both of these being adaptations for seeing in water, just as we have noticed in the case of fishes. The eye in whales is relatively very small and is often placed low down on the side of the head near the angle of the mouth. From the position and comparative immobility of the eyeball it would appear that the whale has a small radius of vision. In a whale seventy feet long the eyeball measures about five inches in diameter. Among the better-known four-footed beasts which have a relatively small eye is the rhinoceros, and this animal has poor eyesight. The eyes are very much reduced in some mammals which are nocturnal or burrowing forms. In the moles there may be a fusion of the lids, but in the mole-like form of Australia (*Notoryctes*) there is no lens and no differentiation of the two outer coats of the eye. The retina also is feebly developed. The group of bats also have poorly developed eyes, but, as in other similar cases, these blind or semi-blind forms have a very acute sense of hearing or smelling, or there may be an extraordinarily acute tactile sense as appears to be the case in the bats themselves.

Neville Kingston

James

UNUSUAL EYES

The rhinoceros lives a life where long vision is unnecessary, and is thus very short-sighted. Also the eyes are placed, not near the ears but, near the snout. The hippo (top) has eyes in the top of its head, so that it can almost submerge itself in water and yet see.

We leave the subject of eyes by mentioning a structure developed on the top of the brain in Vertebrates called the pineal body. In some lizards this is a small vesicle lying just beneath the skin on the top of the head, connected with the brain and having an extraordinary similarity to an unpaired median eye. Whatever may have been the function of this body in past ages, there is no conclusive evidence that it subserves a light-perceiving function in any living form. The French philosopher Descartes believed it to be the seat of the soul.

Chapter XXI

Living Lights in the Animal World

By F. Martin Duncan

Librarian to the Zoological Society of London

AMONG the many marvels of Nature none is more remarkable or dramatically striking than that strange power, possessed by certain members of the animal world, of producing during the hours of darkness that wondrous shining radiance termed phosphorescence, and thereby transforming themselves into veritable living night-lights ; burning with a pale intermittent glow, or brightly scintillating like flashing meteors through the warm darkness of a tropic night, or turning the depths of the sea into a fairy realm—shining with a light that gives out no heat ; burning with a flame that does not consume.

Although this wonderful phenomenon may be observed, in varying degrees, in almost every division of the Animal Kingdom, a careful analysis shows us that it attains its highest development among the forms of animal life that inhabit the sea ; indeed, the only vertebrate, or backboned animals, having true light-producing organs, are to be found among species of marine fishes. On land the power of phosphorescence, or luminescence, which is really a better word to use, for these strange natural fires have nothing to do with phosphorus, reaches its maximum among certain species of insects ; the light that has occasionally been observed on the breast and thighs of the heron and on the plumage of the owl being due to the presence of luminescent bacteria, and not produced by the birds themselves.

Naturally the function and importance of these light-producing organs in the life of animals have been subjects of considerable speculation and controversy. But despite much theory and a certain amount of careful and practical experimental work, knowledge cannot be honestly said to have advanced very far ; much still remains to be ascertained, more particularly in its bearing on the life of the animal and its environment. The chemist may be able to tell us that luminescence in certain groups of animals is the result of the interaction of two substances to which he has given the names luciferin and luciferase, in the presence of water and oxygen, but that does not help us very far along the road to the solution of the puzzling question of why in two closely related species, which we may for simplicity call A and B, and both apparently leading similar lives in a similar environment, species A possesses well-developed light-producing organs, while species B shows, so far as can be ascertained, no trace of them at any stage of its life whatever.

WHILE it may perhaps be right to suppose that metabolic factors, the chemical changes taking place in the living tissues, have played a not unimportant part in the history of luminescence, a closer scrutiny of these light-producing organs and the discovery during recent years of tissues actually serving as lenses and reflectors, would seem to place beyond doubt that such highly developed organs must function for the projection of light in very definite directions, indeed have become natural searchlights ; and that in their presence we are faced with a biological problem of far greater importance and significance. That the marine fishes in which these most highly developed luminescent organs, complete with lens and reflector, are found, use them as searchlights there can be little doubt, though for what particular purpose, whether for alarming foes, attacking prey, recognition of their own kin, or for visual help in locomotion through their dim water world is, indeed, far less certain.

F. M. Duncan

TROPIC FIREFLY

Glowing green and red like jewels in the tropic night, fire flies are often used by women in South America and the West Indies as ornaments for the hair. The fire " fly " is really a small beetle.

The surface waters of the sea are, at certain seasons of the year, densely populated by minute and very varied forms of life, collectively known to the student of marine zoology under the term Plankton, and actually forming the primary source of food supply to the bulk of our marketable marine fish. One of the chief factors that will determine an abundant or a poor harvest of mackerel or herring off our coasts, is the abundance or scarcity of these floating organisms. They are a strange assemblage ; many belong to the simplest forms of animal life, the Protozoa ; others are the young or larval stages of molluscs, of marine worms, and of various species of crabs, starfish and sea-urchins, together with adult crustaceans, and jelly-fish or Medusae of all sorts and sizes ; and a large number are phosphorescent to a greater or less degree.

On a still, warm summer night every rippling wave as it breaks upon the shore sparkles and flashes with gleams of silvery light, and a fishing boat slowly

gliding across the bay leaves a fairy trail in its wake, at every dip the oars scintillating as if surrounded by liquid flames. Far out in mid-ocean, particularly in the warmer tropical and subtropical seas, these phosphorescent displays become more intense and awe-inspiring. No one who has had the good fortune during an ocean voyage to witness what sailors sometimes call a "milk-sea" could ever forget the mystery and beauty of so marvellous a sight. The night is intensely dark, only the stars faintly gleaming in the immense dome of the heavens, while the good ship appears to be sailing mile after mile through a sea of molten silver, the swell breaking against her sides like sheets of leaping, bluish tinted flames.

If we were to lower a glass jar over the side of the ship we should find, on hauling it inboard, that the water with which it is now filled sparkles with myriad points of light that flash out into brighter phosphorescence every time the jar is shaken. In the well-lit cabin we should no longer be able to watch this pyrotechnic display, but we should be able to detect the presence of a number of little, somewhat oval, transparent specks of jelly, not much bigger than a fair sized pin's head, moving rhythmically through the water as if propelled by some unseen force. Our jelly-speck is really a perfect little member of the Protozoa, known as the Noctiluca, and though scarcely measuring one twenty-fifth of an inch in diameter is really a giant of its kind, most of the Protozoa being almost, if not quite, invisible to the naked eye. Seen under a microscope the Noctiluca appears as a tiny crystal globe, rather like a peach in shape, its delicate surface marked with a fine net-work that reminds us of the veining of the skin of a white currant or a gooseberry. Down one side there is a slight indentation in which the mouth of the tiny creature is hidden away, and from a point in this depression arises a short lasher or flagellum, the hidden force that propelled the little creature through the water when we watched it in the jar.

When the surrounding water is agitated, the Noctiluca glows with a bluish or greenish phosphorescence. The light is not constant, but appears and disappears rhythmically, almost like the revolving light in a lighthouse, and is apparently emitted from a number of minute, slightly opaque points scattered over the body of the tiny animal. When the Noctiluca is excited, these points first shine out, the light

J. J. Ward

GLOW WORM, THE FIREFLY'S EUROPEAN RELATIVE

Male glow worms have wings and look like beetles (bottom), but the female of the species (top), which emits the softly shining light of opal tint that is so familiar, is wingless and looks like a grub. The light comes from a number of spots on the abdomen and is used to attract the male in the darkness.

quickly spreading and suffusing the whole of the transparent little body with a brilliant luminosity. So bright is the light produced that a glass test tube fifteen millimetres in diameter filled with a mass of phosphorescent Noctilucae will illuminate the face of a watch sufficiently to enable one to read the time when held at the distance of a foot away.

Many of the so-called jelly-fish, the Medusae, are brilliantly luminescent, and it is a wonderful sight on a warm summer night that is revealed when we

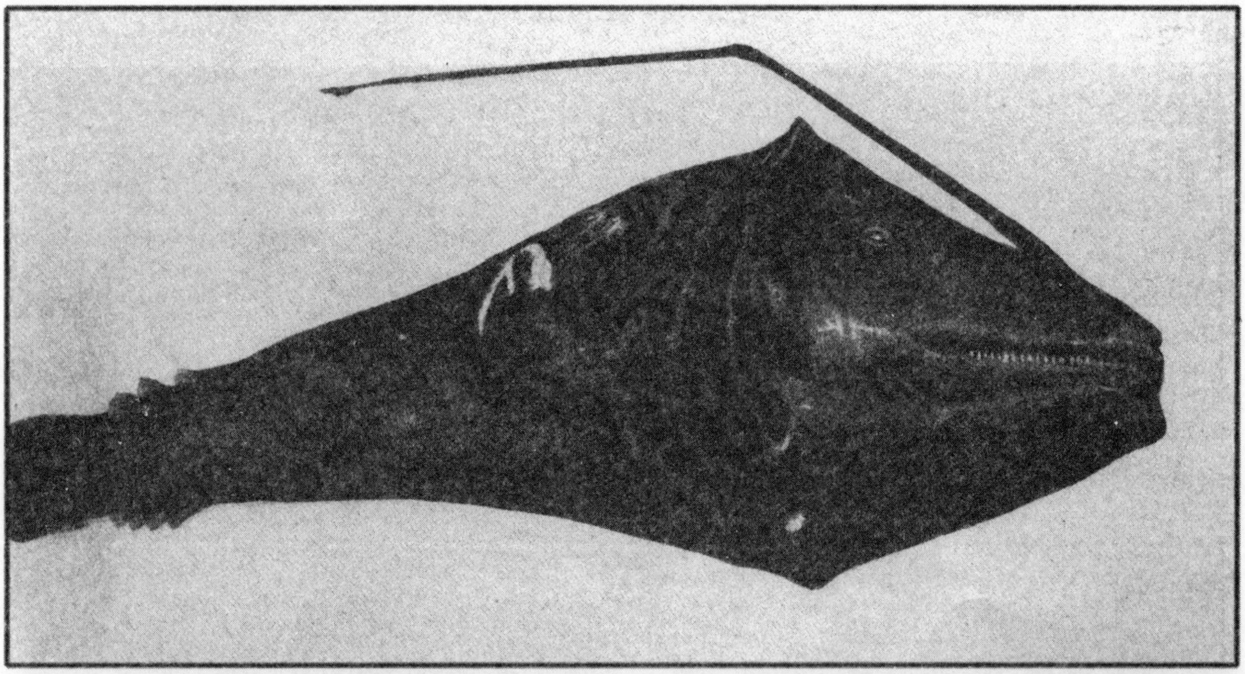

W. S. Berridge

ANGLER FISH WITH LUMINOUS BAIT TO CATCH THEIR PREY

Deep down, far below the slightest influence of sunlight, live these two ugly fish which have evolved a light-generating apparatus for the purpose of picking up a living. The melanocetus (bottom) is known—and very justly, if appearances count for anything—as the sea-devil and is famous for its dreadful teeth. The upper photograph shows us another of the angler fishes which has a lump on the end of its "line" that shines in the dark depths attracting other fish within reach. It is found in the East Pacific at a depth of about 770 fathoms.

Natu al History, N.Y.

EXTRAORDINARY PROTECTIVE MEASURE ON THE PART OF A DEEP-SEA WORM

The power of giving out light is found in some of the worms of the sea. In this illustration we have the scene, constructed from scientific research, enacted when a crab seizes a luminous worm, cutting it in two with its claws. The captured piece of the worm lights up and wriggles, thus distracting attention from the other end which remains unlighted and so escapes. Two of the worm's luminous scales are seen floating near the crab. This and the succeeding illustrations in this chapter are from scientific drawings in the journal of the Franklin Institute.

lean over the side and look into the quiet dark water as the boat slowly passes through a shoal. Lit up with their cold, greenish or bluish fires the Medusae rise out of the inky depths of the ocean and pass by, their " umbrellas " gently pulsating, and their long tentacles streaming out behind like the tails of a comet. In some species the whole surface of the disc or umbrella is illumined ; or the luminescence may be confined to the upper part of the disc, or to the fringing tentacles. Sometimes on a dark night the edge of a sandy shore will be outlined in pulsating phosphorescent gleams, due to hundreds of these jelly-fish being washed up by the tide.

MOST of the Ctenophora, the so-called Comb-bearing jellies, are vividly phosphorescent at night, while in the daytime they glisten with rainbow-tinted iridescence caused by the rhythmic beat of the comb-like bands of cilia by means of which these frail, crystal-like creatures propel themselves in the sea.

These comb-bearers are wonderfully active little creatures, and at certain seasons of the year they literally swarm in the surface waters of the sea, while thousands are left stranded on the shore by the ebbing tide. The so-called Sea-gooseberry (*Homiphora plumosa*) is a very common species on our coasts, and is about the size of a hazel nut, and looks very like a small, glass gooseberry encircled by eight regularly spaced bands of cilia. The little creature is also provided with two long and extremely contractile tentacles, which stream out in graceful curves as their owner slowly moves through the water.

Perhaps the most remarkable comb-bearer is the Venus's Girdle (*Cestus Veneris*), common in the Mediterranean, and also found in the Atlantic. It is quite unlike the rest of its relations in appearance, for they are all more or less globular in form, while the Venus's Girdle resembles a long, delicate ribbon of an exquisite silvery blue hue, and may measure over three feet in length. It moves through the water by graceful undulations of its long, slender body rather than by the movement of the combs of cilia which are grouped along the edge of the ribbon and gleam in the sunlight with a wonderful violet-tinted iridescence. At night these luminous living ribbons are a very lovely sight.

Among the swarms of minute animal life floating in the surface waters of the sea are various species of small Crustacea called Copepods, which are highly luminous, and are at times present in such large

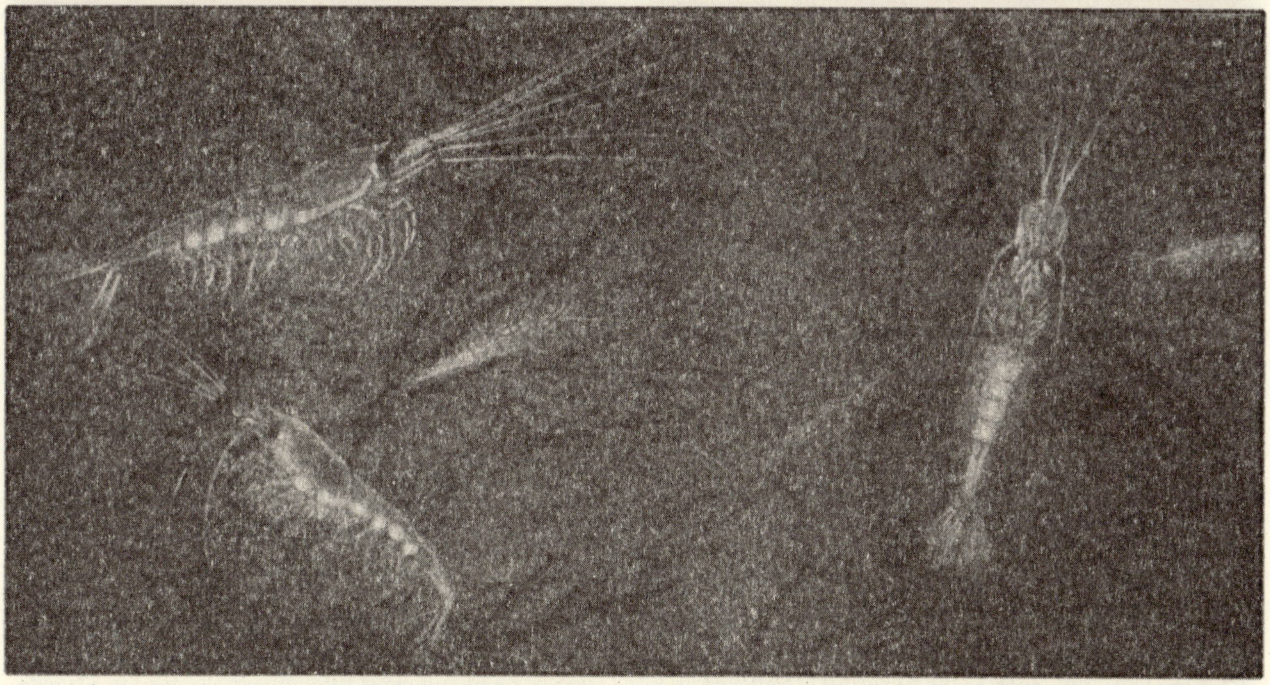

Natural History, N.Y.

SHRIMPS AND PRAWNS LIGHTING UP THE WATERS AS THEY SWIM

Parts of the bodies of certain shrimps (lower drawing) emit a radiance giving them a strange appearance as though they were ships with rows of portholes through which light was shining from within. These strangely equipped crustaceans are shown swimming in and out among the seaweed. In the upper illustration are some deep-sea prawns which, instead of lighting themselves, discharge heavy rings of opaque luminous substance brightening all the water above them. These clouds rather resemble smoke puffed from a pipe.

Natural History, N.Y.

LUMINOUS SQUIDS THAT SWIM DEEP DOWN IN THE SEA OF JAPAN

Phosphorescence—or rather the phenomenon so called, for it has nothing to do with phosphorus—is a most complex matter when its occurrence among the marine animals is studied. While some creatures no doubt use their power of illumination in order to see their prey and others, like the angler fish (page 207), have developed it into a highly specialised lure, yet some fish use their light in a way which one cannot explain on these lines. The deep-sea squids can light up different parts of their bodies as will be seen by a study of this picture.

numbers as to produce long trails of phosphorescent light. The luminosity produced by these active little Copepods is secreted by special glands on the surface of the body, and is due to a substance having the property of becoming luminous on coming into contact with the water when issuing from these glands. Whatever the chemical action thus set up may be, it is not dependent upon the living tissues, for these luminous Copepods have been collected and dried up completely, yet still retained their luminous character; a steady glow being given off when the dried, dead specimens were placed in sea-water.

There is a very interesting little shrimp-like Crustacean called *Meganyctiphanes norvegica*, which is common at no great depth off the British coasts, and can be kept in an aquarium where its pyrotechnic displays can be observed. If the room is darkened, and the glass jar containing the creature is gently tapped, the luminous organs along the sides of its body will flash out like a row of miniature portholes on the side of a ship; the light shining brightly for a few seconds and then gradually fading out, only to appear again directly the tapping is repeated.

CERTAIN Molluscs (shell-fish, as they are often called) are luminous, such as the beautiful little Pteropods of the surface plankton, and the burrowing Pholas that bores its way into rocks on the floor of the sea. While the Pholas conceals its light so that it gleams only faintly from the opening of its tunnel, the little Pteropods, or wing-footed molluscs, are veritable fairy ships, that add their share to the luminescence of the surface waters.

There are many species of Crustacea that live at great depths, far below where the last faint gleam of daylight can possibly penetrate, and while some possess light-producing organs, others do not, but from their large, well-developed eyes obviously are not condemned to grope about in perpetual darkness. Many deep-sea animals are known to be luminous, and probably the large-eyed forms profit by the phosphorescence of these fire-flies of the deep. There is, for example, a deep-sea Hermit Crab (*Parapagurus pilosimanus*) which lives at depths of at least two thousand fathoms, or two nautical miles, in partnership with a colony of sea-anemones which it carries about with it, and probably it is able to see its way about by the light emitted by the anemones, which in return for acting as head-lights receive a share of the banquet when the Hermit dines, capturing the floating fragments of the feast by means of their tentacles. There is also a deep-sea Prawn (*Heterocarpus alphonsi*) which ejects from the orifices of special glands at the base of its antennae, or feelers, copious clouds of bluish phosphorescence that has been seen to be of sufficient intensity to illuminate a bucket of water in which the prawn had been placed so that " all its contents were visible in clearest detail."

That certain regions of the great depths of the ocean are not areas of total darkness would now seem to be clearly established as the result of recent oceanographical investigations which have proved that not only the Prawns and Crabs (*Crustacea*) but the Sea-pens, Starfishes, worms and many other invertebrate forms dwelling at these great depths are brilliantly phosphorescent ; so that the floor of the sea must present an appearance perhaps analogous to a fairly well-lit street at night, with its alternate patches of bright illumination and heavy shadows.

Phosphorescent organs are highly characteristic structures in many deep-sea fishes belonging to widely different families, and vary very greatly in their complexity, number, and mode of distribution. Usually they are found on the sides and ventral surface of the body and head, more rarely on the upper surface. In *Stomias* and *Pachystomias* there are two rows of phosphorescent organs along each side of the body that present the appearance of a chain of brightly glistening jewels set in the skin, while *Pachystomias* has luminous organs beneath its eyes. The family Scopedae contains many deep-sea forms remarkable both for their weird shapes and complex luminous organs. One member of this family which is not known to occur at great depths, will be familiar to many readers who are partial to curries, for in its salted and dried condition it is known as "Bombay-duck." The scientific name of this fish is *Harpodon nehereus*, and when freshly caught it is brilliantly phosphorescent all over its body. Large numbers are caught, salted, and dried, and exported from the west coast of India. A near relation is found in the Indian Ocean at depths of 120 to 300 fathoms.

THE angler-fish or fishing-frog (*Lophius piscatorius*) has a very interesting deep-sea cousin, the sea-devil (*Melanocetus murrazi*) which lives on the floor of the sea at depths of over two thousand fathoms. Like the shallow-water angler-fish of the British seas, this sea-devil has a wide mouth well armed with incurved teeth, a huge head, and tapering body. On the top of its head this uncanny-looking fish has a long fishing-rod tentacle that hangs over its mouth, and at its free end bears a luminous bulb that serves as a phosphorescent bait to attract small fishes and other creatures to their doom.

The whole question of the phosphorescence of marine animals is a very complex matter, and the part that it plays in the life of the animal would appear to differ with the individual. In the clouds of luminous secretion thrown out by the deep-sea prawn described above, and by the surface-dwelling Copepods it may serve, like the inky cloud thrown out by the cuttlefish, to baffle pursuers. In some cases it may serve as a lure to attract prey in much the same way that a lamp attracts moths and other insects ; while the more complex luminous organs would seem to serve to illuminate objects coming within the range of vision. In others, again, it may be of help to individuals of the same species to keep together in a swarm or shoal, or serve as recognition marks by which they may find their mates. But the function of luminescent organs is not always that of giving light for their possessor to see by, for many luminous animals are blind. In these cases, however, it has been noticed that elaborate complex luminescent organs are not present, the animal only exhibiting a diffuse glow, or giving off luminous secretions.

ON land the most important light-bearers are the fire-fly beetles of the tropics, and the glow-worm beetle of the British countryside. On warm summer nights, particularly in the south and west of England, the glow-worm beetles shine out from the hedgerow and banks of the country lanes like tiny fairy lamps. The little creature has gained its popular name of glow-worm from the wingless, long-bodied female, which is much more luminous than the winged male. At every stage of its life, egg, larva, pupa, and adult, this interesting little beetle whose scientific name is *Lampyris noctiluca*, is luminescent ; the amount of light shown increasing with its growth, and reaching its maximum in the adult female in which the lighting apparatus occupies the last three segments on the under surface of the body. In the winged male the light organ is confined to the end of the body, and is visible on both the upper and lower surfaces, whereas the two large belt-like organs of the female shine under her body, only the smaller spots on the end of her body being, as in the male, visible from above.

Watching the unlovely grub-shaped female crawl over one's hand in the daylight, it is impossible to realize how these large luminescent organs can be

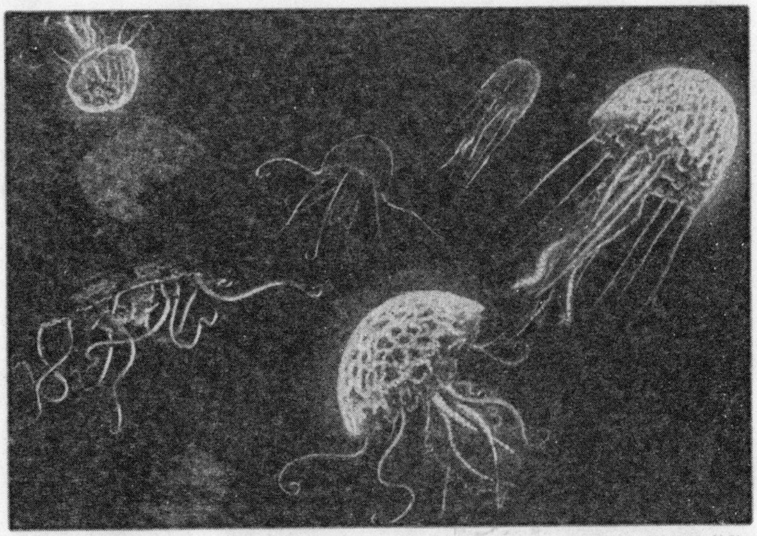

Natural History, N.Y.

SHINING JELLY-FISH OF THE MEDITERRANEAN

Many of the jelly-fish are phosphorescent or rather luminescent, to use the more accurate term. In the Mediterranean it is sometimes possible at night to watch mysterious companies of these things rising, with an increasing glow, from the outer darkness of the sea Our illustration shows some lighted and some unlighted.

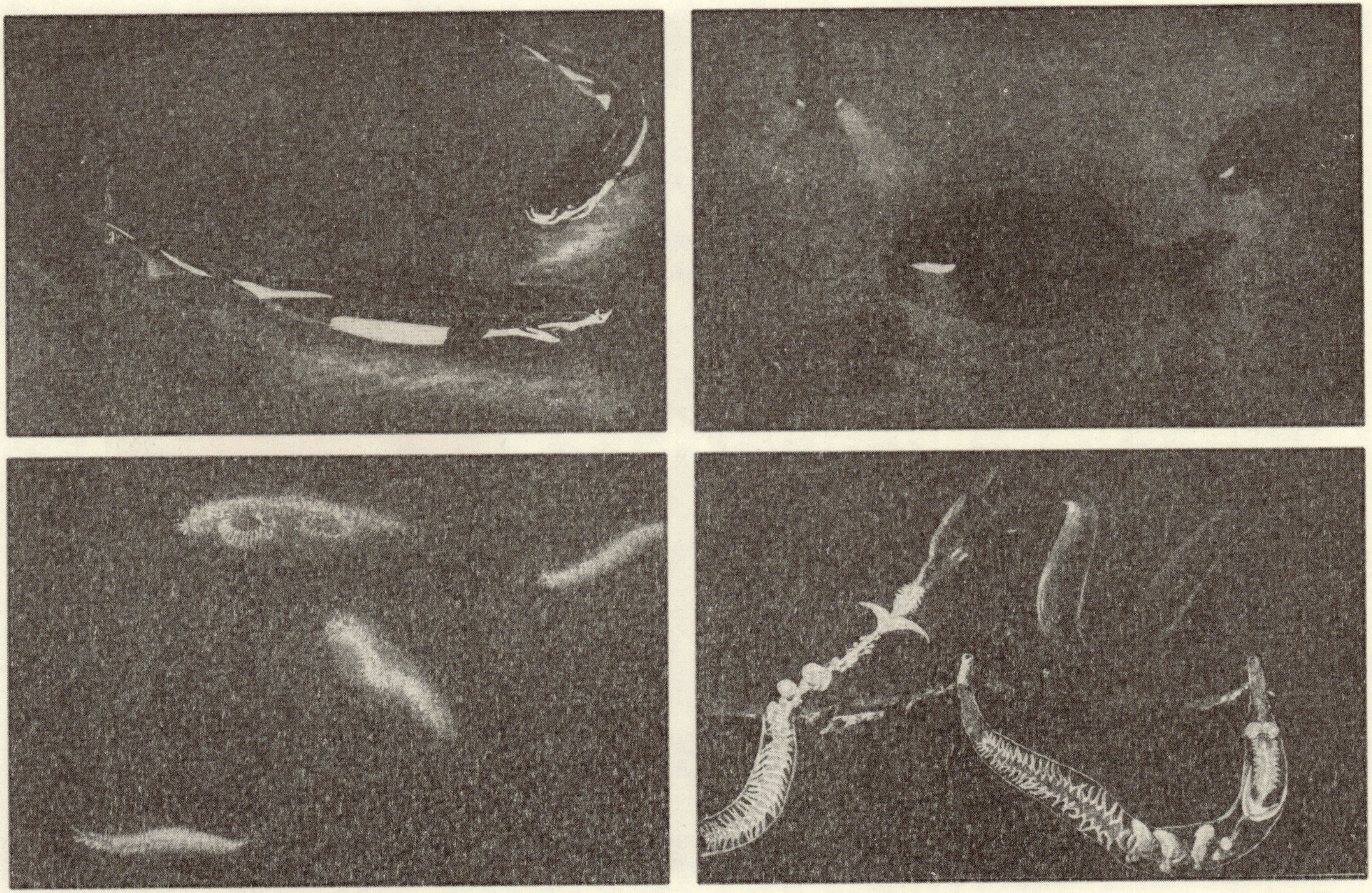

Natural History, N.Y.

DOWN IN THE DEPTHS OF THE SEA WHERE AN EERIE LIGHT IS SHED BY SWIMMING THINGS

Some, among the marine worms (bottom left) spend most of their life in crannies in the coral, but in the summer rise to the surface, where the female becomes luminous and attracts a mate. The chaetopterus (bottom right) lives in a tube. Eels are very partial to it, and here we see an eel which has bitten off the end of the tube and is dragging chaetopterus out. A neighbour, disturbed by the commotion, is "lighting up," and even the one being devoured does not cease to shine. There are luminous sharks, too (top left), found at depths of 500 to 1,500 fathoms. Their light comes from thousands of organs in their skin. Another fish (top right), found off Banda Island, cannot stop its light shining, and so has a curtain of pigment to draw over it.

of service for attracting the male from a distance, for that is their essential function. Under natural conditions, the little lady glow-worm remains more or less quiescent during the daytime, but on a warm, dark, summer night she will ascend the nearest grass stem and proceed to indulge in violent gymnastics, twisting the tip of her flexible abdomen in every direction, so as to expose to view the two broad bands of luminescence on the under-surface of her body ; and it is in this way that she sends forth her nuptial signals, flashing out across the darkness of the night like Hero's lamp to guide her approaching mate.

The fire-fly beetle of tropical America (*Pyrophorus noctilucus*) attracted the attention of the earliest travellers, who were so impressed by the wondrous display produced by hundreds of these insects illuminating the forest glades that detailed descriptions occupy a prominent position in all the accounts written by the old explorers. The *Pyrophorus*, or cucujos, as it is called in Brazil and other parts of tropical South America, is really a cousin of the small but notorious agricultural pest of our fields, the so-called click-beetle, for both belong to the family *Elateridae*. The cucujos, however, is much larger, and has brilliant phosphorescent organs, two that are oval in shape on the upper surface of its body, placed one on each side of the thorax, and a third on the under-surface of the abdomen. The light given out is extraordinarily brilliant, and the natives capture these fire-flies and literally use them as living lanterns to light them on their way on nocturnal excursions through the forests.

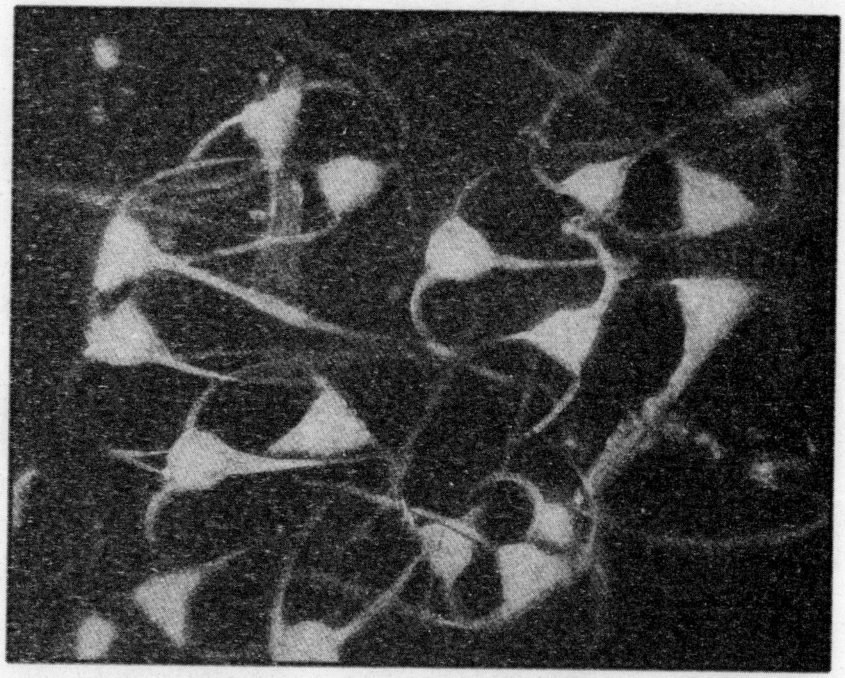

Natural History, N.Y

LOWLY ORGANISMS WHICH BURN BUT ARE NOT BURNT

There exist in the sea certain living organisms known as dinoflagellates, and their name signifies that they move themselves by whirling a small whip-like tail. These creatures are on the borderline where the highest plant life and the lowest animal life meet. Like the other " living lights " they produce light by the oxidisation of a substance called luciferin, which is secreted in the protoplasm of their body cells.

There are certain species of bacteria which are luminescent and, although apparently harmless, occasionally produce rather startling results. Salted haddock and other dried fish occasionally light up the family larder with a phosphorescent glow, which is no sign of putrefaction or being unsuitable for food, but is merely due to a very vigorous growth of those luminous bacteria.

The whole problem of the purpose and use of luminous organs as found in the animal kingdom is an exceedingly complex and difficult one, and still offers a very wide field for original observation into the habits and environment of the light-bearer, and for further microscopical and biochemical research in the laboratory of the expert.

To what extent luminous animals are ever likely to be utilised to the service of man is an equally problematical question. True, the tropical fire-flies have for centuries been used as living lamps and even for adornment by the natives of the West Indies and South America, while the Banda islanders utilise the luminous organs of a fish called *Photoblepharon*, as a bait for their night lines in fishing. Civilized man, so far, has only turned the luminous bacteria to practical account, Beijerinch having used cultures for the testing of bacterial filters, a perfect filter allowing no organisms to pass through ; while Dubois has made phosphorescent " lamps," using luminescent bacteria for the purpose, which might be of value for illumination in high explosive magazines where any heat-producing source of light is a danger. But the use of any luminous animals for practical purposes of illumination would appear to be very doubtful. Perhaps some day the biochemist may discover the secret of the fire-fly and from that knowledge ultimately develop a really efficient light for the use of mankind.

In the exquisite beauty and mystery of these luminescent displays, as in all the beauty of Nature, Man has a treasure which in this mechanistic age he seems ever less and less able to appreciate, fouling the surface of the sea with the black, death-spreading, wasted oil from his ships, and the countryside with the garbage of the town. In the summer the picnicking motorist has been responsible for fires that have destroyed thousands of acres of heather and gorse in Surrey, Sussex, Hampshire, and other southern counties, where the glow-worm also had her home. and will never again display her fairy light.

Oliver G. Pike

KINGFISHER FINDS A GOOD PERCH WHENCE TO DIVE FOR ITS PREY

A commanding position over the water is what the kingfisher seeks when fishing. A post or any projecting object in the water will do, or a reed or, as here, a root exposed by the swirl of winter floods. In this case there is deep water under a sheer bank, and here, out of the current, a shoal of fry—small roach or bleak—will sooner or later appear. Then the bird makes a dive like the flashing of blue lightning, disappears a moment under the water and, in the same second, flies up with fish in beak. Sometimes, however, the bird will hover.

Chapter XXII

The Marvels of An English Brook

By Sir William Beach Thomas

Author of "The English Year"

In the pleasant land of Britain many hundred brooks run down to the rivers and the seas. Towards the west, where the hills are many and steep, they flow fast and free, with a merry sound among the stones. In the south, where the chalk lies beneath they are crystal clear. Towards the east they are more leisurely and wander more like the Lea which, as one of the earliest poets wrote, "oft doth lose its way." But all these brooks, however much they differ in character, have very much in common. Not many animals and not very many plants and insects are peculiar to any one stream. What is true of the inhabitants of one brook is true of most of the others.

Most brooks grow steadily bigger as they come nearer to the sea; but sometimes no part is more spacious and lovely than the source, as on the Pang in Berkshire, where the water comes bubbling out of white chalk and sand, over which the biggest trout lie, for mere pleasure of the feel of the fresh water; and a little lake half covered with heart-shaped water-lily leaves is rounded out before the brook is formed and starts on its journey to the Thames. Almost all water is fuller of life than the land. The best time to observe the wonder of the teeming population is in May or earlier, when the insects we call flies, though they are not properly flies, are wonderfully changed from water-creatures into air creatures.

Both caddis flies and mayflies appear mysteriously in myriads at the surface and as they reach it pause for a second or two before they can open their new wings and take flight. It is then that the struggle for life is most apparent, and you see how the water creatures are dependent on one another. The fish are less numerous than the flies, but they are in shoals in most of the bigger brooks. When May comes, they grow hungry, and a scarcely visible swirl in the water indicates how some spotted trout or silver dace—the chief devourers of these flies—has caught its food on the way to the surface. Sometimes the fish jumps right out of the water in its eagerness for food. The mayfly are called the ephemerids, or one-day flies, though they often live longer; and very soon after their escape into the air and the wedding flight they come back to the water to lay their eggs, which are stuck together like little rafts, but soon sink to the bottom. Very often the mayfly who lays them is drowned. In some years, thousands may be seen floating downstream. But many of these apparently dead flies are only cases, for these ephemerids on first appearance cast a skin that covers the whole of their frame, wings and all; and this is so perfect that often it is scarcely to be distinguished from the living fly itself.

F. Pitt

LITTLE WATER-VOLE

Living in the banks of the brook in a tunnel which has one entrance above the water and another below it, the vole can often be seen quite close by keeping still. It is also called "water-rat."

All through the spring and summer and early autumn births of this sort may be seen. Among the latest in the year, waiting till autumn, are the dragon-flies which laboriously climb up the stems of water plants and go through the marvellous change in the sunlight while they hang on to a stem or leaf. Both before and after the change they are among the most ruthless hunters of all water animals. The animal from which they come is the terror of the floor of the stream. He crawls about for the year or two of his life seeking what he may devour; and the queer mask-like mouth is a marvellously efficient instrument for his purpose. His nearest rival in greediness is the big Dytiscus beetle, which often comes to the surface to breathe and carries down with it a drop of air which it carries under the tail of its case. It will attack even small fish.

Most caterpillars and other creatures that creep and crawl eat voraciously, and the perfect insects into which they change enjoy the sun and air with little thought of food. The perfect mayfly, itself the favourite food of trout, does not feed at all. Its

C. Reid

SHYEST AND LEAST OFTEN SEEN OF WATERSIDE ANIMALS: THE OTTER

While the footprints of the otter are sometimes to be remarked in the soft mud by the water's edge, the animal itself is very rarely seen. The reason for this is that the otter lies snug during the day in its lair, which is tunnelled out of the bank of the stream, sometimes under the roots of a tree. Furthermore, it is only the least frequented parts of the streams that otters seek, and it should be remembered that they are hunted. Occasionally an otter shows himself in daylight as this one, photographed as it was about to enter the water.

C. Reid

OTTER AS IT MOVES IN AND ABOUT THE WINDING ENGLISH BROOK

Many people, especially those who stock streams with trout or preserve salmon water, regard the otter as a pest merely. But there is another opinion which holds that in the delicate " balance of Nature," whereby one animal preys upon another, the otter has its place. For, as in the case of pike, it is usually the weaker fish that get caught, and weak and sickly fish are better out of the way for the sake of the species. At the same time it is exasperating to find a fine trout left with just one piece bitten out ot it.

Neville Kingston

OTTER AT PLAY

One interesting fact about the otter is its love of play. All sorts of antics are performed in and out of the water, and sometimes a family will make a slide down some steep bank and career into the stream one after the other time after time.

form does not permit. The dragon-fly on the other hand springs dragon-like on other winged things, catching them in its queerly-shaped fore-legs, which serve it almost as hands both for this purpose and earlier in clinging to the reed or other water plant while it steps from its shell.

One of the most curious differences between some of these water insects and the land insects is that they do not go through the three different stages of larva or grub, pupa or chrysalis, and winged creature. The dragon-fly, for example, leaves out the middle stage. The grub grows by shedding its skin and passes into the so-called nymph stage without ever becoming still and half-lifeless like the ordinary chrysalis. It passes from the stage of nymph to the imago or perfect insect by slipping off its case directly it leaves the water. The dragon-fly takes the longest time, and unlike the others, must rest some while after escaping from the case before the wings expand to full size and grow hard and brightly coloured in the sun.

The caddis fly on the other hand goes through all the stages in its year of life. The eggs fall to the bottom and the grubs are hatched. They then make themselves cases out of little bits of sand, pebble, stick, or what not, which they fix together by a sort of gummy silk. The grub is rather like a hermit crab. The part within the case is soft, and the part that projects and catches food is hard. When after many months it feels a change coming, it withdraws fully into its room and spins a silk barrier across the doorway, which remains closed till the next change is nearly complete. The larva or grub has become a pupa or chrysalis, and is about to become a winged creature. As soon as it is ready for the air it eats through the silk, with jaws specially constructed for the purpose, and comes to the top of the water as a "nymph." As it clings to some stem or weed the last change is wrought. The nymph case splits and out comes the perfect fly or imago, with four hairy wings and long antennae; and presently after mating, the female lays a mass of eggs held together in a jelly on the surface of the water. The cycle of life is complete.

THE fish feed on the fly, as well as the crawling creatures of the stream, but they are themselves in no little danger. So immense is the number of eggs that a fish lets fall—often in a hollow scooped in the bed of the brook—that if half grew up, the river would be solid with fish within three years. Other fish eat the eggs; and both the fry that came to birth and the bigger fish have a certain number of active enemies.

The greatest enemy from outside the water is the heron, one of the biggest English birds. As Tennyson wrote in The Brook: "I come from haunts of coot and hern." Herons stand, as a rule, in shallow water among reeds, or sedge if possible, and abide as still as the plants, till fish or fly or rat or vole, or even a small bird comes within reach. They then strike with such amazing quickness that you cannot follow the movement, and they very seldom strike in vain. It is thought, though this is not quite certain, that they will eat also the fresh water crayfish, which are almost as numerous as water snails or shrimps in a few English brooks, though rare elsewhere. In one respect the kingfishers, brightest of brook birds, imitate the great grey heron. They keep astonishingly still, on their perch over the river, and when they see a fish below, strike with sudden speed. But they dive, just as an American fish hawk dives, to catch their prey, and seldom make the attempt unless the fish is at the very surface. The kingfisher is more of a brook bird than the heron. It seldom leaves the neighbourhood of the stream, and nests in holes either on the bank or close by, often using fishbones in the structure. The slow beat of the heron's wings carries him long distances, and the heronries in which he builds, high up in lofty trees, are often in distant woods.

More powerful and ruthless than any other enemy of the fish is the otter, which, perhaps, is less often seen by human eyes than any of the bigger animals. Fishermen tell grim tales of its destructive powers. They find big salmon dragged to land, and know the otter for the culprit, because of the deep bites into the shoulder of the fish. But some preservers of fish in the north-west of England, which is the best otter country, claim that the otter, though he kills fish, does more good than harm. The fish is the better swimmer, and it is the fish that are suffering from some malady that the otter more certainly catches. So it comes about, they say, that where some otters are found there the fish are healthier; and though they kill some fish that the fishermen would like to kill themselves, the otters should be allowed their reward. What is called the balance of nature is a strange and sensitive thing, extremely perfect in Britain, and if we interfere with this dependence of one creature upon another we are apt to do more harm than good.

F. Pitt

HERON ALERT

This is the fishing position of the heron, with long neck upstretched. The bird stands as still as a tree and becomes part of the landscape till suddenly there is a lightning movement and a fish is seen flapping in that beak which seldom strikes in vain.

Oliver G. Pike

HERON CONTEMPLATIVE

After feeding the heron stands serene in apparent contemplation, while the process of digestion takes place. In this posture no idea of the real length of the neck is suggested for it folds up between chest and beak. But at a hint of danger it is upstretched immediately.

The otter is a night creature. One often sees his footprint in the soft mud beside the stream, but seldom the living animal. A few people have seen also "the otter's slide." No animal is more playful, as those who have kept tame otters know, and in wild life a family will make a slide down a steep bank, like the slide in some public swimming baths, and career in a festive circle after one another—down the slide into the water and back up the bank to begin the game again.

The otter is certainly less deadly to fish than are some other fish, especially the pike. Pike are almost shark-like, with strong, sharp, teeth-like points. Many fish will swallow other fish not so very much smaller than themselves; few small fish are safe. Perch, which abound in some rivers, are an exception. They eat others, but are not eaten, thanks to the extreme sharpness of their fins. The pike have many things on their side in the struggle for life. They have their powerful and well-armed jaws, they grow very big, flourish both in still and running water, in pond or brook, and are immensely long-lived. No one quite knows how long their life may last, but they certainly survive, on occasion, more than the three score years and ten of human life. It is no wonder that the first step taken by those who preserve trout in our streams is to get rid of the pike;

F. Pitt

Oliver G. Pike

KINGFISHER AND ITS YOUNG

When it has secured a fish (bottom) the bird holds it crosswise in its beak, flies up to its perch, stuns the fish, tosses it up into the air, catches it very neatly and then swallows it head first. Above are some young birds preparing to shift for themselves.

for the pretty, spotted, so-called brown trout, as delicately coloured as the imported "rainbow" trout, are a delicate fish, easily poisoned, and perhaps easier victims to their enemy than the thick-scaled dace or red-finned roach or perch.

The pike, as well as the water rats, will eat many other water animals than fish. Even young birds fall victim. Few birds have flourished more or multiplied more than moorhen, but they lose many of the young to these two enemies. They build, as a rule, almost on the water, as do the coot and the dainty dabchicks, with which they are sometimes confused. The nests are not unlike, but the dabchick is more careful, and generally covers up her eggs with bits of reed or other nesting material when she goes away. The wild duck nests in safer places, further away from the water; generally on the ground, but sometimes in willow trees; and her chief cause of loss is the earliness of her nest-making. Often she takes her brood to the water while spring is so young that insect food is very hard to come by; and starvation is a real danger. If any enemy is threatened the young swim so close to their mother that they seem to stick to her. The young moorhen, on the other hand, generally try to dive, though when they are very young they can do no more than put their heads under. The light, fluffy bodies refuse to follow. The young dabchick can dive with great skill at once, and the bird is so fond of the water that it very seldom flies at all; and when swimming under water, for either food or safety, uses its wings as well as its feet. It swims on the surface smoothly without the quaint jerk of the head that marks the moorhen.

The brooks of the south and east of England are without one charming water-bird. The only small bird that is really at home in water and close to the water is called the dipper, or water ousel. Its nest is usually over or beside the stream, and though the birds are waders, not swimmers, they have been seen by good observers calmly walking along the bottom, though totally submerged for a short space. The dipper is as perky as a wren, but looks more like

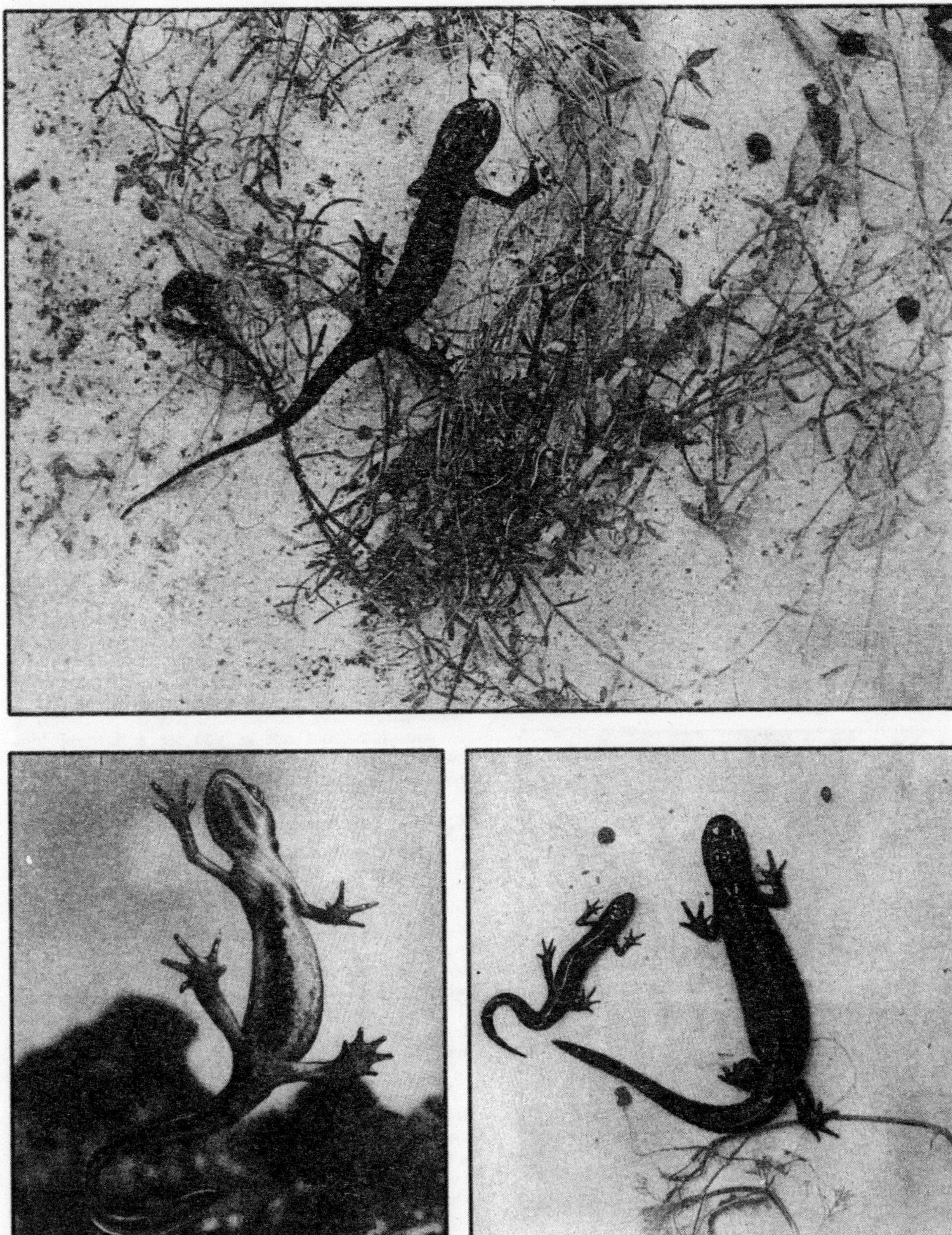

M. H. Crawford

NEWTS AS THEY LIVE IN THEIR UNDER-WATER HOME

Beginning life in a fish-like state with gills, the common newt (top) gradually develops lungs and becomes air-breathing. It spends much of its life, save in the breeding season, on land sometimes at a considerable distance from water, but always prefers damp surroundings. It usually hibernates in the ground, but sometimes spends the winter in the water. The under parts are spotted (bottom left), the tail is flat and coloured red and blue in the male, but red only in the female. The last photograph shows a common and a crested newt or triton.

Minnows

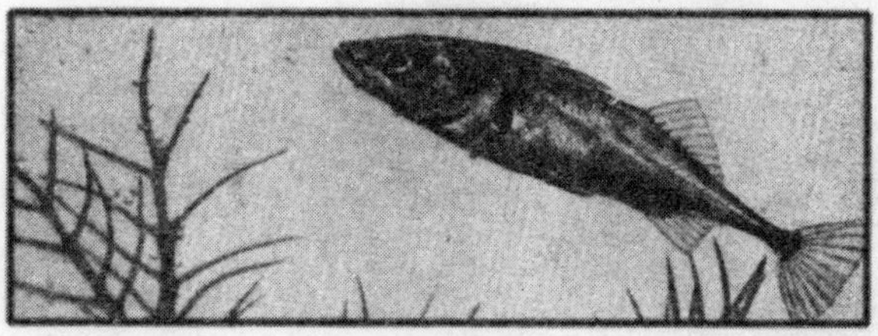

Stickleback

Roach

Chub

Loach

FISHES OF THE BROOK

The loaches that Jan Ridd used to impale with a home-made trident in "Lorna Doone," the chub which lies right under the bushes along the bank, the roach with the lattice-work pattern on its back, the fierce little stickleback and the minnow, all swim the English brook. These photographs are by S. C. Johnson.

a small blackbird that has turned white underneath. In the north-west of England, which is his favourite home, his low, sweet song may be heard even when there is snow on the ground.

The brook is often both a battlefield and a hunting ground; but many of its inhabitants are wholly peaceable. None is more charming to watch than the little water-vole, whose tunnelled house has two entrances at least, one below the other above the water. Almost like the dyticus beetle he can hold air. You may easily see the silver beads of it caught in his close fur, as he dives and swims below you. How bravely he goes about day after day finding reeds and sedge and water weeds, some for his food, some for his nest. He stays round about his home; and is in every way wholly different from his cousin the sewer or water rat, which is a destroyer of life and will travel long distances. This grey rat is a lustier and fiercer creature than the old black rat which has almost disappeared. But the vole was once known and is still often known as the water-rat, for the name vole is recent.

Though he is bigger and when closely seen very different in shape and structure, he may be mistaken by a casual observer for the water-shrew. Both live in holes on the bank of the brook and eat thus living in the water. But the shrew, like the land shrews, is a fiercer little creature living almost wholly on animal food. Everyone can recognize a land shrew at once by the astoundingly long, almost beak-like snout; but this feature is blunter and shorter in the water-shrew, easy enough to detect if the animal is in your hand but not as you see a flash of him swimming past you very fast under water to his home on the bank.

SOME streams never seem quite so full of life as when the caddis fly and mayfly come out; and about the same date the frogs, toads and newts come back to the water. All these hibernate, that is, spend the winter in hiding and shelter; and both frogs and toads prefer the land to the water throughout late summer and winter. But in spring they make for the water in great numbers to lay their eggs. The frogs, which come first, lay their eggs in jelly-like masses. The toads, which come three or four weeks later, in long jelly-like strings, and the lizard-like newts, of which there are three sorts, more neat and careful in many ways, carefully wrap up their eggs in the fold of some water grass or weed. Perhaps one of the strangest things in natural history is the slow change of the tadpole of frog or toad with the gills of a sort of fish into a land creature with lungs; and it is the easiest to observe. One of the oddities is that the long tail of the tadpole is very slowly absorbed by the frog very much as part of the egg by the growing chicken. In the north-west of England is a "batrachian," as these creatures are called, which possesses a tail all its life; but this natterjack is rather surprisingly rare and local.

The newt has one curious likeness to another inhabitant of the water, much studied by children

It develops in spring brilliant red patches of colour round the throat. Now, if you look down into a brook in early morning, you may see a little silvery fish swimming round and round and to and fro; and he catches your eye by the extreme brilliance of a scarlet patch. This is the male stickleback—probably the three-spined stickleback—guarding the female fish. He attacks any and every enemy that approaches; and seems almost as angry against his spouse, for he at once chases her back if she attempts to leave her nest on the bed of the stream.

How the stream teems with life becomes obvious in spring, but a census would show that it is as great or perhaps greater in late summer. Births and deaths follow in endless succession. On the surface of a brook or pond in August, when they are most active, one may see what look like some hundreds of drops of quicksilver sliding about the surface in a mazy pattern, apparently with no particular aim or object. These silver drops are little water beetles very fitly known as whirligigs. They have been well compared with the bats that will fly over the stream in numbers when the evening comes. Both turn and twist with a speed that baffles the eye and they have a like purpose. The bats pursue flying insects, the whirligigs the minute insects that are caught for a moment on the surface of the water. But for their speed of movement most would escape them. Very nearly all the water insects have some of their legs flattened into paddles, as you may see even from a distance with the great dyticus, which may be an inch and a half long, and rather less obviously in the great water beetle, which is sometimes a quarter of an inch larger still. In the whirligig, the back legs are paddles and the short front legs used, like the dragon-fly's, for holding the prey. Another insect, the water boatman, has yet more curious paddles, and he is so well hinged that he can propel himself while he lies on his back, which is shaped like the underside of a boat. So paddled, in this upside down position, these queer insects swim almost as fast as the beetles. The paddle is good and the friction against the water as slight as can be.

Some water beetles and bugs, however, do not need paddles. One in this class is the water scorpion; another the water stick-insect. The scorpion does not need paddles because it spends most of its time hunting along the floor of the water; but it possesses wings, as do several other under-water insects, which use them only when the water dries up and they are thus forced to migrate. The stick-insect is perhaps so well known because of the brilliant patch of red which suddenly shows on his drab, crushed-looking but ample body when the wings are raised. He resembles in this the very common long narrow-bodied, sun-loving insect known as the Soldier, though he is in a different family. The bugs and the beetles, which are two of the biggest classes, resemble one another in many details, in spite of many differences. The scorpion and the boatman are bugs (or Hemiptera). So is the large corixa, which has

Water Scorpion

Water Beetle

Corixa

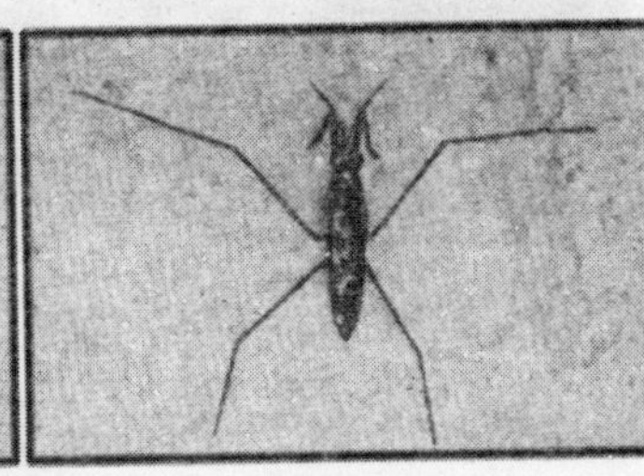

Water Boatman Pupa

Pond Skater

Water Hog or Louse

QUEER CREATURES OF STREAM LIFE

Many forms of brook life need more watching for than the fish. The so-called " hog louse," for instance, lives at the bottom, while the more obvious boatman and pond skater are at the surface The water beetle and water scorpion are well worth studying, too The photographs are by M. H. Crawford and S. C. Johnson.

anchored in a much better protected place, sometimes inside an old crock or bottle. The male which, unlike all other spiders, is bigger than the female, lives in an air chamber alongside, and when the time comes, eats through the division and the air bubbles join.

The brook, unlike the sea, has not very many molluscs, but those it has are curious. The fresh water mussel is the biggest of all the molluscs. It lives nearly all its time well under the mud, and is worth close study because of its queer construction. It possesses a siphon which it thrusts above the mud and by which you may trace its presence; and a yet more curious organ in its huge and powerful 'foot' which it advances even as far as three inches or more and pulls the shell after it, making a tunnel in the mud. The mussel is rightly called a mussel, but the water shrimp is not a shrimp in the sense of the sea animal, but rather more like the 'hopper' commonly found among stranded sea weed.

ALL these creatures serve as food for bird and fish. The hunt goes on continuously; the little boatman devours the lesser insect, the fish live on the flies and other water animals, some like the pike even devouring birds or frogs and rats. The fish themselves are attacked by otter and heron and kingfisher. Even snakes will occasionally invade the water, and though

the dark shiny green colour common to many beetles, but it lacks the regular hard wing cases; and its mode of motion is very much like the boatman's, except that it paddles itself the right way up.

The animal that most ingeniously adapts itself to a life in the water is not insect, mammal, fish or mollusc, but spider. Like the dyticus beetle and the vole it imprisons air in the hairs of its body, coming up to the surface to recharge itself. But it needs more air than this and weaves two sorts of nets to imprison supplies. One is for its nesting hours, the other for its winter quarters. The difference is that the first is closely woven above and is at first like a silk raft; and does not become rounded like a diving bell till the bubble of air is introduced below. The winter home is of rather closer silk and is enclosed all round and is usually

J.J.Ward

DIVING BEETLE AND ITS EGG COCOON

Under-water creatures as small as the diving beetle are sometimes rather hard to find and study, but here are some splendid photographs of the creature. It is a vegetarian and makes a cocoon (bottom) for its eggs. The cocoon has a special ventilation shaft which, as we see, projects through the surface into the air.

only the adder among British reptiles attacks birds, the so-called harmless grass snakes live on frogs and other things. But life is merry in the river. The hunted are not afraid, though they are watchful ; and seldom does the victim know much of his own end, much less feel pain. The variety of life is beyond all reckoning. Some, like the crayfish, live all the time within a square yard or so of the same spot. Some like the otter which shares the love of most so-called vermin for wandering will travel miles, even from one brook to another. All the water-haunting birds and the vermin, including the grey rat, will take considerable journeys, but the little voles are very faithful to one short reach of their home stream, not moving very much farther than the water snails, which swim quite long distances for such a creature, lying on their backs the while like water-boatmen and keeping themselves afloat solely by use of what is known as the surface tension of the water.

J. J. Ward — M. H. Crawford

FRESH-WATER SNAIL AND DRAGON-FLY OF THE BROOK

The most common shell-bearing creature of the English streams is the fresh-water snail of which there are a number of varieties. In the left hand photographs we see its shell (bottom), and (top) the snail crawling up the side of a glass tank with its remarkable "foot" adhering to the glass. The lower illustration on the right shows a dragon-fly resting upon a water plant, and (top) the cast skin left when the insect forsook life beneath the surface for the freedom of the air A dragon-fly is one of the brook's most joyous sights.